Cortinarius traganus

Rozites caperata

Gomphideus roseus

COLLINS GUIDE TO

Mushrooms
&
Toadstools

BY
MORTEN LANGE
AND
F. BAYARD HORA

WITH 96 COLOUR PLATES
FROM
Flora Agaricina Danica
BY
JAKOB E. LANGE (1864–1941)
WITH ADDITIONS BY
EBBE SUNESEN AND
P. DAHLSTRØM

COLLINS
ST. JAMES'S PLACE, LONDON

First Edition 1963
Second Edition 1965
Reprinted 1967
Reprinted 1970
Reprinted 1972
Reprinted 1975
Reprinted 1978

ISBN 0 00 219300 0

Jacob E. Lange and Morton Lange
Illustratet Svampeflora
Copyright 1961 by GEC Gads Forlag

English translation copyright © 1963
by William Collins Sons & Co., Ltd., and
E. P. Dutton & Co. Inc., New York

Printed in Great Britain
Collins Clear-Type Press
London and Glasgow

CONTENTS

PREFACE

This guide is adapted from the Danish *Illustreret Svampeflora* of Jakob E. Lange and Morten Lange. The coloured illustrations of the Gill fungi are reproduced from *Flora Agaricina Danica* by Jakob E. Lange—a work of permanent value and of the highest importance to anyone studying Gill fungi, and in which about 1200 species are superbly illustrated in full colour together with " keys " and descriptive text written in excellent English. However, to give an idea of the range of form in the " larger fungi," the present book also includes representatives of other larger Basidiomycetes and the larger Cup fungi and their allies. These have been painted by Ebbe Sunesen and P. Dahlstrøm and are reproduced here on pages 35-75, 187-95, 215-25. Wherever possible, these additional paintings have been made from living specimens, but four rather rare Cup fungi have been repainted from Boudier's classic work and a few Hypogeous fungi after Hesse. The same artists also painted the coloured illustrations used on the endpapers of this book.

The species selected for illustration are for the most part frequent or common, but some rare or occasional species have also been included as being exceptionally striking, or for various reasons interesting examples of certain fungus groups.

One feature of the present adaptation not included in the Danish work is the addition of microscopical characters, which should prove helpful to the more advanced student. Some chemical aids to field identification have also been added, and the months during which species are to be found in Britain.

The nomenclature of fungi is in a state of rapid transition. In this country, recent Revisions affecting species included in this book are Corner (1950); Dennis (1960); Dennis, Orton & Hora (1960); Hawker (1954). The genera given in the original Danish edition are retained in this Guide but where they differ from those given in these Revisions, each alternative genus has been included, with brackets, between the generic and specific name as here printed. For the convenience of those who may be more familiar with older generic limits, the binomial is followed by the old genus—always beginning with a capital letter— in which the species may once have been placed.

For the specific names, the International Rules have been followed as far as possible. Here also, a few alternative specific names—always beginning with a small letter—have been included, again after the binomial combination.

It is a pleasure to express my thanks to Professor Morten Lange, who entrusted me with the task of preparing an English edition of his work, and to Miss Lise Hansen, for providing me, in lightning time, with an English translation of the Danish text.

I am greatly indebted to Mrs. Ord-Hume for the speed and accuracy with which she typed the whole manuscript.

F. B. Hora

The University, Reading, March 1963

GENERAL STRUCTURE OF FUNGI

The fungi form one of the larger groups within the vegetable kingdom; most species are inconspicuous, appearing only as small dark dots or cobweb-like coverings; many are only properly discernible under the microscope. Nevertheless, in this country alone we have at least 3000 species with fairly large fruit-bodies and it is representatives of these larger fungi that are dealt with in this book. It must, however, be emphasised that the smaller as well as the microscopic fungi have great practical importance in addition to their intrinsic interest to specialists. Thus, the microscopical yeast fungi (Saccharomycetes) are used for brewing and baking, *Penicillium* for the production of the valuable anti-biotic, Penicillin. Other fungi cause serious plant diseases; but many are useful and necessary for the part they play in the decomposition of leaf litter in woods and plantations and for their soil activities in cultivated ground.

All fungi lack the pigment chlorophyll which gives the characteristic green colour to land plants and algae, etc., enabling them to utilise light energy for the synthesis of carbon compounds from the available carbon dioxide and water. Green fungi do exist, but that colour is due to other substances, and in order to grow they must live either as parasites on living organisms or as saprophytes on their dead remains. The absorption of nutrients takes place via the *mycelium* which consists of minute tubes (*hyphae*) usually much thinner than a cobweb. In most species the mycelium is invisible since it spreads in the soil or within the host organism. Not infrequently, however, one can see decaying leaves and other substrates with a superficial covering of white—sometimes coloured—mycelium and in a few cases the constituent hyphal threads may band together to form quite thick strands ("chords," *rhizomorphs*) easily visible to the naked eye. From the mycelium arise the fruit-bodies. These are built up of hyphae as is the mycelium, but they are densely interwoven and transformed in different ways. Thus, fruit-bodies differ very much in form, but common to all is the production of some sort of microscopically small spore which on germination gives rise to a new mycelium.

ASCOMYCETES

Depending on the construction of the spore forming organs, the larger fungi are divided into two main groups: Ascomycetes and Basidiomycetes. In Ascomycetes, the ascospores—most usually eight in number—are formed *inside* a club-shaped cell, the *ascus*, from which at maturity they are shot out: among the larger Ascomycetes, the Pezizales show the most simple construction. Their fruit-bodies are more or less cup-shaped, the asci arising from a dense layer, the *hymenium*, on the inner (upper) side of the cup (Fig. 1 and 2). In the genera

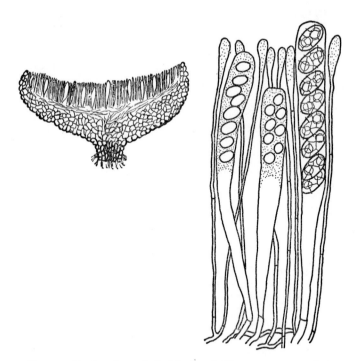

Figure 1   Section through fruit-body of Discomycete, somewhat enlarged. *Right*, highly magnified detail of hymenium with asci and paraphyses

Helvella and *Morchella*, the cup is variously folded into a sort of cap which is raised upon a stem, the hymenium covering the outer side of the cap (Fig. 2).

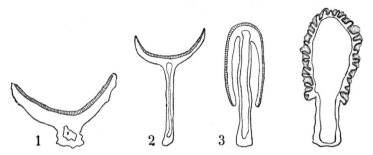

Figure 2   Sections through fruit-bodies of: 1, Peziza; 2, Helvella macropus; 3, Verpa conica; 4, Morchella

This more or less open spore producing layer of asci is often referred to, especially in the Pezizales, as the *disc* and those Ascomycetes having this structure are commonly called Discomycetes, or Cup Fungi.

Some Ascomycetes have tuberous fruit-bodies (within which ascospore formation takes place) and grow below soil surface. Such are the truffles of which there are several different kinds; some of the species, e.g. those of the genus *Elaphomyces* (Hart's truffles) are probably quite common, but their subterranean habitat makes them difficult to find. Most tuffles have a folded hymenium which appears as fine veins in the flesh of the fruit-bodies.

A third group of Ascomycetes has the asci enclosed in small flask-shaped structures (*perithecia*), the spores being finally liberated through a minute opening (*ostiole*) at the top (Fig. 3). This group, the Pyrenomycetes, is exceedingly rich in species, but only a few of the larger ones are figured here. Often several perithecia are grouped into a common structure—the *stroma*—comprised of vegetative hyphae with or without tissue from the host or substratum, the ostioles showing as minute dots on the upper side. The stroma may be soft, but more often it is distinctly hard and black, like coal. The stroma is to be distinguished from the *sclerotium*, which is also a more or less rounded and hard dense mass of vegetative hyphae but does not normally contain spores.

The microscopical yeast fungi belong to the Ascomycetes.

The way in which the ascus opens and other microscopic and chemical characters are of great importance in the classification of the Ascomycetes, and are briefly considered later (page 226).

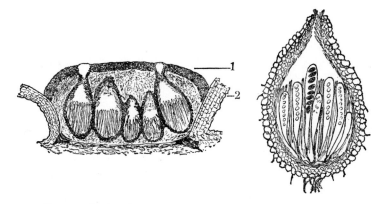

Figure 3 Section through Diatrype (Sphaeriales) with five fruit-bodies in a common stroma with carbonaceous cover (1), bursting through the bark of host (2); low magnification. *Right*, a single perithecium with asci; larger magnification

Although the Ascomycetes are the largest group of fungi, the Basidiomycetes include by far the highest number of larger fungi. The Basidiomycetes form the basidiospores—usually four in number—on small peg-like projections (sterigmata) at the top of club-shaped cells, the basidia; i.e. the spores are borne *outside* the basidium (Fig. 4).

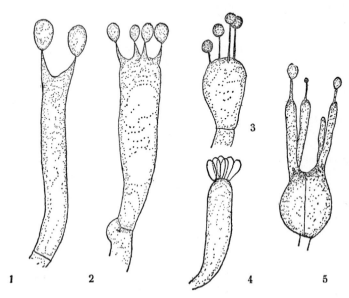

Figure 4   Different types of basidia: 1, two spores, from Clavaria; 2, Agaricales; 3, Lycoperdon; 4, Phallus; 5, Tremellales

APHYLLOPHORALES

In the simplest forms, the fungus consists of a thin crust of hyphal tissue bearing on the upper surface, a hymenial layer with basidia. The genus *Corticium* which grows on rotten wood, belongs amongst others to this type. *Stereum* and related genera are almost as simple, but the receptacles are slightly thicker and form projecting brackets with the hymenium on the lower surface. Also among the more simple forms are the Clavariaceae where the hymenium with its basidia is spread evenly over the upper part of club-like receptacles. But most of the species treated here have a more complex construction. The Polypores (*Polyporaceae*) often possess hoof-like fruit-bodies with a compact layer of tubes on the under side, each tube opening by a pore and lined on the inside by the basidia-bearing hymenial layer. In the *Hydnaceae*, a comparable hymenial layer is developed as downwardly projecting teeth on the under (lower) side of a stalked cap. This stalked cap, umbrella-like type of fructification, with spores developed on and shed from the under surface, is quite common throughout the Basidiomycetes and has reached a high degree of elaboration and variability in those "Gill fungi" to which the terms toadstool and mushroom are most commonly applied and for which the word agaric is coming into favour.

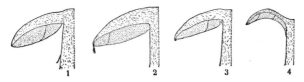

Figure 5   Gill attachment of agarics: 1, free; 2, adnate; 3, sinuate; 4, decurrent

AGARICALES

Here, the hymenium is spread over the gills which radiate from the top of the stipe, like spokes from the hub of a wheel. In the more simple agarics, the gills are exposed from the first. They may be narrow or broad, thick or thin and there may be *intermediate gills* which start at the cap margin and extend for varying distances towards the stipe without actually reaching it. Gills which extend the full length are very variable in their mode of attachment to the stipe (Fig. 5) and this plays an important role in identification, especially at the generic level.

More complicated agarics show additional morphological characters, which are of importance for identification. Thus, the young gills may be covered by a *partial veil* which can be membranous (*Amanita*), or consist of cobweb-like filaments when it is often called a *cortina* (*Cortinarius*). This partial veil ruptures as the cap expands leaving a *ring* (annulus) on the stipe when the partial veil is membranous and sometimes teeth-like remnants at the margin of the cap (*appendiculate veil*). Where there is a cortina, only a ring-like *zone* is likely to be found on the stipe after the cap has expanded (Fig. 6). A further elaboration in some agarics is the presence of a *universal veil* entirely enclosing the young fruit-body, as the shell does an egg. As the stipe elongates, this veil ruptures and remains of it may be seen as detachable scales on the cap and as a bag or cup (*volva*) at the base of the stipe (Fig. 6). In some species the universal veil is more or less granular and appears on the expanded cap as a mealy layer and as a granular sheath on the lower part of the stipe up to the ring. In other species, the universal veil may undergo change and give rise to a slimy coating.

In recent years, the microscopical structure of the fruit-body of agarics has

11

become of great importance for their classification and identification. This is briefly dealt with on pages 226 to 233.

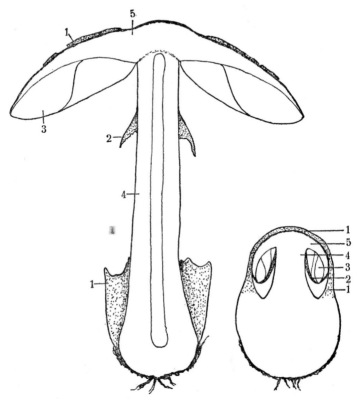

Figure 6 Longitudinal section through expanded fruit-body of Amanita. 1, universal veil forming scales on cap and volva at base of stipe. 2, partial veil, forming ring on stipe. 3, Gill. 4, Stipe. 5, Cap

GASTEROMYCETALES

In this group of Basidiomycetes, the spores are developed within the fruit-body and are not shed until this is fully mature. In the genus *Lycoperdon*, the spores escape through a small hole at the top of a more or less pear-shaped fruit-body. In the genera *Phallus* and *Mutinus*, the spore-mass is carried up on an expanded stem after maturation within a globose " egg." This group also includes some subterranean truffle-like species whose fruit-bodies have no special opening mechanism.

All the above-mentioned groups of Basidiomycetes have rather uniform and simply constructed basidia. The Tremellales is a small divergent group with gelatinous fruit-bodies and more complex basidia these being divided by vertical or horizontal septa *or* are at least deeply furcate (Fig. 4). The Tremellales also differ from the remaining Basidiomycetes in being able to withstand considerable desiccation. In dry weather most of them shrivel up becoming thin and tough, but regain their original shape and gelatinous consistency on re-wetting. They are regarded as being related to the large group of rust fungi.

SPORES

In all groups of fungi, spore colour is of importance. Sometimes the spore colour can be seen directly by examining the spore-bearing surface, but the only really certain way is to place the spore-bearing surface on a glass slide or (preferably) a piece of white paper and cover with a bell-jar or its equivalent. In a few hours (leaving over night is common practice) the spores will have made a distinct spore print. For critical comparison, and when matching a spore print against a colour chart for reference purposes a *thick* spore deposit is essential. This can usually be achieved by scooping up the spores on the paper with a square coverslip and then pressing down the spore mass with the same coverslip.

In the agarics, the spore print is obtained by cutting off the cap and placing it on white paper (with cover) as noted above. In these fungi, the commonest spore colour is white, but large groups are characterised by having spore prints which may be deep salmon-pink, rusty brown or snuff-brown (i.e. brown without red in it); purple brown, or black. *Lactarius* and *Russula* may have more or less yellowish spore prints. Lilac spore prints also occur, but blue or green ones are extremely rare. In the case of white spores, a very important property is the chemical reaction with Melzer's iodine. This is dealt with on page 232.

Microscopical examination of spores shows them to exhibit a high degree of variation as regards shape, size, and whether the wall is smooth or exhibits any sort of ornamentation—warts, spines, crests, etc. These differences are of great value in classification. Thus an agaric which throws down a deep salmon-pink spore print of more or less polygonal spores can at once be referred to the genus *Rhodophyllus*. This microscopical aspect of spores is referred to on page 229.

BIOLOGY OF FUNGI

As already noted, fungi obtain their nutrients by parasitising living organisms or by utilising their dead remains or dead products. In many very simple forms the mycelium grows freely in the soil, weaving its way over small pieces of leaves, dung, etc. In such cases it is very difficult to decide what sort of nutrients the fungus really requires. In a few cases it is possible to follow the growth of the mycelium because its activities, especially the production of fruit-bodies, result in the formation of " fairy rings." Here, in the first year, fruit-bodies are often found in a small cluster. By next season, the mycelium has died at the centre but continues to grow on the outside where fruit-bodies arise and thus form a ring. Every year a new ring is formed round the old one, the old mycelium dying away on the inside of the new. In this way there is a yearly increase in the diameter of the ring. Very often the grass is stimulated by the activities of the fresh mycelium and takes on a ranker growth and greener colour, so that the ring can be seen before the fruit-bodies appear.

Other saprophytic fungi have a more obvious relation to certain nutrient substrates. Thus many so-called coprophilic fungi grow on dung and will appear on fresh horse and cow droppings in 8–10 days. Very many more species are confined to decaying leaves and needles of the forest floor or to decaying wood such as tree stumps or bits of branches. Very often, individual species are restricted to the woods of certain groups of trees, for example, coniferous or deciduous, or in extreme cases, to a single tree genus or even species. Only a few of the larger fungi grow on the decaying parts of animals. A sort of " give and take " relation is very common between fungus mycelium and the roots of trees. This association, for which the term " mycorrhiza " is used, is established by the mycelium forming a dense mantle round the very fine root tips and penetrating the cells of the root cortex. Interchange of nutrients between fungus and tree has been demonstrated and may be beneficial to either partner. The relationship is complex and would seem to be delicately balanced, conditions sometimes favouring the fungus more than the tree and vice versa. Probably most, if not all, of the agarics form mycorrhiza. Here, too, there may be a considerable degree of host specificity: for example, *Boletus elegans* is restricted to larch, while *Amanita muscaria* forms mycorrhiza with birch as well as conifers and occasionally with beech.

Parasitic species are common among the Polypores, many growing on living trees and often killing the host. They may thus become a serious forestry problem. Examples are *Fomes annosus* (root rot, red rot) the most important cause of heart rot in our coniferous woods. *Ganoderma applanatum* is an equally serious cause of heart rot in our beech trees, causing much damage to large, over-mature parkland trees. Among Agarics, *Armillaria mellea* (" Honey Fungus ") is particularly insidious. It causes serious damage throughout the world to standing coniferous trees and under certain conditions may attack shrubs and even herbaceous plants such as potatoes, irises and strawberries. Broad-leaved trees are also attacked and it may also cause extensive decay of felled timber. It is also remarkable for its long, black, boot-lace-like rhizomorphs which occur between bark and wood of infected trees and spread the infection.

Much damage is also done by the essentially saprophytic fungi to constructional

14

timber, telegraph poles, railway sleepers, etc. In this connection, the "dry rot" fungus, *Serpula* (*Merulius*) *lacrymans*, causes extensive and costly damage to house property, almost always getting a hold at a spot where timber has become exposed to an abnormal amount of moisture. It is becoming more prevalent than was usual in newly constructed premises.

SEASONAL APPEARANCE OF FUNGI

Fungus mycelium is present in soil, wood, etc., throughout the year, but the development and appearance of fruit-bodies is restricted to certain times and varies with each species. Very few fungi " fruit " the whole year round. Spring is mainly the season for Cup fungi and Morels (Ascomycetes), but only very few toadstools (Agarics). The main toadstool flush starts, on average, towards the end of August. At about this time, a heavy downpour with continuing warm, humid conditions will be followed in a few days to a week or so by the appearance of fruit-bodies, especially species of *Boletus*, *Lactarius* and *Russula*. On average, the main season, at least for the larger fungi, is from about the beginning of September to about late October. Temperature and moisture are important determining factors. With little or no rainfall, very few fruit-bodies appear: mainly wood-inhabiting species and those in damp situations. In exceptional conditions, for example, prolonged absence of rain, the normal " flush " may fail to appear, but round about November, numerous small species may put in an appearance together with a few of the larger and commonly " late " or frost resistant species such as *Clitocybe nebularis* and *Tricholoma* (*Lepista*) *nudum*. Most Agarics are wiped out by severe frost, especially in open spaces, though a few toadstools like *Polyporus* (*Leucoporus*) *brumalis* and *Flammulina velutipes* may be found throughout a severe winter in periods of thaw. Several inconspicuous *Corticium* species are especially prevalent in winter months and in addition there are the large *Polyporus* species with perennial fruit-bodies.

EDIBLE AND POISONOUS FUNGI

For eating purposes, fungi are conveniently grouped as (1) good to excellent on their own as a main dish, (2) useful as flavouring for soups, stuffings, stews, omelettes, (3) harmless but worthless, (4) unpleasant and likely to cause more or less serious upsets, especially in some people who may be allergic, (5) deadly poisonous.

Judged by reasonably high standards, there are few really good to excellent

15

species. Amongst the best known are certain species of Mushroom (*Agaricus*)[1], Blewits (*Tricholoma [Lepista] personatum, nudum*) Parasols (*Lepiota procera, rhacodes*), the Chantarelle (*Cantharellus cibarius*), several Boleti (*Boletus edulis* especially), Shaggy cap (*Coprinus comatus*), Horn of Plenty (*Craterellus cornucopioides*) and certain species of *Russula* (*R. cyanoxantha, virescens*). In the text, such and similar species are called " edible and good." They may be fried and served with or without a thick sauce as is done for the common cultivated mushroom or they may be put in a greased pie-dish with a little water, covered with grease-proof paper and baked in a moderate oven till tender—usually about twenty minutes. Horn of Plenty, Chantarelle and Boleti are particularly useful for drying on the day of gathering and can subsequently be used to flavour soups, sauces and stews. Those edible species which are most useful as flavourings or for mixing with species of the first group to make these go further are referred to as " good " " good in stews."

The third group, " harmless but worthless," is the largest, mostly small species with little " flesh " in the cap or those of an excessively tough consistency. In the text, these are given no designation or referred to as " worthless." The next group comprises species which, though not deadly, may be slightly poisonous and are " best avoided." Some have a sharp or bitter taste or are known to produce unpleasant symptoms, at least in some people. Perhaps the best known of these, because it is sometimes mistaken for the Field or Cultivated or Horse Mushrooms, is the Yellow Stainer (*Agaricus xanthodermus*).

Other dangerous species in this group are *Rhodophyllus* (*Entoloma*) *sinuatus* and related species; *Hebeloma crustuliniforme; Ramaria formosa;* and a few others. Probably a number of fungi are poisonous when raw such as " The Blusher " (*Amanita rubescens*) which is commonly eaten when cooked. It is, in fact, a real example of an edible toadstool with a thermolabile poisonous principle. For use in the raw state with salads and other uncooked foods, only the best edible fungi should be used such as those in the first group.

A few of the sharp-tasting species have been used as spices. In some countries, an acrid species such as *Russula emetica* is used as food and even " salted down," the burning taste disappearing on cooking. However, for most people, any unpleasant smell or taste tends to discourage gastronomic experiments : such toadstools are best avoided.

The last group, those fungi that are deadly, contains few species. Unfortunately, there is no simple rule-of-thumb method by which a deadly species can be recognised. Quite unrelated genera of the larger fungi contain deadly representatives. They occur in open country as well as in woods; in spring and in autumn. About ninety per cent of deaths are attributable to the not uncommon (in some years) " Death Cap " (*Amanita phalloides*). The closely related " Destroying Angel " (*Amanita virosa*) and " Fool's Mushroom " (*Amanita verna*)

[1] Following Ramsbottom, it is convenient to restrict the word Mushroom to species of the genus *Agaricus* (=*Psalliota*) except for long established names, e.g. St. George's Mushroom (*Tricholoma gambosum*).

are also deadly, but distinctly rare. In Death Cap (*A. phalloides*) the toxic principle is a complex mixture of a and b amanitoxin and phalloidin—both relatively simple polypeptides containing sulphur. The toxin is not destroyed by cooking and is unaffected by human digestive juices. Symptoms do not occur until eight to twenty-four hours after ingestion by which time much of the toxin has been absorbed into the body, so that vomiting and the use of a stomach pump are not very effective as treatment. The symptoms of poisoning include severe stomach pains, vomiting and nervous disorders. The patient remains conscious and may even pass through a period when the symptoms undergo remission only to be followed by their exacerbation. In the absence of continuing improvement, death occurs after two to ten days of great suffering. A single cap of *Amanita phalloides* in a fungus dish is more than sufficient to cause death. *Lepiota fuscovinacea* and related species produce similar results but are rare. " Panther cap " (*Amanita pantherina*) causes a severe atropine poisoning which has been followed by fatalities. The toxin affects the central nervous system causing violent convulsions, dilation of the pupils and palpitations. Symptoms arise after one to three hours. Chances of recovery are quite good. The " Fly Agaric " (*Amanita muscaria*) also contains atropine, but in smaller amounts, together with a second toxin, muscarine. In appropriate amounts, these two toxins tend to neutralise one another, but ingestion of the fungus normally causes an atropine poisoning with symptoms of intoxication. Fatalities from this toadstool seem to be very unusual. Larger amounts of muscarine occur in several other fungi and death has followed their ingestion. Examples are *Clitocybe rivulosa, C. dealbata*, some species of *Inocybe*, especially *I. napipes* and *I. patouillardii*. Other species of *Inocybe* as well as other small white species of *Clitocybe* contain smaller quantities of muscarine and are thus potentially dangerous.

In other species, the nature of the toxin is uncertain. Species of the rare *Gyromitra* are known to contain a haemolytic toxin referred, with much uncertainty, to " Helvellic acid." Nevertheless, they are sometimes eaten, apparently with no ill effects, after a preliminary boiling, the boiling water being thrown away—a procedure which has been claimed to render innocuous any toadstool. This is not true, and fatalities have followed reliance on it. Morels also have been known to give rise to serious symptoms of poisoning and these have been attributed to " Helvellic acid."

Finally, two other fungus toxins have been recently demonstrated. It had been known for some time that the eating of *Coprinus atramentarius*, together with the consumption of alcoholic drinks, caused a series of unpleasant symptoms. The treatment of chronic alcoholism by the substance " Antabuse "[1] was discovered independently but was later found to be identical with a substance in *C. atramentarius*. Also, it has long been known that certain American-Indian tribes of Mexico reached trance-like states by eating certain plants. It has now been shown that the plants are, in fact, fungi; especially small, inconspicuous species of *Psilocybe*. The species concerned are not known from this country,

[1] bis (diethylthio carbamoyl) disulphide.

but some native related species contain similar substances. Attempts at experimenting with these should be discouraged.

Fungus poisonings and fatalities in this country, are, happily, rare. Nevertheless, it cannot be too strongly urged that unfamiliar fungus species should not be consumed in any circumstances unless they have been identified by a competent mycologist so that their properties can be looked up. Even with undoubted edible specimens, a few elementary precautions may be mentioned. Only fresh, healthy-looking specimens should be prepared for the table, and as they decompose rapidly after picking, they should not be kept more than 24 hours before being used, and then preferably in a refrigerator and not in closed tins, polythene bags, or any small enclosed space where the high humidity hastens putrefaction. The keeping of cooked remnants is also ill-advised.

As with the commonest foods, so with the edible fungi: a few people exhibit varying degrees of allergy towards one or more species. This is true of the widely consumed cultivated and wild mushrooms as well as the Chantarelle. To minimise possible upsets, one should not at first, consume a large quantity of a previously untried species of edible fungus, even if its harmlessness is assured by other people from their own personal experience.

In conclusion, it is again emphasised that correct identification is essential; in doubtful cases, the help of a competent mycologist should be sought. In the absence of such help all doubtful specimens should be unhesitatingly discarded. Of those about which one is certain, their preliminary preparation should be done on gathering: stems cut off and any extraneous material such as soil, leaves, the odd animal, removed. Normally, gills, tubes, cuticle are left in place. When about to be cooked, any remaining dirt can be just wiped off. Unless exceedingly dirty, washing of fungi is not required. The peeling of Mushrooms (*Agaricus* spp.), especially the cultivated Mushroom, is quite unnecessary.

GUIDE TO DESCRIPTIONS

For reasons of space, general diagnoses in the descriptive part are given only for the larger genera. In the remaining cases, the generic characters can be obtained from the Key. After the name, a curt diagnosis is given in italics. This seeks to emphasise important differential diagnostic features, especially as between closely related species. Then follows a short description, the average, mature specimen being borne in mind, but in some important cases, younger as well as older stages are described. Size and shape are at once apparent from the illustrations, which unless otherwise stated are reduced to two-thirds natural size. Spore colour is commonly mentioned for the genera and sometimes for individual species if it is divergent.

It is not easy to convey the colour of fruit-bodies, and colour is often important for determination. Much use is made by specialists of " Colour Charts " of which a number are in use but, as yet, no single one is universally accepted. In this book, common everyday colour terms have been used as far as possible. Here, again, the illustrations will prove of great help. Another diagnostic feature difficult to convey in words namely the texture of the flesh. It may be hard and woody, or leathery, or cartilaginous to fibrous, or fleshy. Very often there are characteristic smells which once appreciated can be of great diagnostic value especially at the specific level. Three smells are particularly important: a sweetish smell very like coconut-toffee as in *Lactarius glyciosmus*; the smell of new meal with or without a somewhat rancid overtone as in *Clitocybe langei*; the earthy, so-called spermatic smell, found in many *Inocybe* species. Among other characteristic smells are: the aniseed smell (*Agaricus arvensis; Clitocybe odora*); radish (*Mycena pura, Hebeloma crustuliniforme*).

Taste also is of diagnostic importance particularly in the genera *Lactarius* and *Russula*, where a distinction must be made between acrid (rather like mustard) or mild, which amounts to being not acrid. Very often a farinaceous taste is evident (*Clitopilus prunulus, Tricholoma gambosum*) which runs parallel with the above-noted new meal smell. For tasting, a small piece about the size of a pea should be bitten off and chewed between teeth and tip of the tongue. This procedure is quite harmless, provided always the residue is finally spat out and not swallowed. Usually any taste becomes evident in about 30 seconds, but sometimes a minute or so is required as when a drop of the " milk " of *Lactarius rufus* is placed on the tip of the tongue.

Habitat has also been noted in the descriptions, but not always fully. Whenever appropriate, one should always note the tree under which a fungus is gathered, as this often greatly helps the identification, since, as has already been pointed out, most fungi form a more or less specific relationship with trees. But care must be exercised, especially in mixed woods, and sometimes the host tree may have gone while the fungus still lingers on.

Frequencies have been given and refer to an average season in appropriate habitats. But it must be remembered that even in a good season, some normally common species may be much less common and the contrary may happen, because they have very special habitat requirements.

Finally, edible or poisonous qualities are given, the terms used having been explained in the section beginning page 15.

USE OF THE KEY

The Key should present no difficulties to those familiar with the usual dichotomous (paired, contrasted characters) type. First the fungi are divided into six main divisions on the basis of fruit-body shape, and then within each division, subsequent dichotomies lead for most divisions to a genus   The species is then determined with the help of the illustrations and descriptions.

After a little experience, the main divisions can be spotted on sight.   In the Agaric division (Key A), it is also necessary to know the colour of spores in the mass, i.e. from a thick spore print on white paper.

For those unfamiliar with the dichotomous type of key, it may be pointed out that at each stage, two sets of contrasted characters are given and the appropriate one followed on; or, sometimes, one set of characters only is given.   The alternative being " not so " or " otherwise ".   For example:

> 13. Red, densely scaly, 14
>
> 13. Otherwise, 15

If the fungus under consideration is both red *and* densely scaly, one would proceed to the next set of characters under 14; if the fungus was red and *smooth* or brown and *densely scaly*, one would then go to 15.   Where two sets of contrasted characters are given, only that set is chosen which is wholly applicable.   Thus:

> 15. Brown, flesh thick, on wood, 16
>
> 15. Brown or reddish violet, on soil, 17

If the fungus is brown and thick-fleshed but grows on soil, one would take the second set of characters because " Brown *or* reddish violet, on soil " is wholly applicable.   If neither of the alternatives apply, it is possible that one may have slipped up at an earlier point in the Key, or the specimen under consideration may be abnormal or it may be an excluded species of unusual characters not covered by the Key.

KEY TO GENERA OF LARGER FUNGI

Key A Fruit-body a cap with gills on the underside, typically with central stipe, 20

Key B Fruit-body with stipe and cap or head, but without gills on the underside, 25.

Key C Fruit-body cup-shaped or turbinate, with or without stipe, 26

Key D Fruit-body globose, tuberous, pear-shaped or star-shaped (stellate), 27

Key E Fruit-body ± club-shaped, branched or not, 28

Key F Fruit-body bracket-like; irregularly lobed or forming a crust; on wood, 29

KEY A

a. Spores white; less often *pale* pinkish, cream to egg yellow, lilac, red or blue; mature gills usually taking colour of spores, p. 21

b. Spores *deep* salmon-colour; gills usually white at first, finally of same colour as spores, p. 23

c. Spores rusty, clay, or cigar brown; mature gills ± similarly coloured. p.23

d. Spores purplish or cocoa brown to ± black, mature gills chocolate colour to black, sometimes auto-digesting to inky fluid, p. 24

Spores green or reddish clay colour, cap ± mealy granular, *Lepiota echinata* 126

a. Spores white, etc.

1. Stipe excentric, lateral or absent; on wood, 2
1. Stipe central, 7
2. Edge of gill entire, 3
2. Edge of gill split longitudinally or serrate, 5
3. Fruit-body ligulate; stipe short, flattened, lateral; spores amyloid, *Panellus* 104. (Spores not amyloid in *P. nidulans*)
3. Fruit-body often of several caps; stipe ± terete; spores non-amyloid, 4
4. Brown, leathery, tough and dry, *Panus* 106
4. Grey, greyish blue or pallid; fleshy, *Pleurotus* 104
5. Edge of gill split; cap grey, fibrillose-squamulose, *Schizophyllum* 104
5. Edge of gill serrate, 6
6. Thick fleshed, coarsely squamose, ground colour white; spores non-amyloid, *Lentinus* 106
6. Thin fleshed, almost smooth, brown; spores amyloid, *Lentinellus* 102
7. Fleshy forms without scales on cap; stipe cheesy-brittle; intermediate gills typically absent or latex present, 8
7. Fleshy or delicate forms; stipe ± fleshy-fibrous; intermediate gills present, 9
8. With latex and intermediate gills: cap conical; stipe long, slender, *Mycena* 108: cap ± flat; stipe short, stoutish, *Lactarius* 206
8. No latex; intermediate gills typically absent; stipe + Fe: typically dirty pinkish or olive green, *Russula* 196
9. With distinct volva or volval remains (warts, scales) when young; scales on cap (when present) detachable, *Amanita* 116
9. No volva or remains; scales on cap (when present) not detachable, 10
10. With ring and remnants of veil on stipe, 11
10. No ring or remnants of veil, 17
11. Cap glutinous (moist weather), shining, smooth, 12
11. Cap usually ± scaly, mealy-granular or fibrillose; dry or viscid, 13
12. On the ground; pinkish-clay coloured, *Limacella* 120
12. On branches, esp. beech; porcelain-white, *Oudemansiella mucida* 106
13. Gills (arcuate) decurrent; usually ± tufted, *Armillaria* 92
13. Gills free, adnate or sinuate, 14
14. Cap finely mealy-granular, 15
14. Cap ± scaly or smooth, 16
15. Yellow, orange or flesh coloured; gills ± adnate, *Cystoderma* 128
15. Otherwise coloured; gills free, *Lepiota* 122

16. Cap ± easily separable from stipe by ball and socket-like joint; gills free; spores dextrinoid, *Lepiota* 122

16. Cap not easily separable; gills characteristically sinuate; spores not dextrinoid, *Tricholoma* 82 (With marginate bulb, see *Cortinarius bulbiger* 166)

17. Gills thick and distant; "waxy" species; cap often viscid and shining, *Hygrophorus* 76

17. Gills not thick and distant, or cap dry; not "waxy" species, 18

18. Gills ± markedly decurrent, 19

18. Gills free, adnate or sinuate, 23

19. Gills dichotomous, edge blunt or rounded, 20

19. Gills not dichotomous, edge ± sharp, 21

20. Wholly orange-yellow, spores dextrinoid, *Hygrophoropsis aurantiaca* 184

20. Wholly apricot-yellow or cap brownish-greyish-black; spores not dextrinoid, gills unspotted, *Cantharellus* 58

20. Cap grey to black; gills finally red spotted; spores amyloid, *Cantharellula umbonata* 102

21. Cap typically more than 2–3 cm diam.; stipe unpolished, typically more than 5 mm. diam., *Clitocybe* 92

21. Measurements typically smaller; stipe polished, 22

22. Small tough species; stipe reddish brown, darker towards yellowish brown felty base; spores amyloid, *Xeromphalina campanella* 108

22. Otherwise; spores not amyloid, *Omphalina* 98

23. Cap ± fleshy, i.e. relatively thick at centre; typically more than 2–3 cm diam.; stipe unpolished, typically more than 5 mm diam., 24 (The ± tufted greyish brown or white species of *Lyophyllum* may key out here)

23. Cap flesh relatively thin at centre; above measurements smaller; stipe ± polished, 31 (stipe fibrous in *Laccaria*: see 34 below)

24. Tufted on frondose stumps; cap tawny yellow, ± slimy; stipe velvety with brown tomentum, *Flammulina velutipes* 108

24. Otherwise, 25

25. Tufted on conifer stumps and cap with purplish tomentum on yellow background, or cap greyish to smoky brown, streaked with darker radiating fibrils; gills broad, distant, stipe with thick mycelial cords usually penetrating wood. *Tricholomopsis* 92

25. Otherwise, 26

26. Stipe hard, with long "taproot," springing ultimately from wood; cap brownish, slimy, puckered round central umbo, *Oudemansiella radicata* 106

26. Not this species, 27

27. Stipe fleshy, ± cracking when bent, unpolished; gills characteristically sinuate, 28

27. Stipe cartilaginous, at least externally, ± pliant when bent, ± polished; gills free to adnate, not sinuate, 30

28. ± tufted; greyish brown or white, *Lyophyllum* 80

28. Not tufted 29

29. Cap with relatively thick flesh and not translucid when wet; spores smooth rarely amyloid; gills without harpoon-like cystidia, *Tricholoma* 82

29. Cap with relatively thin flesh, ± translucid when wet; spores rough with amyloid warts; gills with harpoon-like cystidia, *Melanoleuca* 102

30. ± tufted; greyish brown or white, *Lyophyllum* 80

30. Not so, *Collybia* 100

31. Growing on ± rotting gill fungi, *Asterophora* 80
   (See also *Collybia cookei, tuberosa,* 102)

31. Not so, 32

32. Tufted on frondose stumps; cap tawny yellow ± slimy; stipe velvety with brown tomentum, *Flammula velutipes* 108

32. Otherwise, 33

33. Yellowish brick-red, bright red, pinkish lilac or violet, 34

33. Other colours, 35

34. Gills pallid whitish; cap smooth; spores ± oval, smooth, *Mycena* 108

34. Gills ± cap colour: yellowish brick-red or violet; cap scurfy; spores globose or sub-globose, prickly, *Laccaria* 98

35. Tough and leathery; can be dried out and water-revived without putrefying, *Marasmius* 114

35. Not so; ± putrescent, 36

36. On buried cones of conifers, 37

36. Not on cones, 38

37. Gills crowded; stipe minutely tomentose; spores amyloid, *Baeospora myosura* 112

37. Gills more distant; stipe ± smooth; spores non-amyloid, *Pseudohiatula esculenta* 112

38. Wholly ± grey, including flesh; typically with strong new meal smell, *Lyophyllum* 80

38. Otherwise; gills usually white or pale brown, 39

39. With white, red or orange latex, *Mycena* 108

39. No latex, 40

40. With "taproot" springing ultimately from wood; cap brownish, slimy, puckered round central umbo, *Oudemansiella radicata* 106

40. Otherwise, 41

41. Cap mostly conical or campanulate; edge of young cap never incurved; cystidia present, *Mycena* 108

41. Cap mostly convex to ± flat; edge of young cap incurved; cystidia typically absent, *Collybia* 100

b. Spores deep salmon-coloured

42. Cap and stipe easily detachable (ball and socket joint); gills free; often on wood, 43

42. Not so; nearly always on soil, 44

43. With volva at base of stipe, *Volvariella* 120

43. No volva, *Pluteus* 120

44. White, gills decurrent; strong smell of new meal, *Clitopilus* 178

44. Otherwise; spores always angular-polygonal, *Rhodophyllus* 178
(A few species of *Tricholoma*, p. 90, have *pale* pinkish ± oval, prickly spores; see also *Lepiota echinata* p. 126)

c. Spores rusty-brown, or clay- or cigar-brown

45. Fruit-body with rudimentary lateral stipe, *Crepidotus* 176
(See also *Paxillus panuoides*, p. 184)

45. Stipe central or slightly excentric, 46

46. With membranous ring, 47

46. Ring cobweb-like, soon inconspicuous, or absent, 49

47. Cap ± pruinose, yellowish brown; on soil, *Phaeolepiota aurea* 130

47. Cap scaly or smooth, 48

48. Cap white or dull brown, smooth; stipe not scaly; spores cigar brown; on soil; cuticle cellular, *Agrocybe* 152

48. Cap yellow or yellowish brown; stipe ± scaly; spores rusty to yellowish brown; usually on wood; cuticle filamentous, *Pholiota* 148
(See also, *Gymnopilus, Galerina*, p. 174)

49. Gills decurrent, reticulately anastomosing near stipe and easily pushed off from cap flesh, *Paxillus* 184

49. Otherwise, 50

50. Large or medium species with conspicuous flesh layer in cap; spores mostly rough or nodulose, if smooth then cigar brown, not rusty, 51

50. Delicate species without conspicuous flesh layer; spores mostly smooth, if rough then rusty brown, 54

51. On wood; brownish yellow; spores rough, rusty brown, *Gymnopilus* 174

51. On soil, 52

52. Spores rusty brown; young specimens with cobweb-like veil, *Cortinarius* 162

52. Spores dark clay or cigar brown, never rusty; young specimens with or without cobweb-like veil, 53

53. Cap smooth, often viscid, whitish pallid to clay colour, *Hebeloma* 160

53. Cap radially fibrillose or rimose to ± adpressed scaly, usually dry; spores ± nodulose; if smooth then mostly bean-shaped, *Inocybe* 154

54. Shining egg-yellow, ± viscid; very fragile; in rich grass, *Bolbitius* 152

54. Otherwise, 55

55. Cap conical-campanulate, 56

55. Cap ± flat, 59

56. Cap acutely conical; stipe rooting, *Phaeocollybia* 174

51. Cap obtusely conical; stipe not rooting, 57

57. With fishy cucumber smell; cap and gills with large lanceolate cystidia, *Macrocystidia*, 108

24

57. Not this combination, 58

58. Cap surface dull, dark brown or pallid, without veil; cap cuticle cellular, *Conocybe* 152

58. Cap surface ± shining, yellowish brown, often with veil; cap cuticle filamentous, *Galerina* 174

59. Cap surface mealy granular or with recurved scales, *Phaeomarasmius* 176

59. Cap smooth or with marginal white scales, 60

60. Whitish; gills decurrent; edge of cap with minute hairs; spores clay brown, *Ripartites* 176

60. Not this combination; brownish or yellowish brown, 61

61. Cap ± flat with white, marginal scales; spores smooth, *Tubaria* 176

61. Not this combination; under alder or willow; spores rough, *Naucoria* 162

d. Spores purple-brown, cocoa-brown to black

62. Gills and cap auto-digesting into inky fluid at maturity, *Coprinus* 136

62. Not so, 63

63. Thick-fleshed; gills decurrent, veil glutinous, spores bistre-black, *Gomphidius* 184

63. Otherwise, 64

64. Gills mottled by uneven ripening of rough, brown spores or smooth, lemon-shaped black spores, *Panaeolus* 144
    cf. *Psathyrella lacrymabunda* with conspicuous veil and coarsely warted purplish black spores.

64. Otherwise; if gills mottled then spores and gills purple, 65

65. Cap thin fleshed, ± conical, grey or brown and ± striate when moist; ring typically absent; stipe white, mostly longer than twice cap diameter; cap cuticle always cellular, *Psathyrella* 140

65. Not this combination; cap cuticle filamentous, 66

66. Cap ± fleshy, white or brown, often adpressed scaly, never slimy; gills free; membranous ring present; on soil, never tufted; spores cocoa-brown, *Agaricus* 130

66. Otherwise; gills adnate; stipe mostly not white; spores purplish, 67

67. With ± membranous ring; cap bluish green, yellowish brown or brown, with separable pellicle, ± slimy, *Stropharia* 144

67. Not this combination, 68

68. No membranous ring, but young specimens with cobweb-like partial veil; cap bright yellow to reddish brown; species often tufted and on wood, *Hypholoma* 146

68. Without veil or ring; mostly brownish, *Psilocybe* 148

KEY B

Stipe with cap or head, but no real gills.
(With internal powdery spore mass, cf. D.)

1. Cap with pores or tubes on underside, **2**
1. Cap underside smooth, ribbed or veined or with pointed, peg-like " teeth," 4
2. Flesh ± hard; usually "brackets" on wood, *Polyporaceae* 62
2. Flesh ± soft; stipe central; on soil, 3
3. Cap smooth or minutely and softly scaly, *Boletus* 186
    (See also *Caloporus ovinus* 72)
3. Cap with ± overlapping coarse scales; blackish grey; flesh turns reddish, *Strobilomyces* 194
4. Underside of cap with pointed, peg-like " teeth," *Hydnaceae* 58
4. No " teeth," 5
5. Fruit-body funnel-shaped; underside smooth, hairy or with veins or ribs, 6
5. Otherwise, 8
6. With veins or ribs on underside, *Cantharellus* 58. Not so, **7**
7. Blackish brown, blackish grey, margin lobed, *Craterellus* 58
7. Brown or brownish violet, margin frayed-fimbriate, *Thelephora terrestris* 52
8. Apical cap with nasty-smelling spore mass; stipe ± cylindrical, 9
8. Not so, 10
9. Stipe white, cap with green spore mass; smell foetid, *Phallus* 214
9. Stipe orange with olive brownish spore mass at apex; smell faecal, *Mutinus* 214
10. With lacunose, folded, saddle-shaped or smooth cap or head, 11
10. With globose, spathulate or indistinctly delimited cap, 16
11. More than 4 cm high, fleshy or brittle, 12
11. Less than 4 cm high, gelatinous or tough, 15
12. Cap with honeycomb-like pits, *Morchella* 40
12. Cap folded or smooth, 13
13. Cap smooth, campanulate, brown, *Verpa* 40
13. Cap folded or saddle-shaped, 14
14. Cap brown with contorted folds, *Gyromita* 38
14. Cap white, grey, greyish brown or black, irregularly folded or saddle-shaped, *Helvella* 38
15. Gelatinous tough, slimy, amber yellow; stipe smooth, *Leotia* 44
15. Not slimy, but ± dry, leather yellow; stipe ± tomentose, *Cudonia* 44
16. On wood, black, like coal, *Xylaria* 46
16. Not on wood, 17
17. Head minutely punctate; spathulate or globose, *Claviciptales* 48
17. Head not minutely punctate, 18
18. Parasitic on hair, hooves or feathers; a few mm. high, *Onygena* 48
18. On soil, larger, 19
19. Yellow, *Spathularia* 44
19. Black or green, *Geoglossum* 44

Fruit-body cup-shaped to turbinate
(*Tough, leathery.* ± *pitcher-shaped*, see D 11
Papery with brownish spore mass, see D 7)

1. Turbinate; on bark, branches or dung, 2
1. Cup shaped or ± flattened, 5
2. Greyish brown; stipe black tomentose; on horse droppings, *Poronia* 46
2. Not on horse dung, 3
3. Blackish brown, brown tomentose outside; rubbery; on bark of oak or beech, *Bulgaria* 44 (See also F)
3. Otherwise, 4
4. Brown or black; on branches, *Tremella* 224
4. Violet; on trunks or stumps, *Coryne* 44
5. Brightly coloured, 6
5. Black, grey, brown or pale, 10
6. Shining red to reddish orange, *Peziza* 34
6. Yellow, blue-green or violet, 7
7. Yellow, on soil, more than 1 cm. across, *Peziza radiculata* 34
7. On wood, 8
8. Yellow, usually stipitate, a few mm. across; on sticks, acorns, etc., *Helotium* 42
8. Blue-green or violet, 9
9. Blue-green; on wood similarly coloured, *Chlorosplenium* 42
9. Violet; on stumps or trunks, *Coryne* 44
10. Dark brown, with distinct stipe, 11
10. Otherwise, 12
11. On wood, *Rutstroemia* 42
11. From black sclerotia, *Sclerotinia* 42
12. Stipe tall, ribbed and/or lacunose, *Helvella* 38
12. Stipe short ± smooth, or absent, 13
13. Flattened, low bladder-like; conspicuous rhizoids from lower surface; on burnt ground, *Rhizina* 36
13. No such rhizoids on underside, *Peziza* 34

KEY D
Fruit-body globose, tuberous, pear-shaped or stellate

1. Growing on earth or on wood, 2
1. Subterranean, 15
2. With powdery spore mass inside at maturity, 3. Not so, 8
3. Stellate when mature, with ± globose middle part, *Geastrum* 220
3. Not stellate splitting, 4

4. With long, thin ± woody stipe immersed in sand, *Tulostoma* 222
4. With short stipe, or sessile, 5
5. Outer layer thick and hard, smooth or cracked, yellowish or yellowish brown; spore mass slate-grey, *Scleroderma* 222
5. Outer layer smooth or spiny, more papery (at maturity), greyish to brown, 6
6. Globose; more than 20 cm. across, *Lycoperdon giganteum* 216
6. Pear-shaped, or globose; smaller, 7
7. Outer layer white, peeling off at maturity; no sterile tissue at base, *Bovista* 218
7. Outer layer spiny or ± coarsely granular (at least when young); usually with sterile tissue at base, *Lycoperdon* 216
8. Leathery or fleshy; yellow, grey or white, 9
8. Red, rufous or black, globose; on wood, 12
9. Tuberous to globose; slate-grey inside, *Scleroderma* 222
9. Pitcher-shaped, or stellate, 10
10. Stellate, 1–3 mm. across, *Sphaerobolus* 222
10. Pitcher-shaped, with lentoid "eggs" at bottom, 11
11. Straw-yellow to tan coloured, cylindric *Crucibulum* 222
11. Brown or greyish brown, funnel shaped, *Cyathus* 222
12. Like charcoal, globose, black more than 1 cm. across; concentrically zoned internally, *Daldinia* 46
12. Red, rufous or brownish black, 13
13. Like charcoal; rufous to brownish black, 3–10 mm. across, *Hypoxylon* 46
13. Red or reddish yellow, 1–3 mm. across, 14
14. Coral red, rather hard; on sticks, often crowded, *Nectria cinnabarina* 46
14. Reddish yellow, gelatinous; on wood, *Dacrymyces* 224
15. Internally chambered; outside smooth, 16
15. Internally veined or with labyrinthine canals opening on surface; outisde smooth, spiny or warty, 21
16. White; size of marble or egg; slimy inner layer over greenish spore mass, *Phallus* and *Mutinus* " eggs," 214
16. Without slimy layer, etc., 17
17. White, greyish brown or slightly greenish, 18
17. Yellowish brown or dark brown, attached to brown cord-like rhizomorphs, 20
18. White with greenish tinge; mature spore mass purple brown, *Arcangeliella* 214
18. Otherwise, 19
19. Spore mass greenish olive, solid; outer layer easily detachable, *Hysterangium* 214
19. Spore chambers more open, *Hymenogaster* 214
20. Yellowish brown to tan with distinct chambers, *Rhizopogon* 214
20. Dark brown with indistinct chambers, *Melanogaster* 214
21. Minutely warty-spiny, yellowish brown; spore mass dark with few veins, finally powdery, *Elaphomyces* 48
   (See also subterranean forms of *Scleroderma*, 222)

21. Spore mass not finally powdery, 22
22. Rufous; internally with contorted veins opening on surface, *Hydnotrya* 42
22. Without such veins, 23
23. Brown or yellowish brown; internally pale to rufous, *Tuber* 42
23. Black and coarsely warty, 24
24. Internally greenish yellow, often somewhat hollow, *Pachyphloeus* 42
24. Internally pale to reddish violet, *Tuber* 42

KEY E
Fruit-body club-shaped or branched

1. Unbranched or sparingly branched, 2
1. Branched, 4
2. Brown, white or yellow, *Clavaria* 54
2. Otherwise coloured, 3
3. Black, tough to coal-like; on wood, *Xylaria* 46
3. Black or brightly coloured; not on wood: see Key B 17–19
4. Shining yellow; tough, horny, somewhat slimy, *Calocera* 224
4. Otherwise, 5
5. Dark brown, leathery; branches slightly flattened, *Thelephora* 52
5. Not leathery, 6
6. Black often with white powdered tips; on wood, *Xylaria* 46
6. Otherwise coloured, 7
7. Cauliflower-like with flat branches, pale brown; base of pine stump, *Sparassis* 56
7. Branching coralloid; branches terete, 8
8. Branches pendulous, ± awl-shaped; on wood, *Hydnaceae* 58
8. On soil, often erect, 9
9. Branches numerous, thread-like, feathery, *Pterula* 56
9. Branches thicker, *Ramaria* 56
   (Branches few; fruit-body soft, like wax, *Clavaria* 54)

KEY F
Fruit-bodies bracket-shaped, irregularly lobed or crust-like; on wood

1. Fruit-bodies bracket-shaped, ligulate or crust-like with distinctly expanded margins, 2
1. Forming a crust, or irregularly lobed and gelatinous, 12
2. Underside with pores or gills, 3
2. Underside with teeth, tuberculate, reticulate or smooth, 7
3. Underside with round or angular pores, 4
3. Underside with greatly elongated gill-like pores, 5

4. Flesh soft, red, exuding red juice, *Fistulina* 74

4. Otherwise, *Polyporaceae* 62

5. Flesh bright rusty brown to yellowish brown, *Gloeophyllum* 70

5. Flesh white or dull brown, 6

6. Flesh thick, woody; on stumps especially of oak, *Daedalea* 66

6. Flesh thin, woody; upper surface ± woolly-hairy, *Trametes betulinus* 70

7. Underside smooth or tuberculate, 8

7. Underside reticulate or with teeth, 9

8. Yellow, greyish or violet; hymenium smooth, *Stereum* 50

8. Dark (reddish) brown; hymenium bristly (lens), *Hymenochaete* 52

9. Underside with teeth, 10

9. Underside (sometimes upper side) reticulately veined, 11

10. Greyish, gelatinous, *Pseudohydnum gelatinosum* 224

10. Whitish, yellow; brittle, *Hydnaceae* 58

11. Upper surface greyish white, silky hairy, *Merulius tremellosus* 52

11. Upper surface greyish brown, *Serpula* 52

12. Crust-like, 13

12. Ear-shaped or folded-contorted; distinctly gelatinous, 18

13. Under surface with pores; orifices sometimes jagged, *Polyporaceae* 62

13. Under surface smooth or tuberculate, 14

14. Hard, coal-black, 15

14. Soft-fleshed, 16

15. Large irregular, crust-like, *Ustulina* 46

15. 0.5 cm across, bursting through bark; disc-like, angular, *Diatrype* 46

16. Orange; somewhat tuberculate, *Phlebia radiata* 52

16. Whitish, greyish or brown, 17

17. Whitish, greyish or pale brown, *Corticium* 50

17. Yellowish brown with small brown warts, *Coniophora puteana* 52

18. Ear-shaped, brownish; especially on Elder, *Auricularia* 224

18. Contorted; yellow, white, black or blackish-brown, *Tremella* 224

GLOSSARY

adnate, (gill attachment), see Fig. 5, p.11.

adpressed, closely flattened down, as if by flat-iron; commonly of scales on a fruit-body; see p. 149, *Pholiota destruens*.

amyloid, (of spores), when spore mass on glass slide turns blue-black in Melzer's iodine.

anastomosing, joining together.

annulate, (of stipe), having a ring (annulus).

annulus, same as ring on stipe of many agarics.

appendiculate, of gill fungi, where ± expanded cap edge is fringed with tooth-like velar remains, e.g. *Psathyrella candolleana*, p. 141.

arachmoid, pertaining to spiders; esp. "arachnoid veil" = cobweb-like.

apothecium, the (open) cup or saucer-like fertile part of a Discomycete; see Fig. 1 and p. 35.

ascocarp, general term for an ascus-producing structure.

ascus, sac-like body bearing spores internally (see p. 7).

basidium, club-shaped body, bearing spores externally (see p. 10).

campanulate, bell-shaped; like flower of Canterbury bell.

capillitium, (Gasteromycetales), branched or unbranched thread-like fibres among spore mass.

chlamydospore, thick walled, asexual spore formed by enlargement of hyphal cell or cells, as in *Asterophora*.

clavate, club-shaped.

concolorous, of same colour as.

concrescent, of structures becoming joined as they grow together.

connate, joined together.

coriaceous, of leathery consistency.

cortina, (of agarics), the cobweb-like partial veil between cap margin and stipe in many young toadstools, e.g. in *Cortinarius*, p. 165.

crenate, where an edge is shallowly and finely wavy, e.g. *Hygrophorus turundus*, p. 79 (cap margin).

crust-like, spread over and forming a usually thin, closely adherent layer (crust) on the substratum.

cusp, a small ± pulled-out point.

cuticle, the outermost layer, e.g. of cap or stipe in an agaric.

decurrent, (of gill attachment) see Fig. 5, p. 11.

dentate, toothed.

denticulate, with little teeth.

depressed, (of toadstool caps), with the middle at lower level than edge, like a saucer.

dextrinoid, (of spores), when spore mass on glass slide turns red-brown in Melzer's iodine.

dichotomous, (usually of gills), forked into ± equal branches.

disc, (of toadstool cap) the surface part immediately above stipe; (of Discomycete) the layer of the apothecium comprising asci and associated structures.

discomycete, a Cup fungus; a sub-class of Ascomycetes, having the asci ± exposed on a ± cup-or saucer-shaped apothecium, e.g. Pezizales, see Fig. 1, p. 8., cf. pyrenomycete.

double ring, where partial and universal veils combine to make a ring, the outer veil often becoming stellately stretched or torn; see *Agaricus arvensis*, p. 135.

effused, ± irregularly spread over substrate.

effused-reflex, as previous, but the edges ± turned up.

emarginate, (of gill attachment), ± same as sinuate (q.v.) but the sinus where gill almost joins stipe, is much more cut-away and conspicuous.

farinaceous, farinose, like meal in form or smell.

fibrils, small fibres ± visible to naked eye.

fimbriate, with tassel-like edge.

flocci, cotton-like tufts.

floccose, ± cottony.

flocculose, with delicate flocci.

free, (of gill attachment), see Fig. 5, p. 11.

frondose, (of trees), deciduous or broad-leaved trees, shrubs.

fugacious, soon disappearing; e.g. the

ring on some toadstool stipes.

fulvous, (colour), palish yellow-tawny; paler than a lion's mane.

fusiform, spindle shaped, tapering at both ends.

glabrous, free of hair, smooth.

gleba, the spore-bearing tissue especially of Gasteromycetales and Tuberales.

globose, globe-shaped.

hispid, with short stiff hairs.

hymenium, the fertile layer of asci, basidia and associated structures.

imbricate, $\pm$ overlapping, like tiles on a roof.

infundibuliform, funnel-shaped.

inoperculate, of ascus, which opens by an irregular apical slit to release spores. cf. operculate.

intermediate, (of gills), short gills which do not extend the full length, e.g. do not reach stipe in a gill fungus.

involute, having the edge turned under.

lacinate, of edges, as if shortly cut into slender segments.

lacunose, of a surface having layer of sunken gaps, e.g. stipe of *Phallus impudicus*, p. 215; stipe of *Helvella lacunosa*, p. 39.

ligulate, shaped $\pm$ like a tongue.

marginate, (of basal bulb of stipe), having a circular, gutter-like rim, e.g. *Inocybe asterospora*, p. 159; *Cortinarius bulbiger*, p. 167.

nodulose, (of spores), with broad-based, blunt wart-like excrescences.

operculate, of ascus, which opens by apical lid to release spores, cf. inoperculate.

papillate, (of caps) with small central conical process, e.g. *Lactarius tabidus*, p. 209.

pellicle, (of gill fungi), detachable, skin-like cuticle of the cap.

pellucid-striate, (of gill fungi), where water-soaked caps of certain species are sufficiently transparent for gills to be seen through them, especially towards margin, when viewed from above.

peridum, the wall(s) or limiting membrane of a fruit-body, e.g. of Gasteromycetales.

perithecium, a flask-shaped structure containing asci and opening by apical pore; characteristic of the Pyrenomycetes, see Fig. 3, p. 9; cf. apothecium.

peronate, sheathed, esp. of stipe which is sheathed from below upwards.

pilose, covered with easily visible, longish hairs.

pruinose, appearing as if frosted or dusted with powder.

pyrenomycete, a Flask fungus, the asci being grouped in a perithecium.

resupinate, (of fruit-bodies), lying flat on the substratum, with the hymenium facing outwards, e.g. many Aphyllophorales, *Phlebia*, p. 53; occasionally in Agaricales, *Crepidotus variabilis*, p. 177.

reticulate, in the form of a net.

revolute, (of caps), where extreme edge is rolled up and (usu.) back.

rhizoids, root-like structures, e.g. *Rhizina undulata*, p. 37.

rhizomorph, easily visible thread or cord-like structure made up of closely packed hyphae, e.g. *Armillaria mellea*, p. 93, base of stipe.

rimose, (of gill fungi), where hyphae of cap become slightly separated radially, showing underlying tissue, e.g. many species *Inocybe*, p. 159.

rugose, $\pm$ wrinkled rough.

saprophyte, organism living on dead

organic material as food; adj. saprophytic.

sclerotium,—ia, a ± hard, often round mass of closely packed hyphae, e.g. *Collybia cirrhata, tuberosa,* p. 103.

septate, divided by cross wall(s).

serous, (of "milk," latex), like serum: watery opalescent; neither clearlike water nor opaque like drop of oil paint.

serrate, edged with teeth, like a saw, gill of *Lentinellus cochleatus,* p. 102.

sessile, without stipe.

spatulate, shaped ± like a flat spoon or spatula.

spermatic, (smell), a distinctive rank, unpleasant, strong "earthy" smell.

squamose, having scales (squamae).

squamulose, having smaller scales (squamae).

squarrose, turned back ± at right angles esp. of scales, e.g. *Pholiota squarrosa,* p. 149.

sterile base, (puff balls), rubber-sponge like tissue at base of some species of *Lycoperdon,* e.g. *L. depressum,* p. 219.

stipe, commonly used by many mycologists for the supporting stalk of fungus fruit-bodies. The words stipe, stem, stalk are often interchanged.

stipitate, having a stipe.

stratified, in ± horizontal layers, esp. the tubes of perennial polypores.

striate, marked with ± thin lines, as in margin of some water soaked agaric caps.

strigose, beset with long, ± firm coarse hairs, e.g. stipe base of many spp. of *Mycena,* p. 111.

sub-globose, roughly globe-shaped.

sulcate, grooved, furrowed, e.g. cap margin of *Russula foetens,* p. 197.

terete, circular in cross-section.

thermolabile, of poisons, enzymes, etc.; destroyed, rendered inactive by heating.

tomentose, thickly downy with soft, matted hairs.

tuberculate, having small, wart-like pimples, visible to naked eye.

turbinate, shaped like a top.

umbilicate, having a small, localised depression, e.g. cap of *Omphalina swartzii,* p. 99.

umbo, a central, broad swelling like the boss on a shield, e.g. caps of many gill fungi, as *Mycena galericulata,* p. 109.

umbonate, having an umbo.

velar, pertaining to universal or partial veil.

venose, looking like veins, often raised above general surface.

ventricose, protruding at the middle of a structure, usually to one side.

verrucose, having wart-like protuberances.

ABBREVIATIONS

In the gill fungi, a " small " cap can be covered by about a half-penny.

ASCOMYCETES—CUP FUNGI AND ALLIES

PEZIZALES

Peziza (Sarcoscypha) coccinea. *Disc scarlet; cup whitish-yellow outside, tomentose; stipe short.* Cup 2–6 cm diam., finally ± expanded; stipe tomentose. Decayed branches in woods on rich soil. XII–II (–III). C (local).

Peziza (Pseudoplectania) nigrella. *Disc ± shining, coal-black; outside of cup brown tomentose.* Cup 1–4 cm diam., at first involute, finally ± expanded. On conifer needles. III. R.

Peziza (Sowerbyella) radiculata. *Wholly lemon-yellow with long hairy rooting stripe.* Cup 2–6 cm diam., disc paler somewhat irregularly saucer-shaped. Under conifers (? always). IX–XI. R–O.

Peziza (Pustularia) catinus. Geopyxis. *Cup pale clay, margin crenate; ± stalked.* Cup 1–3 cm diam., covered by thin membrane when young, downy outside. Light, rich soil in woods, esp. by paths. VI—IX. O–F.

Peziza (Humaria) hemisphaerica. Lachnea. *Cup dark brown outside with black, septate hairs; disc whitish.* Cup 0.5–2 cm diam., sessile, ± deep saucer-shaped. In woods, on soil esp. along paths. VII–X. C.

Peziza (Scutellinia) scutellata. Lachnea. *Cup scarlet with black marginal hairs.* Cup 0.5–1 cm diam., finally ± flat, sl. paler outside. Damp soil, branches, and roots. V–XI. C.

Peziza (Neotiella) rutilans. *Cup orange-red, hyaline, hairy outside; stipe short.* Cup 0.5–1.5 cm diam., finally ± expanding, paler outside; stipe often buried in soil. Heaths, esp. among *Polytrichum*. X–I. F–C.

Peziza (Aleuria) aurantia. *Cup large, sessile, scarlet-orange inside, whitish and downy outside.* Cup 1–12 cm diam., irregular, ± cup-shaped, often split, finally ± expanded. Esp. on bare gravels; also paths, lawns, bare soil in woods. IX–I. C.

Peziza saniosa. Galactinia. *Disc bluish-grey inside; cup blackish-brown outside, ± mealy; flesh yields bluish juice.* Cup 1–2 cm diam. finally ± expanded. On rich soil in woods. X. R.

Peziza succosa. Galactinia. *Cup grey-brownish outside, sl. pruinose; disc brownish with olive or violet tinge; flesh yields yellowish juice.* Cup 1–4 cm diam., cup-shaped, margin involute, finally irregularly flattened. Bare soil, esp. on woodland paths. VII–IX. C.

Peziza coccinea

Peziza nigrella

Peziza catinus

Peziza rutilans

Peziza scutellata

Peziza saniosa

Peziza radiculata

Peziza hemisphaerica

Peziza aurantia
"Orange peel Peziza"

Peziza succosa

Peziza badia. *Dark brown, outside paler and mealy.* 2–7(8) cm high ± cup shaped margin soon flexuose, sessile disc liver-brown with olive tint. On ground in woods. VIII–X. F–C.

Peziza repanda. *Light brownish, cup-shaped to flattened, 3–10 (12) cm.* Margin soon irregularly flexuose-undulate; disc dark tan to pale hazel, outside paler ± mealy; often with stem-like base. On rich soil, leaves, esp. round tree stumps in frondose woods; large forms on sawdust. IX–XI, V. O.

Peziza vesiculosa. *Pale yellowish-brown, at first globose, soon irregularly cup-shaped with incurved, flexuose, notched margin, 2–5(8) cm high, often in groups.* Disc yellowish-tan to honey, outside paler, mealy. On rich soil, manure heaps. VIII–IV. F–C.

Peziza (Otidea) leporina Batsch ex. Fr. *Ear-shaped, dull tan, 2–6 cm high, on spruce needles.* At first pitcher-shaped, soon narrowly ear-shaped with inrolled margin; disc dark tan to hazel, outside paler and mealy; base stem-like, short, hairy. VIII–X. O.

Peziza (Otidea) onotica. *Yellowish with flesh tinge, slender to broad, ear-shaped, 3–10 cm high, ear-shaped lobes to 5 cm wide, margin inrolled or ± flattened, in clusters.* Disc yellowish with flesh tinge, outside yellowish-tan, finely mealy; stipe short, whitish, densely hairy. On ground in frondose woods. IX. O.

The cup fungi mentioned above are but a selection of our largest, commonest, or at least most striking, species.

Rhizina undulata, inflata. *Dark brownish to black, lower surface with numerous whitish root-like structures.* 2–8 cm high, at first disc-shaped, then cushion-shaped and irregularly lobed; margin paler; very tough. Coniferous debris, esp. after fires. VI–X. C. × 1

Peziza badia

Peziza vesiculosa

Peziza repanda

Peziza leporina

Rhizina undulata

Peziza onotica

Gyromitra esculenta. *Mop-like, to 12 cm high, cap sub-globose, contorted, convolute.* Cap 3–8 cm each way, dark date-brown to sooty-brown; stem short, stout, about half diam. of cap, whitish, somewhat grooved, irregularly hollow. Sandy soils in conifer areas. Spring (IV). O–F, more common northwards. *Poisonous to some, even deadly* (though often eaten after special treatment). *To be avoided.*

Helvella—False Morels

Fertile head ± cup-shaped to saddle-shaped, folded. Stipe usually distinct, cylindrical, smooth, ribbed or furrowed. The species are sometimes eaten, but cause indigestion in some people. Best avoided.

Helvella (Cyathipodia) macropus. *Solitary, head saucer-shaped, mouse-grey, edge and underside hairy* 2–4(5) cm diam. stipe 2–7 cm., thick, terete, sometimes flattened and grooved below, covered with downy grey hairs. In woods, esp. moist ground among nettles. VII–X. C.

Helvella (Paxina) acetabula. *Deeply cup-shaped, to 6 cm diam. tapering into ± strongly ribbed stipe, dark brownish within.* Outside paler brown, powdery; stipe to 8 cm tall, thick, tapering, ribs branching almost to margin. Calcareous ground, often woods, heaths, gravelly soils. IV–VI (VIII). O–F.

Helvella costifera Nannf. Acetabula ancilis (Pers. ex Fr.) Lamb. *Irregularly funnel-shaped, greyish-brown; stipe paler, ribbed.* 4–6 cm high, 2–4 cm broad, at first cup-shaped, later irregularly expanded; stipe ribs branching to half-way up cup. Calcareous soil. V–VI. R.

Helvella (Leptopodia) elastica. *To 10 cm high; Saddle-shaped to expanded, ± lobed, greyish above; stipe pale, terete, smooth.* Cap 1–3 cm wide, lobes sometimes irregular, drying brownish; lower surface glabrous, drying ± ochre; stipe white to pale greyish-brown, hollow, sl. grooved below, minutely pruinose above. Paths in woods in grass. VII–IX. F.

Helvella lacunosa. *To 10 cm high, cap saddle-shaped, dark greyish-black; stipe deeply grooved, greyish.* Cap 2–4 cm wide, lobes irregular, undulating; stipe hollow or chambered. Mostly frondose woods, esp. burnt soil. IX–X. F–C.

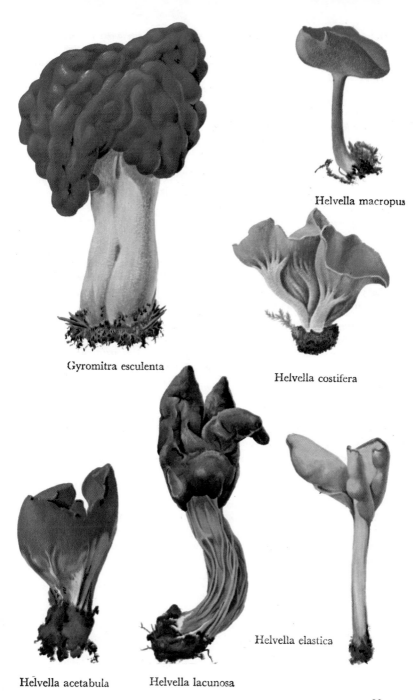

Gyromitra esculenta

Helvella macropus

Helvella costifera

Helvella acetabula

Helvella lacunosa

Helvella elastica

39

Helvella crispa. *Whitish; cap saddle-shaped, lobed; stipe deeply grooved, lacunose.* Cap 2–5 cm high, lobes 2(3) irregularly folded, underside pale tan; stipe 3–6 cm high, stout, white. Damp frondose woods on rich soil, usually along paths. III–IV, VIII–X. C.

Morchella—Morels

Cap with honey-comb like pits; stipe hollow, $\pm$ fragile. Vernal (March, April, May).

a. Base of cap not free from stipe.

Morchella esculenta. *Cap light yellowish-brown; pits and acute sterile ridges irregularly arranged.* Cap 6–12 cm high, obtusely ovoid; pits large, ridges sinuous; stipe 6–12 cm high, almost smooth, terete or faintly grooved above, sometimes pitted grooved below, minutely scurfy, yellowish, browning with age. Under frondose trees on rich soil, hedgerows, banks, grassland, esp. S.E. England, widespread. O–F. *Edible and good.*

Morchella vulgaris [Pers.] Boud. *Cap dark greyish-brown to bistre; pits with obtuse ridges irregularly arranged.* Cap 3–6 cm high, ovoid, sometimes with olive tinge; stipe 2–5 cm, terete but enlarged and somewhat grooved below, $\pm$ smooth, white to yellowish. On rich soil in woods, also gardens. O. *Edible and good.*

Morchella conica. Pers. ex Fr. *Cap conical, primary ridges in vertical $\pm$ straight lines, blackening.* Cap 2–5 cm high, dark brownish-olive, pits in $\pm$ horizontal rows; stipe 3–5 cm high, apex almost as broad as cap, sl. grooved, mealy, whitish yellow to pale brown. Copses on rich soil, also conifer plantations. O. V. *Edible but thin-fleshed.*

b. Base of cap free from stipe (Mitrophora)

Morchella (Mitrophora) semi-libera, rimosipes. *Cap small relative to stipe; pits few.* Cap 2–4 cm high, conical, short pointed, usually dark brownish with olive tinge; primary ridges in $\pm$ vertical rows, coarse, often enlongated; stipe 4–8 cm high, terete or a little grooved below, minutely mealy, whitish, later pale tan. Damp woods on rich soil. O–F. *Edible but thin fleshed.* × 1.

Verpa conica. *Cap brown, campanulate, supported at centre, otherwise wholly free of pale yellowish stipe.* Cap 2–4 cm high, smooth or sl. wrinkled, yellowish on underside; stipe 3–8 cm high, cylindric, with $\pm$ pronounced, irregularly arranged, incomplete transverse reddish-yellowish granular belts. Sandy and heathy soils; in roadside grass. R(-O). V. × 1.

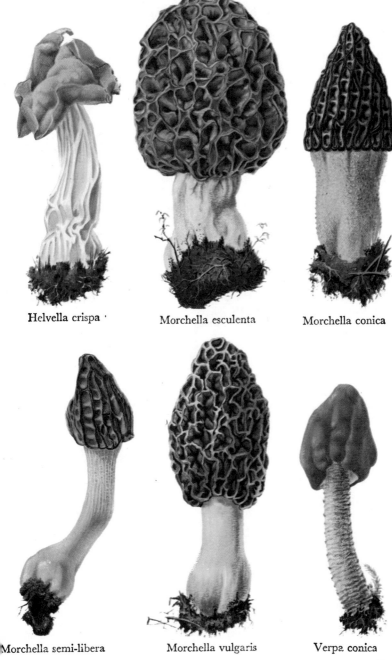

Helvella crispa ·   Morchella esculenta   Morchella conica

Morchella semi-libera   Morchella vulgaris   Verpa conica

TUBERALES—TRUFFLES

A series of tuberous, subterranean fungi with spores in asci.

Hydnotria tulasnei. *Reddish brown, oblong tuberiform, knobbly; internal chambers convoluted, vein-like, opening on surface.* 1–4(6) cm long, small specimens almost smooth; section paler in colour; discolours by bruising and eel-worm attacks. Smell faint, sweetish. Frondose woods in light soil, or under leaf cover. Late summer. F, often in groups. *Edible.*

Pachyphloeus melanoxanthus. *Black, globose, densely angular warted; interior olive greenish.* 0.5–1.5 cm, sometimes with short stalk; apical or lateral opening to somewhat hollowed interior. Rich soil or under leaves in woods. XI. R. × 1.

Tuber rufum. *Foxy red, irregularly globose, minutely warted, interior pale greyish lilac.* 0.5–2.5 cm, interior first white, sometimes finally red brown; veins much branched, pale; flesh firm, taste nutty; sweetish to unpleasant (phenolic) smell when old. Frondose woods in rich soil along paths. (II) VII–VIII. F–C. This and the rare *T. nitidum* are the only small species of *Tuber* with spiny as distinct from reticulate spores. × 1.

Tuber aestivum. *Dark brownish to (purplish) black, irreg. globose, densely covered with 5–6 sided pyramidal warts.* 2–7(9) cm, interior greyish or putty coloured, often tinged violaceous, with close network of pale veins; taste ± nutty. Calcareous soil (mostly under beech). VIII (–X). R. *Edible;* esteemed less than Truffle of commerce (*T. melanosporum* Vitt.), which is not found here.

HELOTIALES

Helotium (Calycella) citrinum. *Gregarious, bright yellow, cup-shaped to flat with short thin stipe.* 0.5 cm diam., drying orange-yellow; outside smooth. Bursting through decaying branches. IX–XII. C. Similar species on herbaceous stems, acorns, hazel nuts. × 1.

Rutstroemia firma. *Solitary, brownish, cup-shaped to flat with short stipe.* 1 cm diam. varying dark hazel to paler tan, toughish; stipe distinct, a little shorter than cap width, sl. hairy. Dead branches, esp. oak. IX–XII. Widespread. O. × 1.

Sclerotinia (Ciboria) batschiana. *Brown, funnel-shaped becoming flat, stalk slender.* 0.5–1 cm diam. sometimes tinged olive, stipe short to rather long. On acorns. IX–XI. O. *Sclerotinia tuberosa* is larger and paler with longer stipe from black sclerotia in *Anemone* rhizomes. III–IV(V). O. × 1.

Chlorosplenium (Chlorociboria) aeruginascens, aeruginosum. *Blue-Green cups on decayed wood, the mycelium turning it green.* 0.5(1) cm diam., soon flattened expanded, sometimes yellowing. Frondose wood esp. oak. (IV–VIII) IX–XI Green wood common, fruit bodies much less so. × 1.

Hydnotria tulasnei

Pachyphloeus melanoxanthus

Tuber rufum

Tuber aestivum

Helotium citrinum

Chlorosplenium aeruginascens

Sclerotinia batschiana

Rutstroemia firma

Bulgaria inquinans. *Clustered, turbinate, blackish-brown, on bark; consistency of indiarubber.* 1–3(4) cm diam., margin involute at first; disc shining smooth, outside ± scurfy. Often on oak, less frequently on beech; often surrounded by black spore deposit. C. X–XI. × 1.

Coryne sarcoides. *Reddish-purple, gelatinous, irregularly ligulate to ± turbinate.* To 1 cm across, disc concave to flat; outside minutely mealy; stipe present or not. Clustered on decaying stumps and logs. C. IX–XII. × 1.

GEOGLOSSALES—EARTH TONGUES

Geoglossum

Tall, stalked, head ± flattened club-shaped. Mostly black rarely olive species of grassland.

Geoglossum (Trichoglossum) hirsutum. *Black to 8 cm high, head dry ± flattened fusiform; stipe densely velvety, terete.* Stipe and sometimes head dark to sooty brown. Acid grass, often clustered. VIII–IX. F–C.

Geoglossum fallax. *Similar to above, but stipe smooth or minutely squamulose above.* In grass, esp. on woodland meadows. (The larger specimen figured is *G. cookeianum*, which is virtually without squamules. The genus contains several other black species.) X–XI. O.

Geoglossum (Microglossum) viride. *Olive green, stipe mealy or scaly.* 2–5(6) cm high, head often with longitudinal groove. On soil in frondose woods, often in small tufts. IX–XI. C.

Spathularia flavida. *Head bright yellow ± flattened, usually wrinkled.* 2–5 cm high; stipe round, wedged into head, whitish yellow. Coniferous plantations, solitary. VIII–X. O.

Cudonia circinans. *Head flattened, leather-yellow, hat-shaped, folded.* To 4 cm high, head 1–2 cm across, somewhat veined and drying darker beneath, waxy; stipe greyish-tan, flesh colour below, downy. In conifer plantations on needle cover, often clustered. VIII–IX. R.

Leotia lubrica. *Gelatinous and slimy, head brownish-olive, ± folded, edge inrolled; stipe amber.* 1–3(6) cm high; head ageing ± convex, irregular, greenish-black; stipe slimy, minutely squamulose, sometimes green dotted. Rich wettish soils of frondose woods. VIII–X. C.

Bulgaria inquinans

Coryne sarcoides

Geoglossum fallax

Geoglossum hirsutum

Geoglossum viride

Spathularia flavida

Cudonia circinans

Leotia lubrica

SPHAERIALES

Mature receptacles hard, carbonaceous, brown or black; fertile part papillate from openings of immersed perithecia. Only the largest species of this big group are mentioned. All illustrations × 1.

Xylaria (Xylosphæra) hypoxylon. *Usually forked, tips white powdered with conidia when young, black when mature.* Antler-like, 2–6 cm high with black felty stipe; tips finally black and rough with protruding tips of perithecia; flesh white; unbranched forms have only perithecia. Dead wood stumps, branches of deciduous trees. I–XII. C.

Xylaria (Xylosphaera) polymorpha. *Irregularly club-shaped, tapering below, coal-black.* Peri-thecial tips prominent in fertile (swollen) part; flesh white, tough. Mostly gregarious on stumps of deciduous trees, esp. beech. I–XII. C.

Poronia punctata. *Turbinate-stipitate, ± flat-topped, mostly greyish-tan; stipe black.* 1–2 cm high, disc 1.5 cm diam. white powdered by conidia at first, finally sparsely blackish papillate with perithecial tips; outside ± feltv. On horse dung. IX–XI. R, becoming rarer.

Ustulina deusta. *Irregularly lobed cushion or thick crust, finally black and brittle.* To 40 cm wide by 3–4 mm thick, at first dark greyish-brown, finally papillate with tips of large perithecia and crumbling between fingers. Stumps, butts, dead roots of trees, esp. beech. I–XII. C.

Hypoxylon fragiforme, coccineum. *Sub-globose, finely papillate with perithecial tips, pink to brick-red, ± blackening.* 0.5–1.5 cm diam.; flesh hard, brownish-black, brittle. Gregarious, mostly on newly felled trunks of frondose trees, esp. beech. VIII–III. C.

Daldinia concentrica. *± sub-globose, black, concentrically zoned in section.* 2.5–6(9) cm. diam., at first chocolate-brown, finally dull shining black, minutely papillate; internal zones greyish-black, silky. On dead branches of frondose trees, mostly ash; also beech and others. C.

Diatrype disciformis. *Discoid-polygonal, minutely papillate, buff to dark brown or blackish.* 2–3(5) mm across, 5–6 angled, at first whitish with blackish tips of protruding perithecia; flesh white; single or confluent. Bursting through bark of frondose trees, mostly beech. C.

HYPOCREALES

Differ from Sphaeriales by the soft, ± highly coloured fruit-bodies.

Nectria cinnabarina. *Pinkish to dark-red, ± globose receptacles to 3(4) mm diam.* Minutely warted when mature. Densely clustered and bursting through sticks, newly fallen branches of all kinds. I–XII. C.
(A number of other, mostly smaller, species occur including *N.* (*Dialonectria*) *galligena,* the cause of canker on apple trees.)

Xylaria polymorpha

Xylaria hypoxylon

Poronia punctata

Hypoxylon fragiforme

Diatrype disciformis

Ustulina deusta

Nectria cinnabarina

Daldinia concentrica

47

CLAVICIPITALES

Ligulate to drum-stick shaped, parasitic on insects, false truffles (Elaphomyces) or grasses.

Claviceps purpurea. Ergot. *Black, fusiform or ± contorted sclerotia (" ergots ") on grass.* At first flesh-coloured; white inside. Small club-shaped fruit bodies develop on fallen sclerotia in spring, singly or in clusters. Ergots on inflorescences of many grasses, esp. rye. F–C, rarely in grains. Fruit bodies R. **Deadly Poisonous.**

Cordyceps

Cordyceps ophioglossoides, parasitica. *± club-shaped; head olive-black; stipe yellowish.* 3–8(10) cm high, head finally rough with perithecial tips, often white powdered from spores; stipe smooth, terete. On *Elaphomyces.* IX–X. O–F.

Cordyceps capitata. *Drumstick-shaped, head black, tinged olive, 0.5–1 cm. diam.* 3–9(10) cm high, head minutely rough, often white powdered from spores; stipe smooth or grooved ± mealy above, dull olive-brown, toughish. On *Elaphomyces.* IX–X. O.

Cordyceps militaris. *Tapering downwards from sl. swollen head, reddish orange.* 1–4(5) cm high, head sl. delimited from stipe, minutely rough. On caterpillars and pupæ of Lepidoptera in woods and meadows, usually buried in soil. IX–X. F.

Cordyceps entomorrhiza (Dicks.) Link. C. cinera. *Head globose, grey, rough, on long stipes.* 3–8 cm high, head 0.5 cm diam., stipe thin, hard, usually twisted. Recorded on a beetle larva. R.

PLECTASCALES

Onygena corvina. *0.5–1 cm high; drum-stick shaped, powdered, on owl pellets and rotting feathers.* Head sub-globose, grey-brown; stipe short, pale whitish. Often in groups. R–O. The allied *O. equina* is larger with pale brown head 2–4 mm diam. On shed horns, hooves, etc. C.

Elaphomyces granulatus, cervinus. *Yellowish clay, finely warted, not marbled in section.* ± globose, 2–4(5) cm diam., varying to dull straw-colour; in section pale brown to vinaceous; gleba soon dust-like, blackish grey. Mostly in surface layers of soil under *Pinus,* less often in frondose woods. I–XII. F–C.

Elaphomyces muricatus sensu M. Lange. *Bright yellowish-brown, with conspicuous pointed warts; marbled in section by pale veins.* Globose, often lobed, 2–5 cm diam.; section purple-brown; dust-like gleba blackish-grey. In soil of conifer plantations. O.

E.variegatus Vitt. sensu M. Lange is smaller (0.5 cm diam.) and is restricted to frondose woods, esp. beech. I–XII. C.

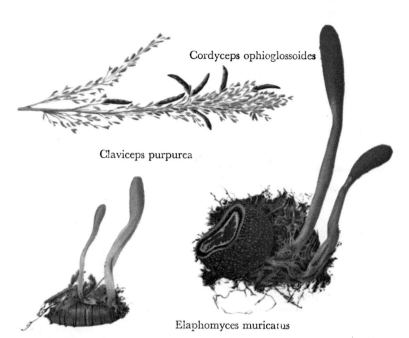

Cordyceps ophioglossoides

Claviceps purpurea

Elaphomyces muricatus

Cordyceps militaris

Cordyceps capitata

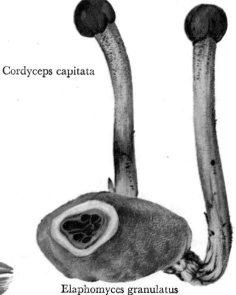

Cordyceps entomorrhiza

Elaphomyces granulatus

Onygena corvina

BASIDIOMYCETES

APHYLLOPHORALES

THELEPHORACEAE

Corticium

Resupinate, mostly crustaceous, on wood or bark, rarely on soil. A genus of very many species, hard to distinguish without a microscope and often broken up into several smaller genera.

Corticium (Peniophora) quercinum. *Greyish-violet, cracking.* Hymenium greyish-violet, warty rough when moist, cracked when dry; margin usually free, revolute, showing black underside. In crust-like rows on bark of dead branches of frondose trees, esp. oak. I–XII. C.

Corticium comedens. *Dull flesh coloured to yellowish-grey thin crust beneath rolled-back bark.* Inconspicuous; best recognised on attacked branches between rolled-back bark and wood. Dead branches and young stems of frondose trees. I–XII. C.

Stereum

Coriaceous, often resupinate or effuso-reflexed; upper surface often strigose-felty; hymenium smooth to ± warty. On wood.

Stereum hirsutum. *Lower surface (hymenium) yellowish; upper strigose-hairy.* Small brackets 1–4 cm broad; upper surface ± zoned, varying to yellowish-grey; underside somewhat uneven varying pinkish or tan or becoming grey. Stumps, trunks, logs, palings, fallen branches of frondose trees, etc. I–XII. C.

Stereum purpureum. *Purplish to lilac.* Brackets 1–3 cm broad, often in tiers on a vertical surface; upper surface ± woolly, often lobed; hymenium becoming dirty grey with age. Similar habitats to above. Parasitises plum trees, causing "silver leaf" disease. I–XII. C.

Stereum rugosum. *Hymenium ± buff, uneven, greying with age, ± blood red when wounded; on frondose wood.* Mostly resupinate, spreading, margin upturned, upper surface brown, wrinkled. Stumps, trunks etc., also on living trees. I–XII. C.

Stereum sanguinolentum. *Hymenium greyish-yellow to tan, ± blood-red where wounded; on coniferous wood.* Resupinate, papery thin, spreading or ± bracket-shaped; upper surface ± zoned hairy. On dead wood. I–XII. F.

Corticium quercinum   Corticium comedens   Stereum hirsutum

Stereum sanguinolentum   Stereum rugosum

Stereum purpureum

G.M.T.—D

Corticium quercinum   Corticium comedens   Stereum hirsutum

Stereum sanguinolentum   Stereum rugosum

Stereum purpureum

G.M.T.—D

Hymenochaete rubiginosa. *Hard, chestnut, at first velvety, often zoned and wavy. blackening with age.* 2–5 cm broad, usually in long intricate brackets; dull yellowish-brown when young; hymenium rust brown or bistre, minutely, bristly rough; flesh tough, brownish. Decaying trunks, stumps of frondose trees, esp. oak. I–XII. F.

Thelephora terrestris, laciniata ± *Fan-shaped, tinged violaceous-brown with pale fringed margin.* 3–8 cm broad, sometimes effused and ± irregularly funnel-shaped, or circular; upper surface radially fibrillose; hymenium wrinkled or granular, more violaceous-grey. Often in clusters on needle cover in pine plantations and on heathy soils; sometimes around stems. (VII) VIII–XII. C.

Thelephora (Phylacteria) palmata. *Erect, clustered, much branched above, purple-brown, foetid garlic smell.* 3–5(6) cm high, branches ± flattened, tips laciniate, paler; flesh leathery. Soil of conifer plantations. VIII–XI. O.

Coniophora puteana, cerebella. *Effused resupinate; central brownish-tuberculate hymenium, olive-yellow sterile margin.* To 40 cm broad, closely pressed to substrate, margin ± radially fibrillose. On dead wood in forests. I–XII. Sometimes attacks structural timber.

MERULIACEAE

Phlebia radiata. *Orange-red to flesh-colour with raised radiating vein-like ridges.* To 30 cm broad, resupinate; margin free, raised, fimbriate; flesh tough. Around stumps or on bark of frondose trees, esp. alder. VII–V. C. (Often considered to be a colour form of *Ph. merismoides*.)

Serpula lacrymans. Merulius. *Spongy to cottony soft; fruit-body of honeycomb-like yellowish-rusty shallow pores.* Fruit body usually resupinate, 5–50 cm across, bracket-like on vertical substrate, yellow towards a white sterile tomentose margin; arising from strands of white to greyish mycelium by which it spreads; colours vary flesh, olive-yellow, brownish-yellow, chestnut; often with unpleasant (? fishy) smell. I–XII. C. The serious " Dry rot " of buildings. Closely related species occur on wood in nature.

Merulius tremellosus. *Gelatinous; ± bracket-like, often super-imposed; lower surface reticulately shallow pored, orange buff to pinkish.* Caps 1–4 cm broad, reflexed. upper surface pale greyish adpressed woolly. Old rotten stumps, esp. the insides of frondose trees. IX–III. O–F.

All illustrations × 1

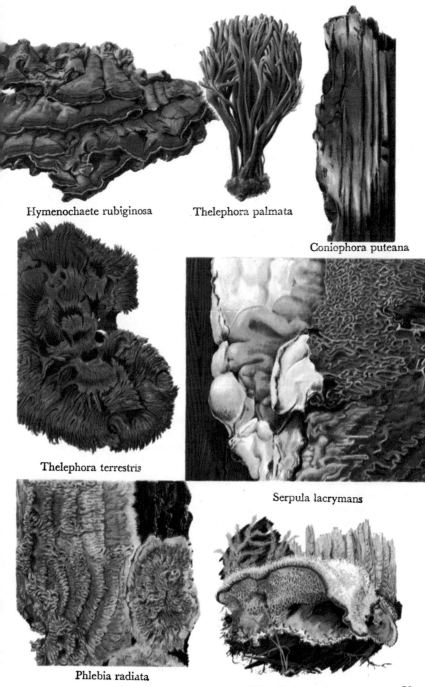

Hymenochaete rubiginosa

Thelephora palmata

Coniophora puteana

Thelephora terrestris

Serpula lacrymans

Phlebia radiata

Merulius tremellosus

53

CLAVARIACEAE

Clavaria—Fairy Clubs

Erect, fleshy, branched or unbranched club-like bodies, covered by hymenium except at base; spores white, yellowish, brown. All illustrations × 1.

Clavaria (Clavariadelphus) fistulosa. *Unbranched, leather brown, yellowish below, becoming hollow, spores white.* 10–20 cm high, sl. swollen upwards to 0.5 cm diam., fragile, stipe darker, tough. Solitary or in twos or threes on branches, leaves, esp. beech. IX–II. O. *Edible.*

Clavaria (Clavariadelphus) pistillaris. *Unbranched, ± pestle-shaped, yellowish tan.* 10–15–30 cm high; 2–4–6 cm wide above, often wrinkled and tinged flesh colour, primrose; flesh white, soft. Spores pale yellowish. On ground of frondose woods. IX–XII. O–F. *Edible.*

Clavaria (Clavariadelphus) juncea. *Unbranched, filiform ± leather-brown, creeping base fibrillose.* 6–10(15) cm high, *c.*1 mm wide; sl. tapering upwards to acute apex; very brittle. Spores white. On damp leaves, often clustered. IX—XI. O.

Clavaria (Clavulinopsis) helvola Fr., inaequalis. *Unbranched, slender sl. tapering downwards, apex blunt, bright- to orange-yellow, solid, fibrous.* 2–5(8) cm high, sometimes sl. flattened; stipe paler; spores white to yellowish. Solitary or in small clusters. VIII–XII. C.

Clavaria (Clavulinopsis) corniculata. *Branched, clear bright yellow, tough.* 2–6 cm high, ± regular and dichotomously branched, branches tapering; spores white. In grass of fields, woods etc. VIV–XII. C.

Clavaria argillacea. *Unbranched, clavate, lemon-yellow to alutaceous, often sl. flattened.* 3–6(8) cm high, often grooved; stipe ± distinct, yellow; flesh yellowish with tallow-like taste. Spores white. Among mosses on peaty gravels, heather moors. VII–XI. C.

Clavaria (Clavulina) cristata. *Branched, white, tinged pinkish to sl. greyish, tips ± crested.* 3–8 cm high, irregularly branched, branches ± flattened, few to many, ultimate crests few. Spores white. On ground, esp. of paths in woods. VI–XII. C. Very variable, with transition forms to *C. cinerea* which is distinctly grey (sometimes with purple tinge).

Clavaria (Clavulina) rugosa. *Unbranched or irregularly branched above, white rugose.* 4–12 cm high, ± longitudinally wrinkled, apex blunt; sometimes with greyish or yellowish tinge; flesh brittle; spores white. On ground of woodland paths, meadows. VIII–XII. C.

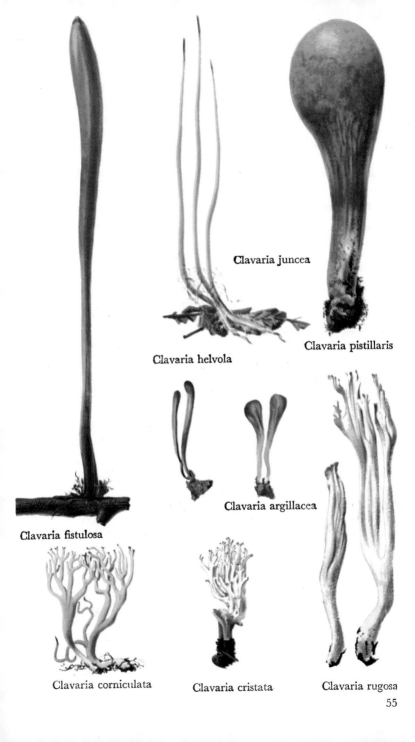

Clavaria juncea

Clavaria helvola

Clavaria pistillaris

Clavaria fistulosa

Clavaria argillacea

Clavaria corniculata

Clavaria cristata

Clavaria rugosa

55

Ramaria—Fairy Clubs

Densely branched species with tough, tan-coloured, often ± reddening flesh; spores yellowish-to yellowish brown. Formerly a section of Clavaria, but differing from Clavaria proper by dense branching, tougher flesh, coloured fruit bodies and spores which are never white.

Ramaria invalii. *Leather-brown, branched almost from base; in conifer plantations.* 3–7(8) cm high, branches thin, often sl. flattened; stipe 1–2 cm, white, felty; flesh white, ± bitter. On conifer needles. *R. ochraceo-virens*, found in similar habitats, bruises and weathers greenish. *Worthless.* × 1.

Ramaria stricta. *Yellowish-pale brown; branches erect, parallel; on wood.* 3–10 cm high, branches slender, tips pale yellow; stipe sometimes distinct, often violet tinged; flesh tough, bitterish, smell faintly spicy. On decayed stumps, buried branches, penetrated by white mycelial strands. VIII–I. F. *Worthless.* × 1.

Ramaria botrytis. *Stipe stout, massive, with dense branching, ± reddish at tips.* 5–10(15) cm high, up to 20 cm broad, ± yellowish-brown or tan; stipe massive 3–4 cm high, to 6 cm wide, branchlet tips varying red to purplish; flesh brittle, mild, smell fruity. Acid humus in frondose woods. VIII–XI. O. *Edible, but may be mistaken for following species which has bitter flesh.*

Ramaria formosa. *Pinkish buff to orange-rose; tips lemon-yellow; flesh bitterish.* 10–25 cm high; stipe stout, height and width *c.* 3–6 cm paler; flesh fragile often bruising brownish to black. In humus, usually of frondose woods. VII–XI. O. *Poisonous (very bitter when cooked).*

Ramaria flava. *Branches ± bright sulphur-yellow; stipe whitish, bruising or ageing ± reddish.* 7–15 cm high; branchlets very numerous browning somewhat with age; stipe *c.* 5–8 x 4.5 cm. Frondose and coniferous woods. IX–X. O. *Edible, but may be confused with previous species.*

Sparassis crispa. *Like a cauliflower; pale yellowish-tan with flat lobed branches; base of pine stump.* ± globose, 25–35 cm across, densely branched, at first creamy colour; flesh brittle, mild. VIII–XI. F. *Edible.*

Pterula multifida. *Much branched from base, greyish, dirty pale ochre to ± brownish, sometimes ± lilac tinged, branches thin almost hair-like.* 1–5 (6) cm high; stipe almost nil. Whole plant dries black. Under conifers on needles, branches etc. IX-XI. R. × 1.

Ramaria invalii

Ramaria stricta

Ramaria botrytis

Ramaria formosa

Ramaria flava

Sparassis crispa

Pterula multifida

57

Funnel-shaped fungi; hymenium of much branched, decurrent, shallow, blunt " gills " ; or ± wrinkled. Spores white. All species edible.

Craterellus cornucopioides. " Horn of plenty." ± *funnel-shaped, dark brown to blackish, drying paler, margin wavy.* 5–12 cm high, deeply hollowed, upper surface ± scaly, lower surface smooth or sl. wrinkled, greyish; stipe usually short; flesh tough. Amongst dead leaves of frondose woods, esp. beech; often clustered. VIII–XI. C. *Edible and good; easily dried.*

Cantharellus cinereus. *Irregularly funnel-shaped, margin crisped, whole plant ± grey.* Cap 1–3(5) cm across, often perforate to base, upper surface more brownish, lower distinctly grey, primrose with irregularly branched, distant rib-like " gills "; stipe ± grooved, tapering below. Fasciculate, esp. round stump of frondose trees. IX–XI. O.

Cantharellus cibarius. " Chantarelle." *Wholly apricot-yellow; " gills " forked, shallow, blunt.* Cap 3–10 cm across, at first ± top-shaped finally depressed towards centre, margin often wavy-crisped; stipe to *c.* 5 x 2 cm, smooth, paler; flesh yellowish with ± apricot smell. In frondose woods. VII–XII. C. *Edible and excellent.* Can be confused with the harmless but worthless *Hygrophoropsis aurantiaca.* (*q.v.*)

Cantharellus infundibuliformis, tubaeformis. *Cap dark brown, margin wavy to crisped, stipe deep yellow.* Cap 2–5 cm across, deeply funnel-shaped; " gills " vein- or fold-like, blunt, irregular, branched, yellow at first, then greyish; stipe 2–7 cm long deep yellow, often grooved or compressed; flesh tough, aromatic, bitterish. Frondose and coniferous woods on acid soils, often clustered. VII–I. C. *Edible, quite good.*

Var. *lutescens* is a form entirely yellowish in colour.

HYDNACEAE—*Tooth fungi*

Fruit body with central or lateral stipe, or sessile; spore forming layer covers individualised " teeth " or " spines " on lower surface of cap. Mostly fleshy and tough fungi; spores white or coloured. Formerly referred to the single genus, Hydnum.

Hericium coralloides. *Densely branched from thick trunk, whitish then dull yellowish; free teeth pendant in clusters like tassels.* To 35 cm across; pendant spines 6–10 mm; spores white. Dead trunks of fir and frondose trees esp. beech. X–XI. R. *Edible and good when young.*

Sarcodon imbricatum. *Greyish-brown; cap imbricately scaly; teeth greyish.* Cap 5–15 cm diam. ± convex to sl. depressed; teeth dense, decurrent; stipe whitish or concolorous to brownish; spores reddish brown; flesh thick, firm. Sandy coniferous woods. IX–XI. O–F. *Edible.*

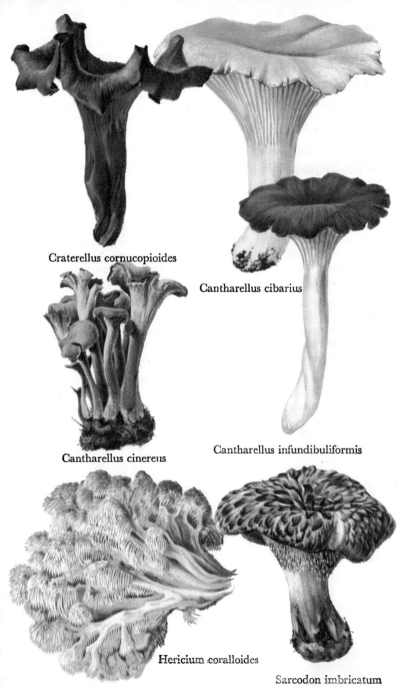

Craterellus cornucopioides

Cantharellus cibarius

Cantharellus cinereus

Cantharellus infundibuliformis

Hericium coralloides

Sarcodon imbricatum

Hydnum repandum. *Pale yellowish to pinkish-buff, fleshy, cap margin incurved* ± *lobed.* Cap 5–10(15) cm diam., often sl. cracked; stipe short, stout, often eccentric, paler; teeth ± decurrent, crowded, paler; flesh firm, white, bitter; spores white. Often grouped or in rings in frondose woods. VIII–XI. C. *Edible and good: best after boiling to remove bitterish taste.*

Hydnum rufescens. *As above, but cap more reddish-brown and concolorous not decurrent spines.* Smaller, cap 3–10 cm diam. Also in coniferous woods. Frequency, edibility etc., as previous species.

Hydnellum aurantiacum. *Corky; cap orange-yellow finally dirty brownish, stipe orange-reddish-brown, tomentose.* Cap 4–10 cm diam. at first downy-white, turbinate then flat to ± depressed, surface often ± wavy-nodulose, margin whitish; teeth pale, becoming orange-brown; stipe attenuated upwards, tomentum ± rusty. Spores yellowish. Coniferous woods. IX–XI. R.

Hydnellum zonatum. *Coriaceous,* ± *funnel-shaped, cap reddish-brown, zoned, teeth brownish, grey-tipped.* Cap 3–6 cm silky-fibrillose, margin paler, uneven; teeth decurrent, ± brown-bistre. Often clustered in woods. IX–XI. R–O. The rare *Phellodon melaleucus* is somewhat similar but smaller and more slender with a smell of melilot.

Phellodon niger. *Rigid corky, cap blue-(blackish), tomentose-fibrillose, margin usually whitish; flesh* ± *black.* Cap 3–7(10) cm diam. ± expanded, margin lobed; spines crowded, white then grey-blue; stipe often ± clavate, brown-black, tomentose at base; young flesh pale bluish when cut, almost black in old specimens. Spores off-white. Often connate. In coniferous woods. IX–XI. O–F.

Auriscalpium vulgare. *Dark brown, reniform, hairy cap and mostly lateral stipe; on pine cones.* Cap 1–3 cm across, at first yellowish chestnut, sometimes lobed; spines paler, at first ± flesh coloured; stipe densely hairy, concolorous; flesh leathery. Spores white. V–II. C. × 1.

Hydnum repandum

Hydnum **rufescens**

Phellodon niger

Hydnellum **zonatum**

Auriscalpium vulgare

Hydnellum aurantiacum

A large group of very different fungi, the spore forming layer (hymenium) lining tubes, opening to the air by pores. The majority grow on wood (" brackets ").

Inonotus radiatus. Polyporus. *Yellowish-tawny to rusty-brown, ± radially furrowed; pores minute, greyish-brown, glistening in oblique view.* Brackets 2–6 cm across, often overlapping, at first finely tomentose and ± zoned; flesh yellowish to rusty with silky sheen, corky, rigid. Spores creamy. On dead or weakened trunks of frondose trees, esp. alder. IX–IV. **C.**

Inonotus hispidus. Polyporus. *Shaggy-haired above ± dark rusty-brown, flesh thick, fibrous, spongy-soft.* Bracket 15–20 cm across, at first yellowish-brown, ageing blackish, faintly zoned; pores yellowish, finally dark brown, often " weeping " drops; flesh dark reddish-brown. Spores yellowish-brown. Trunks of frondose trees, esp. apple and ash. V–II. **C.**

Phellinus igniarius. Fomes. *Very hard, upper surface grey- to blackish-brown, concentrically furrowed, usually radially and irregularly cracked; flesh rusty-brown; mostly on Salicaceae.* Bracket or hoof-shaped 5–25 cm across, sl. tomentose when young, margin thick, rounded, pale; pores minute, long remaining closed, whitish grey, finally cinnamon; old fruit bodies may have 20–30 layers of tubes; flesh reddish-brown, very hard. Spores white. Mostly on living trunks of poplar and willow. I–XII. **O–F.** × $\frac{1}{2}$.

Phellinus pomaceus. Fomes. *Cushion-shaped to effused, very hard; flesh ± cinnamon; on rosaceous fruit trees.* Sometimes ± hoof-shaped; cap *c.* 6 cm across, upper surface finally greyish and cracked, at first sl. velvety at the rounded margin; pores long remaining closed, minute. Tubes stratified in older specimens; flesh very hard. Spores white, becoming pale brown. On living trunks; detachable only with difficulty. I–XII. **C.**

Coltrichia perennis. Polyporus, Polystictus. *Stipitate cap ± funnel-shaped, then zonate, rusty-brownish, coriaceous.* Cap 3–8 cm diam., concentrically zoned from alternating light and dark colour shades, at first finely silky-hairy; tubes short, decurrent, pores minute, greyish-primrose finally dark brownish; stipe 2–4 cm long, sl. swollen below, tomentose, concolorous; flesh brown; spores yellowish-brown. Sandy soil in woods, heathy places, esp. where ground has been burnt. I–XII. **C.** × 1.

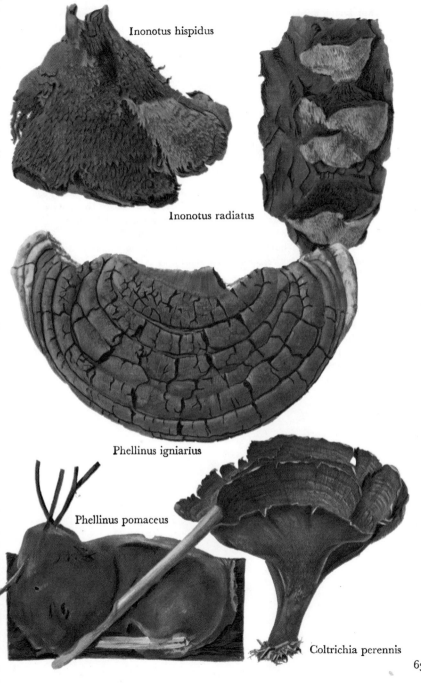

Inonotus hispidus

Inonotus radiatus

Phellinus igniarius

Phellinus pomaceus

Coltrichia perennis

63

Ganoderma applanatum. *Bracket-like; upper surface with low humps formed from hard laccate crust, ± red-brown, often cocoa-brown from deposited spores; whitish pores brown when scratched.* Caps 5–30 cm across, ± flat, solitary or a few caps overlapping, ± zoned, humps ± radial, margin paler at first, rounded; pores finally ageing brown; tubes often (obscurely) stratified; flesh brown, corky-hard, thick. Spores cocoa-brown. On trunks of frondose trees esp. ageing beeches, where it causes a serious and damaging heart rot. I–XII. C. × ½.

Ganoderma lucidum. *Laterally stipitate reniform cap; whole fungus enclosed in hard, shining, laccate, dark chestnut crust.* (The purplish-black colour of the plate is exceptional.) Cap 5–20 cm wide, sometimes ± circular or ligulate, concentrically sulcate; pores off-white, finally dull brown, minute; flesh corky-fibrous. Spores brown. On stumps of frondose trees. O–F. × ½.

Fomes fomentarius. *Hoof-shaped, sessile and broadly attached, concentrically sulcate to zoned, pale brownish to greyish black, margin blunt; woody hard.* To 50 cm across, sl. tomentose at first; flesh brown, firmly spongy, compact; tubes many layered in old specimens; pores off-white then dirty brownish. Spores white. Scottish Highlands only, on birch. Formerly thought common in England owing to confusion with *Ganoderma applanatum* (see above). I–XII. C. Causes a white rot. × ½.

Fomes pinicola. (Sw.) Cooke, marginatus. *Bracket to hoof-shaped, upper surface with varnish-like reddish-brown crust, margin often paler.* To 25 cm across, ± flat, sl. concentrically sulcate; crust cracking somewhat irregularly; margin, when distinct, yellowish to pinkish-buff; pores pale yellowish, later brown; flesh corky-hard, ± pinkish buff; spores white. Cause of heart rot, mainly in conifers but also frondose trees. Rare, but sometimes attached to imported timber. The whole specimen shown × ½. Lower section shows stratified tubes.

Ganoderma applanatum

Fomes fomentarius

Ganoderma lucidum

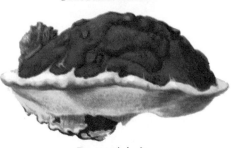

Fomes pinicola

Fomes annosus. *Bracket-like, rarely resupinate, upper surface crust-like, thin, irregularly bubbly, ± bright reddish brown; growing margin and pores white.* 2–40 cm across, varying from shell-shaped bracket to effused; upper surface sl. tomentose at first; old pores often with cream to flesh tinge; flesh whitish at first tough leathery, finally woody hard. Spores white. The most important cause here of heart rot in conifers esp. Norway spruce; also attacks frondose trees and structural timber (pit props). C. × ½.

Oxyporus populinus. Fomes. *Bracket-shaped, imbricate upper surface moss-covered.* Caps 3–6 cm across, often concrescent, thickish, upper surface whitish, greyish to pale watery-brown, villose; pores whitish-yellow, minute; flesh ± corky-fibrous, dirty whitish to pale brown. Spores white. On frondose trees, esp. poplars, mostly high up. O–F.

Phaeolus schweinitzii. Polyporus. *Bracket-like, ± rusty-brown, densely tomentose; margin yellow; greenish-yellow pores bruising brownish; on conifers.* To 30 cm across, sometimes shortly stalked, stipe brown tomentose; pores large, irregular, angular ageing to brownish; flesh thick, spongy-fibrous. Spores white or tinged citron. Usually at ground level, sometimes on roots; a serious butt rot, esp. of pines. F–C. × ½.

Piptoporus betulinus. Polyporus. *Reniform or shell-shaped, upper surface smooth, greyish to pale watery brown, pores and flesh white; on birch.* 5–30 cm across, sessile or very shortly stalked, edge projecting, incurved; pores minute sl. discolouring with age; flesh dry, corky, very even. Spores white. Causes decay and eventual death in sapwood; often found saprophytically. C. × ½.

Daedalea quercina. *Bracket to almost hoof-shaped, corky, hard, upper surface grey to pale greyish-brown; pores labyrinthiform;* 5–30 cm across, attached by broad base; upper surface concentrically zoned, furrowed; pores ± round at blunt margin, becoming more elongated and wavy further away; walls thick; flesh pale wood-colour. Spores white. On dead wood of living trees; on stumps and worked wood—mostly oak; also chestnut, beech, other hardwoods; not known as a parasite. C. (Figured fruit body × ½; details of labyrinthine pores (*right*) × 1.)

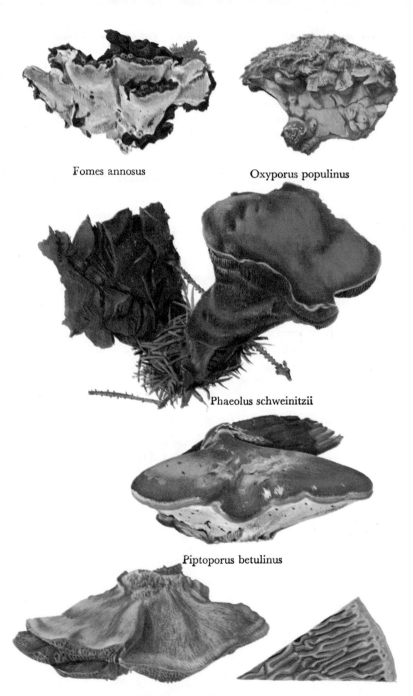

Fomes annosus

Oxyporus populinus

Phaeolus schweinitzii

Piptoporus betulinus

Daedalea quercina

Poria vaillantii (DC) Fr. (P. vaporaria auct.). *Very variable; resupinate-effused, 20-30 cm, skin-like or thicker, margin white fimbriate cottony; fruiting stage soft, sometimes with tubes to 12 mm; usually with spreading white cord-like mycelial strands.* Pores angular, $\frac{1}{2}$-1 mm across, $\pm$ toothed on vertical substrate; often hangs from above in tassel like columns. Saprophytic. A serious cause of wood decay esp. in damp mines, but also in buildings where water is leaking. C. A number of closely related species have been confused under the binomial *Poria vaporaria*. The above description applies to the prevalent British species.

Trametes

Bracket-like or resupinate corky to woody fungi; tubes continuous with tough flesh. Spores white. On wood. Annual.

Trametes serialis. *Effused usually resupinate, often much elongated; pores 2-4 mm across.* At first white, greyish or greyish brown; pores creamy to pale buff; flesh thin, white; tubes 1-8 mm long. On conifer trunks and stumps; also on timber in houses. O.

Trametes gibbosa. *Bracket; upper surface often with central algal growth,* whitish to greyish, $\pm$ zoned and densely tomentose; margin rounded. 8-15 cm across mostly sessile and broadly attached; pores $\pm$ radially elongated 3-5 times longer than wide; flesh white, corky, tough. On stumps of frondose trees, esp. beech. VIII-III. F. (Figured fruit body $\times\frac{1}{2}$; pore details to right $\times$ 1.)

Trametes versicolor. Polystictus. *Thin brackets, upper surface $\pm$ silky-velvety, with usually multi-coloured concentric zones.* 3-5 cm across, often in long, tiered, rows; colours variable: brown, greyish, greenish, yellow, near black; tubes very short; pores white to dirty yellowish; flesh thin, tough, thinner at wavy margin. On stumps, branches of frondose trees. Causes much decay on felled, rarely on structural timber. I-XII. C.

Trametes hirsuta. Polystictus. *Uniformly $\pm$ yellowish-brown, zoned but not variegated, strigose above.* 3-5 cm broad, varying greyish or greyish-brown; pore layer thin, pores pale grey becoming dirty yellowish-brown. On newly fallen branches of frondose trees. VI-III. O-F. Causes rot indistinguishable from above.

Poria vaillantii

Trametes gibbosa

Trametes versicolor

Trametes serialis

Trametes hirsuta

Trametes cinnabarina. *Bright reddish-orange bracket with deep blood-red to vermilion pores.* 3–6(9) cm across, sometimes in rows or imbricate; upper surface sl. tuberculate, ± zoned, fading to dull orange-yellow; pores minute; flesh rather thick, corky. Mainly on birch; also beech. VII–X. O.

Trametes abietina. Polystictus. *Small brackets, thin; upper surface greyish often tinged violet, esp. at wavy margin; pores ± violet.* 1–2(3) cm broad, often united and imbricate; rarely resupinate; pores often angular and torn; flesh thin, tough, leathery. Saprophytic on trunks, stumps, fallen branches of conifers, esp. where trees have been killed by fire. I–XII. C.

Trametes betulina. Lenzites. *Bracket; upper surface ± hairy-woolly, whitish to grey or tinged brownish, zoned; hymenium of gill-like plates.* 4–8 cm broad, often imbricate; gill plates branched, yellowish grey-white, drying ± ochre; flesh thin, soft to corky. On stumps and stout branches of frondose trees, esp. birch; also beech. I–XII. O.

Irpex obliquus. *Thin ± cream coloured ' skin ' having wide pores with toothed orifices.* Effused, margin indistinct, often 20–30 cm wide; pore layer becomes entirely disintegrated into short irregular often oblique teeth. Spores white. On bark of dead frondose trees; stumps, twigs, esp. oak; reduces wood to spongy ± fibrous mass. I–XII. F–C. May be a form of the common *Poria versispora* (Pers.) Baxt.

Gloeophyllum sepiarium. Lenzites. *Rusty-brown, corky, usually ± bracket-shaped, upper surface ± tuberculate, strigose and hairy at first, zoned, finally ± squamulose; hymenium gill-like, firm, irregularly forked, paler.* 3–6 cm broad, rusty brown finally blackish-brown to chestnut, margin long paler, more yellowish; flesh brownish-yellow, tough. Spores white. Serious cause of conifer timber decay in open; rare in houses and then probably from imported infected timber. I–XII. O.

Gloeoporus adustus. Polyporus. *Bracket-like, upper surface greyish to pale smoky-brown, minutely tomentose, ± zonate; pores minute, smoky-grey to sooty-black.* Caps 2–4 cm wide, often grouped and densely imbricate; margin (like pores) at first whitish, finally ± black; flesh pliable, coriaceous, whitish, then grey. Spores white. On trunks, stumps and fallen hardwoods generally. I–XII. C.

G. fumosus is thicker, with pale grey, finally smoky-brown, larger and irregular pores; pore layer separated from overlying context by dark line visible in section. Smell often like anise. On frondose trees, esp. willows and poplars. VIII–V. O.

All illustrations × 1.

Trametes cinnabarina

Trametes abietina

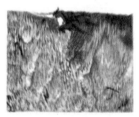

Irpex obliquus

Trametes betulina

Gloeoporus adustus

Gloeophyllum sepiarium

Caloporus ovinus. *Stipitate; fleshy; tubes short, pores small; on ground under conifers in mountains.* Cap 5–10 cm, irregularly convex to depressed, margin sometimes lobed, white and smooth when young, then brownish-yellow, finally often with olive tinge, scaly cracked; pores at first white, finally lemon-yellow or when bruised, irregularly decurrent; stipe central or not, short, thick, curved, same as colour on cap; flesh yellowish-white, fragile; smell of almonds. No British record; might occur in Scotland. *Edible when young.*

Leptoporus

Fruit bodies bracket-shaped to hoof-shaped; white, yellowish or bluish; flesh soft, cheesy.

Leptoporus stipticus (Pers.) Quél. Polyporus albidus. *Bracket to hoof-shaped, flesh bitter.* 2–6(8) cm across, sometimes concrescent; upper surface ± pubescent, whitish or margin tinged rusty; pores white, often weeping in active growth; flesh white, drying hard and brittle. Spores white. On stumps, trunks etc. of felled conifer wood. There are several closely related species. VIII–X. C. × 1.

Leptoporus caesius. Polyporus. *Bracket to hoof-shaped, woolly-tomentose on top at first, usually bluish-grey and flesh or pores bruising bluish.* 2–5(7) cm across; upper surface sometimes white; fades to grey; flesh white, watery, spongy, ± bluish on cutting. Spores pale blue. Especially on conifer stumps and dead wood; usually solitary or a few together. I–XII. C. × 1.

Grifola

Large forms with soft, not corky flesh; fruit bodies usually compound.

Grifola sulphurea. Polyporus. *Bracket-shaped, at first orange-yellow on top with sulphur-yellow margin and pores.* Often imbricate from common stipe, 30–40 cm across; fades to yellowish-tan; pores minute; flesh spongy, thick, yellowish. Attacks frondose and coniferous trees, esp. oaks. A serious cause of decay. V–XI. C. *Worthless, though sometimes eaten.* × ½. (Also shown: part of underside with pore layer.)

Grifola gigantea. Polyporus. *Caps fan-shaped, imbricate, leather-brown and scurfy fibrillose on top; minute whitish pores bruising blackish.* Often in groups to 1 metre across, individual caps 10–30 cm wide, merging into short, tuberous stipe; flesh rather brittle at first, finally tougher, blackening on cutting. Base of frondose trees esp. beech, oak. VII–I. C. *Worthless.* × ½.

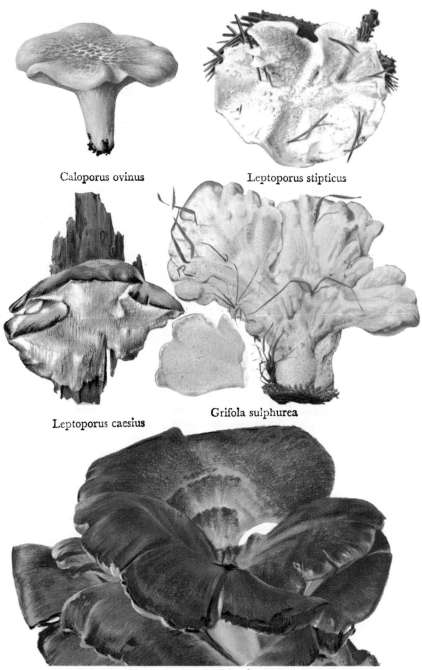

Caloporus ovinus

Leptoporus stipticus

Leptoporus caesius

Grifola sulphurea

Grifola gigantea

Grifola frondosa. Polyporus intybaceus. *Densely tufted, branched, spatulate to narrowly fan-shaped, imbricated, greyish brown caps.* Individual caps 4–6 cm wide, sl. fibrillose, sometimes yellowish-brown; tubes decurrent; pores irregular, whitish; flesh soft, white, smell somewhat rancid (" of mice "). Spores white. The richly branched stipe arises from a large dark sclerotium. At base of frondose trees, esp. oak. IX–X. R–O. *Sometimes eaten, but tough.*

G. (*Polyporus*) *umbellata* is similar, but individual caps have almost central stipes. × ⅓.

Polyporus *sensu restricto*

Stipe distinct, simple, central or lateral; flesh coriaceous.

Polyporus squamosus. *Reniform to circular, leather yellow on top with brown adpressed feathery scales; stipe lateral to almost eccentric.* 10–30 cm across; stipe short, stout; blackish below, pallid above; tubes decurrent; pores white finally dirty yellow with ± dentate orifices; flesh white at first soft, finally tough. On frondose trees, esp. elm; also *Acer* spp., *Pyrus* spp. and others. IV–XII. C. × ½. (Illustrated specimen more centrally stalked than usual.)

Polyporus brumalis. ± *Centrally stipitate with greyish brown to bistre cap and grey stipe.* Cap 2–5(7) cm diam., convex to flattened and depressed, finely downy at first, margin ± pubescent; tubes shallow, decurrent; pores whitish to yellowish, rather coarse, orifice often jagged; flesh white, thin, tough. Spores white. On stumps, branches, etc. of frondose trees, often on partially buried wood giving appearance of growing on soil. IX–V. F. × 1.

Polyporus varius. *Centrally or excentrically stipitate brownish-yellow cap; stipe black tomentose below.* Cap 2–8(10) cm diam., ligulate to shell-shaped or circular, flattened or depressed, varying ochre-yellow to cinnamon, often flecked and radiating dark-brown lines; tubes white to creamy, shallow, decurrent; pores ± creamy, greying; stipe short (2–3 cm), pallid above; flesh tough to almost woody, dirty yellowish. On stumps, trunks, fallen branches of frondose trees. VII–XI. C.

P. nummularius is a similar but smaller (cap 2–3 cm) sp. paler and with central blackish stipe. On buried sticks. F–C.

Fistulina—Ox-tongue; poor man's beefsteak

Fistulina hepatica. *Shaped like a hoof, tongue or bracket; reddish brown and rough on top; tubes on lower side close but free from each other; cut flesh yields a reddish juice.* 5–30 cm wide, sticky or jelly-like above; tubes minute, yellowish flushed pinkish; stipe short or absent; flesh looks and feels like red meat. Spores pinkish brown. Esp. on living oaks, also other frondose trees. The cause of so-called " Brown oak " timber. × ½. VIII–XI. F–C. *Edible; best after boiling, but hardly exciting.*

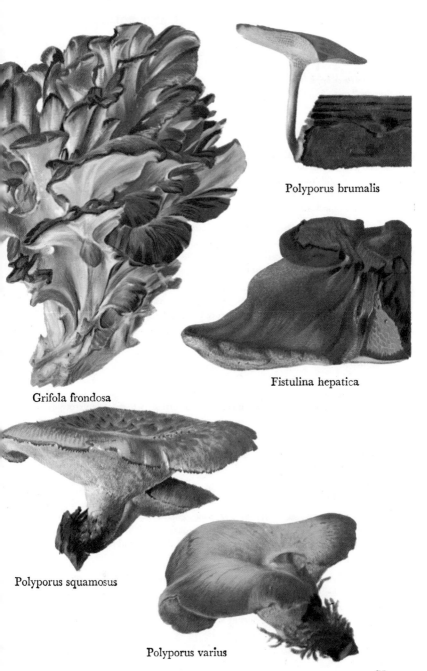

Polyporus brumalis

Fistulina hepatica

Grifola frondosa

Polyporus squamosus

Polyporus varius

AGARICALES—GILL FUNGI AND BOLETI
AGARICINEAE—GILL FUNGI
Hygrophorus

Often white or brightly coloured fleshy species, gills thick (esp. at base) ± distant character-istically "waxy"; spores white, smooth. All species edible, but mostly not much valued. For sub-genera, see footnote,[1] page 78.

Sub-genus Limacium

Hygrophorus eburneus. *Wholly white cap, stipe slender, glutinous, tapering down-wards, mealy-granulate above.* Cap 2–6 cm, smooth, convex, expanding to sl. umbonate; gills decurrent. No smell or reaction with KOH. Probably common and more tied to oak than beech; much confused in past with the common beechwood species *H. chrysaspis*, which stains brownish with KOH. VIII-XI. F.

Hygrophorus hypothejus. *Cap ± olivaceous-brown, sl. depressed, radially fibrillose, slimy; gills decurrent, yellow.* Cap 2–6 cm, shining darker towards centre; gills almost saffron with age; stipe slime-coated upwards to ring-like zone, paler than cap, apex pallid. Resistant to frost. Pine woods. X–XI. C.

Hygrophorus dichrous. *Stoutish; cap slimy, brown, sea-green with drop of ammonia; gills white; stipe slime-coated with brownish scales; frondose woods.* Cap 3–6(8); stipe apex white floccose. IX–XI. F. Figured specimen unusually stout.

Hygrophorus olivaceo-albus. *Slender; cap whitish; slimy centre ± brown, no ammonia reaction; gills white; stipe smooth; under conifers.* Cap 3–4; stipe slimy to ring-like zone. IX–XI. o.

Hygrophorus agathosmus. *Cap viscid, convex-umbonate, pale grey; stipe stoutish, whitish, apex pale brownish granulate; smell of bitter almonds.* Cap 3–8 cm, middle often with granules in dry weather; gills decurrent, white. Coniferous woods. IX–XI. O-F.

Hygrophorus pustulatus. *Cap dark mouse-grey ± viscid, with granular squamules, convex-depressed; stipe paler, brownish floccose esp. above; odourless.* Cap 2–5 cm; Coniferous woods. IX–X. O.

Sub-genus Camarophyllus

Hygrophorus niveus. *Wholly ivory-white, gills arcuate-decurrent.* Cap 1–5 cm, convex expanded to ± gibbous, smooth, sometimes faintly greyish in middle, margin striate; stipe dry tapering downwards. Pastures and meadows. IX–XII. C. *Edible and good.*

Hygrophorus pratensis. *Compact, ± top-shaped, convex to umbonate, pale tan-yellowish to buff; stipe and decurrent gills paler.* Cap 2–7 cm; gills often connected at base; stipe stout, finely striate; flesh thick, buff. In pastures, meadows. Colours tend to fade; some forms almost white. VIII-XII. C. *Edible and good.*

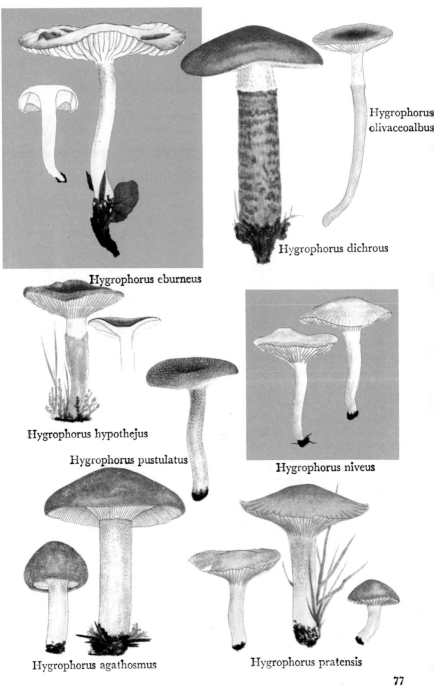

Hygrophorus olivaceoalbus

Hygrophorus dichrous

Hygrophorus eburneus

Hygrophorus hypothejus

Hygrophorus pustulatus

Hygrophorus niveus

Hygrophorus agathosmus

Hygrophorus pratensis

77

Hygrophorus camarophyllus, caprinus. *Large, cap soot-brown beset radially (lens) with blackish fibrils; gills greyish white; stipe dry.* Cap 5–10 cm ± convex, purple tinged towards edge; gills thick ± decurrent; stipe paler than cap, whitish above ± pruinose. In conifer woods. *Edible and good.*

Sub-genus Hygrocybe

Hygrophorus puniceus. *Cap scarlet or blood-red, smooth; stipe concolorous but white at base, fibrillose; gills yellow becoming flushed red, emarginate-adnate to almost free.* Cap 4–8(10) cm, ± campanulate, often irregular and lobed, colour soon fading; stipe fibrils coarse, dark on paler background. Grassy places: commons, fields, roadsides. VIII–XII. C. *Edible.*

H. coccineus is smaller; gills ± decurrent; stipe smooth.

Hygrophorus turundus. *Cap orange to scarlet with brownish, hairy squamules, esp. towards centre; margin thin, crenate; gills weakly decurrent, white at first, then sl. sulphur-yellow; in Sphagnum.* Cap 1–2 cm, flattened-depressed, dry; stipe often sl. white tomentose below. Mostly in open bogs. VII–X. O.

H. miniatus is similar but has cap less squamulose; gills ± golden-yellow; grows in grass.

Hygrophorus conicus. *Cap acutely conical, yellow often flushed orange to scarlet; blackening with age:* Cap 1–5 cm, ± fibrillose, viscid, margin splitting ± recurved; gills whitish-yellow, ± free; stipe dry, yellowish or with reddish flush, blackening, stiff. Grassy places: meadows etc., copses, heaths. VII–XI. C.

H. nigrescens is very similar, but has blunter cap and white base to stipe.

Hygrophorus citrinus sensu J. Lange (? H. glutinipes). *Wholly lemon-yellow except for horizontal, whitish-yellow, weakly decurrent gills.* Cap 1–2 cm, ± viscid, flat-convex to sl. depressed, margin striate; stipe ± viscid. Colour soon fades. Meadows, copses. IX–XI. R–O.

Hygrophorus psittacinus. *Cap glutinous, varying brownish, dull yellow, usually with marginal greenish flush; stipe slimy, apex distinctly green.* Cap 1–3(5) cm, convex, umbonate, margin sl. striate; gills adnate, yellow, green at base. Grassy places, lawns, meadows, copses. VII–XI. C.

Hygrophorus laetus. *Cap flesh colour to brownish, glutinous; gills decurrent; stipe apex bluish-violet.* Cap 1–3 cm, convex, finally ± flat, margin sl. striate; gills greyish, finally flesh colour; stipe slimy colour of cap below apex. Grassy places, pastures, heaths, somewhat boggy places. IX–XII. F.

---

[1] Sub-genera of Hygrophorus, sometimes regarded as separate genera:

Limacium. Cap viscid to glutinous; gills ± decurrent; veil manifest or rudimentary; stipe apex usually rough with dots. Spp. of woods and plantations.

Camarophyllus. Includes white spp. with dry cap; cap never viscid, nor stipe apex rough with dots; veil absent. White or dull coloured spp. of grassland or grassy places in wood clearings.

Hygrocybe. Mostly brightly coloured spp.; cap thin, fragile, often slimy when moist; stipe smooth or fibrillose. Grassland spp.

Hygrophorus turundus

Hygrophorus puniceus

Hygrophorus psittacinus

Hygrophorus conicus

Hygrophorus citrinus

Hygrophorus laetus

Hygrophorus camarophyllus

Small; on usually rotting species of Lactarius and Russula.

Asterophora parasitica. *Cap smooth, silky grey, thin; stipe long, slender.* Cap 1–2 cm, convex to flattened, sl. fibrillose or pruinose, sometimes lilac tinged; gills at first thick, distant, later ± obscured by brownish powder-like chlamydospores; stipe ± flexuose, 2–4 cm long, greyish. Smell nauseous. Often clustered. VII–XII. F.

Asterophora lycoperdoides, asterophora. *Cap soon densely powdered with brownish chlamydospores.* Thick; stipe short, stout. Cap 1–2 cm, sub-globose, white when young; gills obscure; stipe white then brownish. Smell strongly rancid or mealy. Singly or clustered. VII–XI. C.

Lyophyllum

Nearly all the species[1] have grey gills; frequently the fruit-bodies are also grey all over. Large species were formerly referred to Clitocybe, or Tricholoma. The smaller ones (with ± strong mealy smell) are by some authorities still retained in Collybia.

Lyophyllum decastes. Tricholoma aggregatum. *In large tufts; cap greyish, but varying greyish-brown to yellowish-brown.* Cap 4–12 cm, convex, expanding, somewhat undulate in large specimens; margin long, remaining incurved; gills white at first, finally grey to straw coloured, adnate to sl. decurrent, rather crowded; stipe whitish-grey, apex whitish, floccose, variable: long, short, ± eccentric, brownish below; flesh in cap thin, generally fibrous-elastic throughout; taste and smell not conspicuous. In woods, parks on rich soil. VII–X. F. *Edible.*

There are a few very closely allied species, sometimes regarded as varieties of the above.

Lyophyllum connatum. Clitocybe. *Tufted, almost chalk-white; iron reaction (ferrous sulphate) on gills: violet in 1 minute.* Cap 4–8 cm, smooth convex-flat, expanding, margin somewhat wavy; gills crowded, narrow, sl. decurrent, ageing sl. yellowish-grey; stipe slender, rather tall, white floccose above; flesh watery white, rather tough; smell and taste inconspicuous. Usually 3–4 fruit bodies together in grass on rich soil, esp. by paths in frondose woods. IX–XII. R–O. *Edible;* but poisonous, even deadly, white species of *Clitocybe* (q.v.) may be mistaken for it; iron reaction is differential.

---

[1]All spp. of *Lyophyllum* have basidia with numerous granules staining deeply when heated with aceto-carmine (see p. 233). Such *carminophil basidia* also occur in *Asterophora* and in the section *Calocybe* of *Tricholoma.* (See next page, first two spp. of *Tricholoma.*) For this reason, the section *Calocybe* is placed by some authorities under *Lyophyllum.*

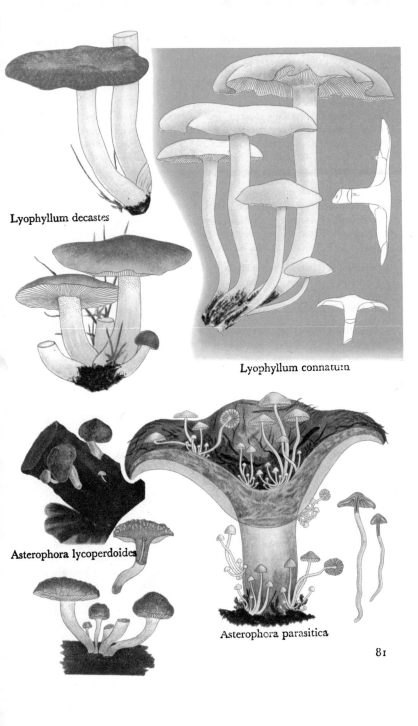

Lyophyllum decastes

Lyophyllum connatum

Asterophora lycoperdoides

Asterophora parasitica

81

Lyophyllum (Collybia) carbonarium, ambustum. *Blackish-brown with new or rancid meal smell; on charcoal heaps, burnt soil.* Cap 1–2 cm, convex to saucer-shaped, margin sl. striate; gills whitish then greyish, adnate, rather distant; stipe slender, flexuose, colour of cap except paler apex. Often 2–3 plants ± clustered. VIII–XI. F.

Lyophyllum (Collybia) palustre, leucomyosotis. *Cap pale watery greyish-brown, margin sl. striate; gills pale grey; in Sphagnum.* Cap. 1–2 cm, convex, finally ± saucer- shaped; gills rather distant; stipe long slender, smooth, toughish, paler than cap, ± hairy to strigose below where attached to Sphagnum. In heathy bogs. V–X. F.

Lyophyllum (Collybia) tesquorum, erosum. *Dwarfish; cap campanulate-umbonate, tinged brownish-grey, with darker course striae; stipe rooting.* Cap 1 cm, rarely more; gills distant, rather thick, pale grey; stipe slender silky-fibrillose apex sl. pruinose, flexuose. In small groups often on almost vanished remains of fungi. IX–X. R–O. (Best known by the broadly oval prickly spores.)

Lyophyllum (Collybia) rancidum. *Wholly dark ash-grey; stipe villous at base deeply rooting; strong rancid mealy smell.* Cap 2–5 cm, ± expanded or flat, sometimes with olive-brown tinge; umbo darker, becoming shiny silky-pruinose; gills crowded, ash-grey; stipe stiff, rigid. Mainly in frondose woods. IX–XII. O–F.

Lyophyllum (Collybia) murinum. *Cap dark greyish brown, convex then ± expanded; stipe ± flexuose, paler, white plumulose above.* Cap 2–3 cm, darker at middle; flesh of stipe dark brown. Esp. along woodland paths. Not yet definitely known from this country.

Tricholoma

A large genus of mostly ± fleshy species with white spores and sinuate gills; a few species have a veil.

Tricholoma pseudoflammula J. Lge. ± wholly orange yellow, sl. felty cap with darker and more tawny centre. Cap 2–5 cm; margin incurved; gills very narrow (1–2 mm) and crowded, arcuate-sinuate to sl. decurrent; stipe stoutish, tapering downwards, base white felty; flesh ± bitterish. Coniferous woods. Not yet recorded here. Very close to *T. cerinum*, which has more brownish cap, stipe soon hollow and not white felty at base. R.

Tricholoma gambosum. " St. George's Mushroom." *Cap and stipe creamy to whitish buff; white crowded gills; strong mealy smell and taste. April to June* Cap 5–15 cm, convex-expanded, ± wavy, whiter when young; stipe stout thick, curved; flesh white, brittle. Grassy places, esp. calcareous pastures. IV–VI. O–F. *Edible and very good.*

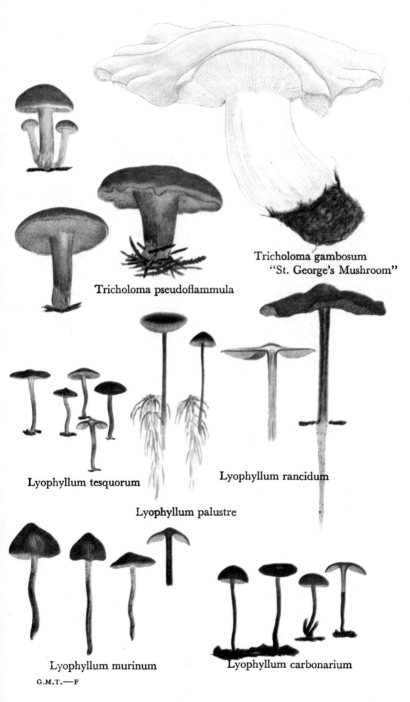

Tricholoma gambosum
"St. George's Mushroom"

Tricholoma pseudoflammula

Lyophyllum tesquorum

Lyophyllum palustre

Lyophyllum rancidum

Lyophyllum murinum

Lyophyllum carbonarium

Tricholoma sudum. *Cap smooth mouse-grey or pale brownish, edge paler; gills greyish to flesh coloured.* Cap 5–8 cm, soon flattened, almost dry; gills rather crowded, broadly emarginate; stipe cylindric, sl. rooting, becoming flesh coloured with age; flesh firm white to tinged pinkish; smell and taste faintly rancid mealy. Coniferous woods. Not known with certainty here.

Tricholoma saponaceum. *Gills distant, white to tinged pale sulphur; distinctive smell of kitchen soap.* Cap 3–8 cm, ± umbonate and sl. fibrillose to squamulose at middle, blackish-grey to olive-grey or brownish; gills sometimes glaucous tinged or spotted reddish; stipe pale, smooth, fibrillose or ± squamulose, rooting; flesh firm. Flesh tints sometimes develop, esp. on gills and at stipe base. Frondose and coniferous woods. VIII–XI. C.

Tricholoma sulphureum. *Wholly sulphur-yellow; strong smell of gas tar.* Cap 4–8 cm, convex or irregularly flattened, smooth, centre sometimes tinged brownish; gills rather distant and thick; stipe long, ± flexuose. Frondose woods, esp. oak.

Tricholoma inamoenum. *Similar to T. sudum, including smell, but stipe taller and, like gills, almost white.* Cap ± tinged yellowish, pale brownish towards centre; stipe slender and tall in proportion to cap, somewhat rooting. On mossy ground in conifer woods, esp. on calcareous soil. IV–XI. R–O.

Tricholoma lascivum. *Cap sl. umbonate, very pale yellowish-tan, ± darker at disc; smell and taste faintly sweetish, then ± gassy.* Cap 5–8 cm, sometimes almost white towards margin; gills emarginate rather distant, white; stipe white, usually with pale tan flesh midway on one side. Gregarious in frondose woods, esp. oak. IX–XI. F. *T. album* is more leather greyish, larger, cap margin ± grooved. gills often brown spotted with age; found in boggy ground under birch.

Tricholoma columbetta. *Wholly white, cap almost shining, minutely silky with fibrils, often ± blue spotted when old; no smell.* Cap 6–10 cm, convex to expanded. margin ± fibrillose; gills crowded; stipe rooting, stout, ± fibrillose; flesh solid, tasteless. In frondose woods, on acid soil, often beech. VIII–IX. O–F. *Edible and good.*

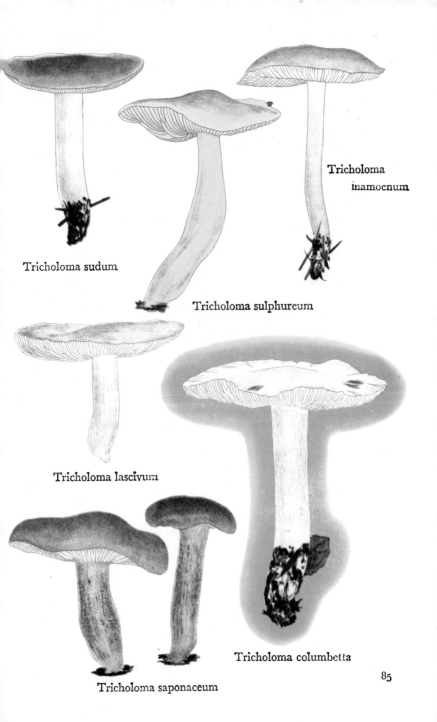

Tricholoma sudum

Tricholoma
inamoenum

Tricholoma sulphureum

Tricholoma lascivum

Tricholoma columbetta

Tricholoma saponaceum

Tricholoma flavovirens, equestre. *Cap greenish-yellow, viscid; gills sulphur-yellow; stipe pale yellow; no unpleasant smell.* Cap 5–10 cm, soon flattened and somewhat undulate, brownish tinged towards sl. scaly middle; stipe stout, ± fibrillose; flesh firm with faint mealy smell. Sandy pine woods. VIII–IX. F. *Edible and good.*

Tricholoma portentosum. *Cap greyish-brown with fibrils from almost black centre.* Cap 6–10 cm with thin flesh; gills first white then faint yellow; stipe stout, white tinged sulphur, sl. rooting; flesh firm without taste or smell. Esp. under old pine trees. IX–XI. O–F. *Edible.*

Tricholoma cingulatum. *Cap ± mouse-grey, squamulose-fibrillose; stipe with distinct cottony ring; flesh with mealy taste.* Cap 3–6 cm, expanded to umbonate, sometimes tinged brownish; gills white, rather distant; stipe slender, white, often flexuose, sl. fibrillose below ring, ± hollow; flesh whitish-grey. On damp ground mostly under willows, rarely pines. VIII–XI. O. *Edible.*

Tricholoma argyraceum, scalpturatum. *Cap ± mouse-grey, densely squamulose-fibrillose; stipe without ring; taste mealy.* Cap 3–7 cm, convex-flat, sometimes acutely umbonate, may be tinged brownish, margin somewhat shaggy-tomentose; gills white to tinged greyish, yellowing with age; stipe white or grey flushed, ± hollow; flesh whitish-grey. In litter of frondose woods, esp. beech on chalk, also coniferous woods. VIII–XI. F. *Edible.*

Tricholoma virgatum. *Cap ash-grey, with darker radiating fibrillose lines, ± conical; gills mostly white edged; flesh peppery after few minutes.* Cap 5–7 cm, gills broad, rather distant, often with jagged edge; stipe tallish, slender, white to pale grey, sl. fibrillose, apex ± white pruinose; flesh firm, whitish grey. Coniferous woods. XI. O–F.

Very closely related is *T. sciodes:* same peppery taste, cap felty-squamulose, gills mostly edged with black; frondose woods, esp. beech. VIII–XI. F–C.

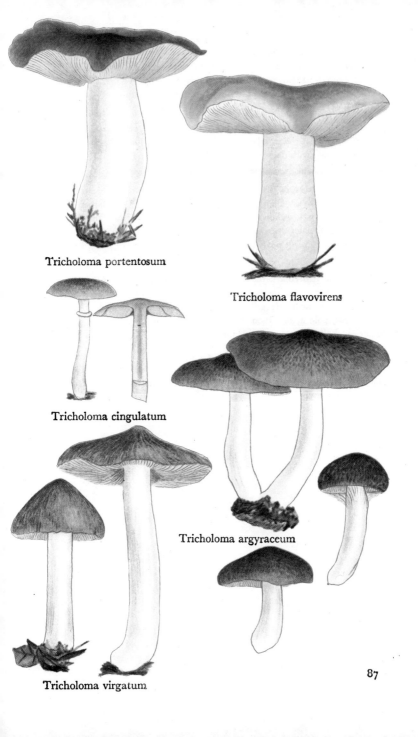

Tricholoma portentosum

Tricholoma flavovirens

Tricholoma cingulatum

Tricholoma argyraceum

Tricholoma virgatum

87

Tricholoma terreum. *Cap blackish-grey, usually acutely umbonate, ± fibrillosely felty-squamulose; gills grey; flesh with no mealy taste or smell.* Cap 5–7 cm, convex to ± expanded, middle often almost blackish, margin incurved; gills rather distant, not edged with black; stipe whitish-grey, apex white mealy, rather stout; flesh whitish-grey, spongy, quite mild to taste. Predominantly coniferous wood species. VIII–XI. F–C.

Tricholoma psammopus. *Cap pale reddish-tan; stipe densely granular with brownish flocci, denser and darker downwards; under larch.* Cap 3–6 cm, ± convex; gills pale brown with darker brown discolorations; stipe slender, whitish at apex; flesh pale brownish. Confined to larch. IX–XI. O.

Tricholoma fulvum, flavobrunneum. *Cap reddish-brown to chestnut; flesh in stipe distinctly yellow.* Cap 5–8 cm, ± viscid; expanded umbonate ± radially streaked; gills pale yellow, brown spotted with age; stipe cylindric concolour with cap, or sl. paler at apex, fibrillose; flesh white in cap with ± rancid mealy taste and smell. In ± peaty ground of frondose woods, heaths, esp. under birches. IX–XI. C.

Tricholoma imbricatum. *Cap dry ± conical, reddish-brown breaking up into ± coarse imbricating scales; confined to pines.* Cap 5–9 cm, smooth when young, margin long remaining incurved; gills whitish, rufous spotted with age; stipe thickening downwards, pale at first then ± brownish-red, fibrillose, sl. rooting; flesh firm somewhat hollow in stipe, smell faintly mealy. IX–XI. O–F.

Tricholoma vaccinum. *Cap ± rufous, dry, softly but coarsely squamulose, margin shaggy.* Cap 4–6 cm, convex ± umbonate, margin involute; gills whitish discolouring brownish with age; stipe slender, fibrillose or ± squamulose, sl. paler than cap, hollow; flesh pallid. Coniferous woods. VIII–XI. O–F.

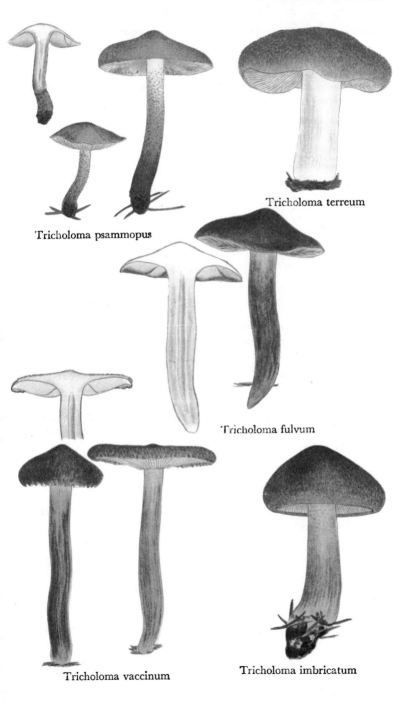

Tricholoma terreum

Tricholoma psammopus

Tricholoma fulvum

Tricholoma vaccinum

Tricholoma imbricatum

89

Tricholoma aurantium. *Cap fleshy viscid ± rusty-orange, stipe with closely-set concolorous scaly belts.* Cap 5-10(12) cm, convex, disc with mealy scales, sometimes more brownish, margin incurved; gills rather narrow, emarginate-free, at first whitish discolouring rufous; stipe stout, apex pale yellow, belts becoming more brownish downwards; flesh with cucumber smell and bitter taste. Coniferous woods, often in groups or fairy rings. IX-XI. R-O.

Tricholoma ustale. *Cap reddish bay-brown, darkening with age, ± viscid, gills soon rufous spotted; no smell of new meal on cutting; frondose woods.* Cap 5-8 cm, smooth, convex to flattened, margin incurved; gills at first white; stipe slender, sl. clavate below, pallid then flushing brownish from base. Esp. beech woods. VIII-XI. F.

The following two species are very similar: in similar habitats is *T. ustaloides* Romagn., with persistent strong mealy smell; *T. albobrunnea* has a faint mealy smell, cap minutely radially streaked with darker lines; a common species of coniferous woods, esp. pines.

Tricholoma populinum. *Cap pale brown tinged with flesh colour; ± tufted; always under poplars.* Cap 8-12 cm, smooth, sl. viscid, almost flat, darkening with age; gills white, discolouring rufous; stipe stout, white, soon pale rufous; flesh whitish, smell and taste strongly mealy. Usually in grass. IX-X. F. *Presumably edible.*

Tricholoma (Lepista) nudum. " Wood Blewits ". *± wholly lilac to fuscous violet.* Cap 6-10 cm, convex to flat, smooth, sl. moist, somewhat darker violet towards centre, more reddish-brown when old; gills pale lilac, crowded; stipe solid, elastic apex, mealy, ± cap colour; flesh pale violet. Spores pale pinkish. Frondose and coniferous woods, gardens. (IX)X-XII. C. *Edible and good.*

Tricholoma (Lepista) saevum, personatum. " Blewits ". *Cap and gills ± pale clay colour; stipe ± flushed bluish, with more violet scaly fibrils.* Cap 6-12 cm, almost flat, dry, varying pale tan to greyish; gills crowded, white or flesh colour never bluish; stipe stout, often swollen below; flesh white, firm. Spores pale pinkish. In grass, often in rings, mainly pastures; less often in frondose woods or by hedges. (IX)X-XII. F-C. *Edible and good.*

Tricholoma (Lepista) irinum is similar but with paler cap, pallid stipe and characteristic pleasant, sweet smell—Iris, Violet, Mock orange (*Philadelphus*). *Edible and good.*

The genus Lepista, to which the above 3 species are often referred, is distinguished from typical Tricholoma spp. by the pale pinkish spore print and the spores prickly under the microscope, not smooth.

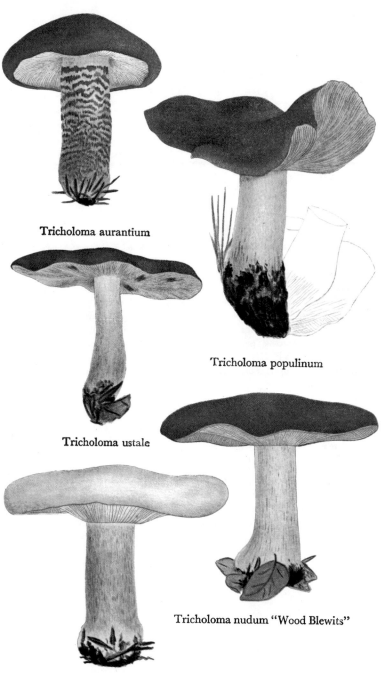

Tricholoma aurantium

Tricholoma populinum

Tricholoma ustale

Tricholoma nudum "Wood Blewits"

Tricholoma saevum "Blewits"

Tricholomopsis

Tricholomopsis rutilans. Tricholoma. *Cap with purplish downy scales on yellow background; gills chrome-yellow; on conifer stumps.* Cap 5–9 cm, convex to ± flat, more densely scaly towards centre; gill edge sl. fluffy; stipe paler than cap below, yellowish above; flesh yellowish. Spores white. VIII–XI. C.

Tricholomopsis platyphylla. Collybia. *Cap horn-grey to smoky-brown, radically streaked with darker fibrils; gills broad, distant; stipe with prominent basal mycelial cords.* Cap 4–9(12) cm, dry, ± flat; gills to 1.25 cm broad, white; stipe equal, straight, pale greyish fibrillose; flesh white, quite thin towards cap margin. Frondose woods, probably always in contact with wood, at least via the mycelial strands. V–XI(XII). F–C.

Armillaria *sensu restricto*

Restricted to the following two species by several authorites.

Armillaria mellea. " Honey fungus ". *Cap yellowish to brownish, with recurved fibrillose scales; ring ± membranous, yellow-flecked; ± tufted from black rhizomorphs.* Cap 3–10(14) cm, the scales yellow to brownish, disappearing with age; gills arcuate, adnate or sl. decurrent, whitish then pale brownish-yellow, often brown-spotted; stipe often bulbous below, whitish to dull ochre, yellow-flecked like, ring; flesh pale, spongy. Solitary specimens sometimes occur. Spreads extensively by black rhizomorphs which may be found between bark and wood. A serious and destructive parasite of frondose and coniferous trees; also lives saprophytically. VII–XII. C. *Edible; some find it too rich.*

A. tabescens is superficially identical except for complete absence of ring. It is uncommon.

Clitocybe

Medium to large infundibuliform species with decurrent gills, fleshy stipe, tissue of cap continuous with that of stipe. Spores white.

Clitocybe nebularis. *Very fleshy, cap pale greyish ± broadly umbonate at first; gil and stipe paler, stipe tapering upwards.* Cap 6–15 cm, finally expanded or sl. depressed hardly infundibuliform, smooth, darker towards centre, at first with slight bloom; gills crowded not very decurrent, whitish then pale yellowish-grey; stipe stout; striate fibrillose; flesh white, soft, with faint sweetish smell. Woods generally esp. coniferous. VIII–XI(XII). C. *Edible and enjoyed by many; a few find indigestible.*

Clitocybe nebularis

Tricholomopsis platyphylla

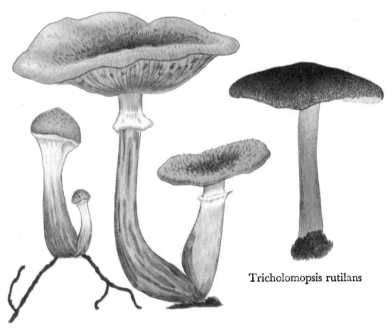

Tricholomopsis rutilans

Armillaria mellea "Honey fungus"

Clitocybe clavipes. *Cap grey-brown with sl. olive tinge, margin paler; gills pale primrose; stipe clavate below.* Cap 4–7 cm, sl. umbonate at first, finally sl. depressed, smooth; gills deeply decurrent; stipe cap colour but paler, $\pm$ fibrillose, hairy below. Esp. beech, conifer woods. IX–XI. C.

Clitocybe odora. *Cap blue-green; strong sweet smell of aniseed.* Cap 4–8 cm, flattened, $\pm$ umbonate, irregularly lobed; gills paler than cap; stipe flushed with cap colour, swollen below; flesh soft, greenish. In litter mainly of deciduous woods. VIII–XI. F–C. *Used as a flavouring.*

Clitocybe flaccida, inversa. *Cap reddish leather-brown, $\pm$ spotted, funnel-shaped; leathery.* Cap 5–8 cm, smooth, darkening with age, paler when dry, margin expanded, $\pm$ lobed; gills narrow, deeply decurrent; stipe cap colour, usually shorter than cap diam., base woolly; flesh pale tan. Mainly coniferous woods, often clustered or in rings. IX–XII. C. *Edible.*

Clitocybe infundibuliformis. *Cap yellowish or pinkish flesh-colour to tan, thin fleshed, funnel-shaped.* Cap 4–8 cm, usually faintly silky and scaly at middle, margin wavy; gills crowded, deeply decurrent, white; stipe whitish, tinged cap colour, sl. swollen and hairy below; flesh rather tough, smell faint, pleasant. Woods, usually in deep litter; also heaths and among grass. VII–XI. F–C.

Clitocybe geotropa. *Large; cap depressed round central umbo, pale pinkish-tan, smooth; stipe longer than cap diam.* Cap 10–15(20) cm, at first convex to flat with incurved margin, margin finally scalloped; gills cap colour, decurrent; stipe sl. paler than cap, fibrillose, enlarging and downy or hairy below. Wood clearings on damp rich soil, sometimes in rings. IX–XI. F–C. *Edible and good.*

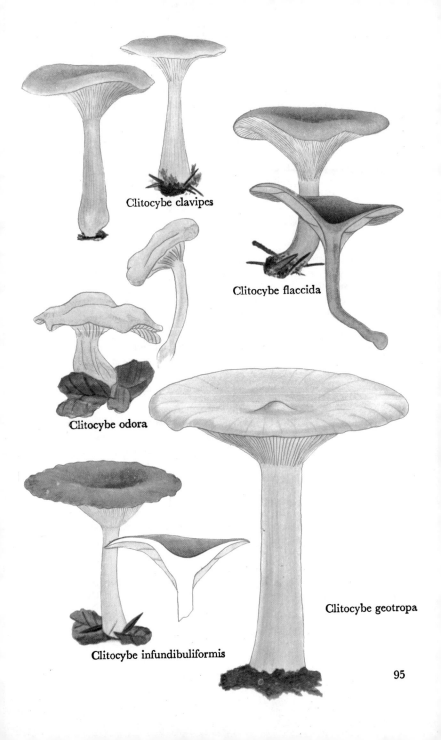

Clitocybe clavipes

Clitocybe flaccida

Clitocybe odora

Clitocybe infundibuliformis

Clitocybe geotropa

95

Clitocybe (Leucopaxillus) gigantea. *Large, cap cream coloured, margin incurved at first, sl. pubescent, finally expanded and grooved.* Cap to 30 cm, broadly infundibuliform, smooth or sl. squamulose at disc, finally tinged pale tan; gills narrow, crowded, often forked, creamy; stipe short, thick, fibrillose, whitish; flesh white firm, smell faint, pleasant. Spores amyloid. In grassy places, pastures, roadsides, hedgerows, often in rings and killing the grass. VIII–XI. F. *Edible.*

Clitocybe rivulosa. *Dull, whitish flesh-coloured, ± zoned; delicately powdered at first with a bloom; stipe short.* Cap 2–4(5) cm, flattened to sl. depressed, margin powdered, incurved, dry, smooth, the delicate bloom soon disappearing, varying to pale pinkish tan; gills crowded, paler than cap, sl. decurrent; stipe usually shorter than cap diam., cap colour, sl. hairy-downy at apex, often twisted; flesh white, firm, little or no smell. In short grass, lawns, pastures, in troops or rings. VIII–XI. C. **Poisonous, sometimes deadly.** *Might be gathered as Marasmius oreades with which it commonly grows.*

Clitocybe dealbata. *Very similar to previous, in similar habitats, but cap whitish or whitish-tan; not zoned.* Cap 2–4 cm, flattened-convex, dry, dull; the bloom remaining; gills white with faint yellow tinge, crowded sl. decurrent; stipe short, thin, smooth, sl. primrose above; smell mealy. Grassy places, pastures etc. VII–XI. C. **Poisonous, sometimes deadly.** *A few other related white spp. of Clitocybe occur, some found in woods, and are equally poisonous.*

Clitocybe langei, vibecina p.p. *Cap flat-convex to depressed, hygrophanous mouse-grey, tinged tan; margin striate when moist, off white, striations absent when dry; taste and smell mealy.* Cap 2–5 cm, drying from centre, gills greyish-brown, decurrent narrow; stipe paler than cap, smooth, elastic. In coniferous woods, esp. pine, on heathy soils under birch, esp. under bracken. (X)XI–XII. C.
There are a number of closely related spp.

Clitocybe asterospora. Omphalina. *Cap striate and brownish-grey when moist, off-white and no striations when dry, convex-flat then ± depressed; spores round, blunt, echinulate.* Cap 2–5 cm, gills sl. paler than cap, short-decurrent; stipe cap colour, elastic; flesh with faint smell of cucumber or meal. In soil, usually among moss, along woodland paths. Best recognized by microscopical examination of spores. IX–XI. R-O.

Clitocybe fragrans. *Cap yellowish-grey and margin striate when moist, uniformly whitish and non-striate when dry; convex-flat to sl. depressed; distinct aniseed smell.* Cap 2–4 cm, somewhat shining; gills tinged with colour of cap, sl. decurrent; stipe usually flexuous, slender, longer than cap diam. Amongst grass and moss mainly in frondose woods. VIII–XII. O-F.
C. suaveolens, with same aniseed smell, is very similar but dried cap has dark ± brownish disc and is essentially a species of coniferous woods. IX–XI. O-F.

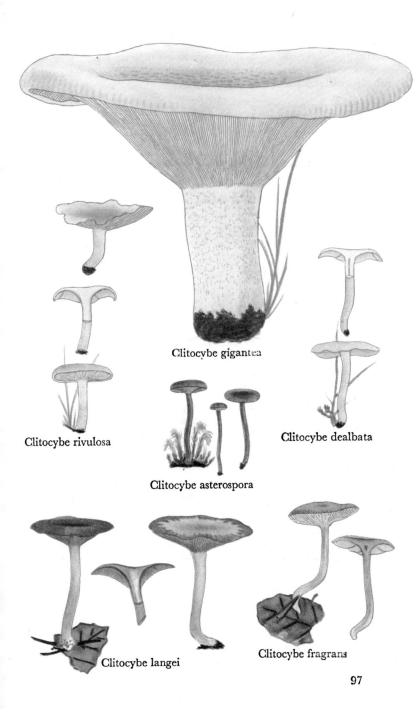

Clitocybe gigantea

Clitocybe rivulosa

Clitocybe asterospora

Clitocybe dealbata

Clitocybe langei

Clitocybe fragrans

97

Clitocybe (Cantharellula) cyathiformis. *Cap dark greyish-brown to bistre when wet, paler when dry, ± deeply cup-shaped, margin incurved; spores amyloid.* Cap 3–7 cm; gills ± decurrent, greyish-tan; stipe longer than cap diam., paler than cap, fibrils, apex with ± network of fibrils; flesh greyish. Woods generally, on rich soil, esp. along paths. IX—I. O. *Edible.*

Laccaria

Differs from Clitocybe by thick, widely-spaced, hardly decurrent gills, dusty with spores.

Laccaria amethystina. *Wholly deep violet when moist, drying paler.* Cap 1–4 cm, convex-flat, scurfy towards centre; stipe fibrous-elastic. Frondose woods. VIII–XII. C. *Edible.*

Laccaria laccata. *Dull rufous flesh-colour when moist, drying out dull yellowish.* Cap 1–6 cm, somewhat convex, scaly-squamulose towards centre; gills flesh-colour; stipe fibrous-elastic, cap colour. Woods generally and heaths. VII–XII. CC. Very variable. Illustration shows large form from *Sphagnum* bog.

Omphalina. Omphalia

Small, cap convex or umbilicate; gills ± decurrent; stipe thin, ± cartilaginous.

Omphalina fibula. *Cap yellowish-orange, striate, gills pallid;* Cap 0.5–1 cm, convex depressed varying pale orange; gills arcuate, deeply decurrent; stipe filiform, ± pale orange, longer than cap diam. In grass and moss, moist shady places. V–XI. C.

Omphalina swartzii. *Stipe apex, and often cap centre, dark violet.* As previous sp., but colours duller: more brownish. Similar habitats. VIII–XII. F.

Omphalina ericetorum, umbellifera. *Cap convex-umbilicate, coarsely striate, colours variable, usually pale brownish olive; gills wide, distant.* Cap 1–2 cm, darker in middle, margin ± crenate to grooved; gills white to pale yellowish, deeply decurrent; stipe ± cap colour. On peaty ground, heaths. V–XI. F–C.

Omphalina sphagnicola. *Cap ± sooty-brown, middle ± squamulose, funnel-shaped; confined to Sphagnum.* Cap 1–2 cm, varying brownish-black or olive-brown, striate; gills pale greyish-brown, deeply decurrent; stipe paler than cap. VI–VIII. O–F.

A larger species, *O. epichysium*, is found in similar places late in the season.

Omphalina pyxidata. *Cap ± orange-brown with rufous striations and coarsely striate; gills yellowish.* Cap 1–2 cm, at first deeply umbilicate, finally ± funnel-shaped; stipe flexuose, paler than cap. In grass on moist sandy soil. VIII–XI. F–C.

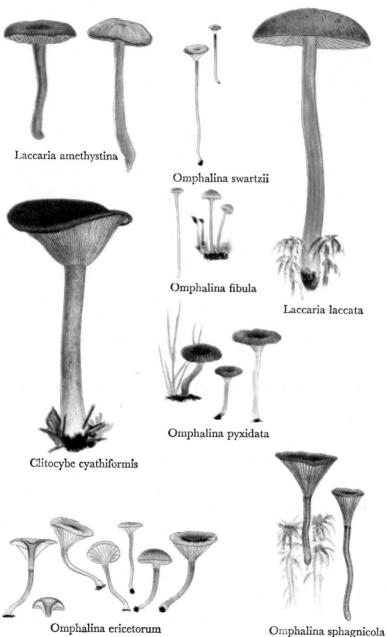

Laccaria amethystina

Omphalina swartzii

Omphalina fibula

Laccaria laccata

Clitocybe cyathiformis

Omphalina pyxidata

Omphalina ericetorum

Omphalina sphagnicola

Collybia

Small to medium species with generally convex cap and incurved edge; gills never decurrent; stipe usually slender, ± cartilaginous.

Collybia dryophila. *Cap light to dark yellowish-tan; gills crowded, white to tinged sulphur; stipe smooth, ± cap colour.* Cap 2–5 cm, convex–flat, quite smooth; gills adnexed or free, narrow; stipe tough pliable, usually darker towards swollen base. Frondose woods, esp. oak. V–XI. C.

Collybia fusipes. *Cap dark rufous, stipe fusiform, longitudinally grooved, darker downwards than cap; ± tufted from rooting base.* Cap 3–8 cm, convex-umbonate to expanded, fading to reddish-tan, often spotted; gills distant, broad, much paler than cap, sometimes spotted, tough, pliant; flesh firm. Base of frondose trees, esp. beech, oak. (IV)V–XII. C.

Collybia butyracea. *Cap sl. umbonate, greasy, brownish-rufous when moist, drying greyish, but not umbo.* Cap 3–7 cm, ± convex, smooth; gills broad, crowded, whitish; stipe tapering upwards from swollen base, striate, brownish. Frondose and coniferous woods. (I–VIII) IX–XII. C.

Collybia maculata. *Entirely white, soon spotted reddish-brown, tough.* Cap 4–8 cm, convex to flat, margin strongly incurved; gills whitish to creamy, crowded; stipe sl. swollen midway, striate or furrowed longitudinally; flesh tough, bitterish. Spores tinged pink. Predominantly in coniferous woods; often clustered. All parts become ± spotted. VII–XI. C.

Collybia peronata. Marasmius. "Wood woolly-foot". *Cap yellowish- to reddish-brown, fading; stipe more yellowish, thickly woolly-hairy towards litter-binding curved base; tastes peppery after few minutes chewing.* Cap 2–5 cm, convex to flat, often ± wrinkled; gills distant, cap colour but often yellow when young; stipe yellowish to brownish-yellow; whole plant leathery and pliant. Woods generally, esp. frondose. VIII–XI. C.

Collybia confluens. *Cap ± flattened, pale clay, flesh-colour to almost white; gills crowded; stipes confluent, shortly but densely pubescent.* Cap 2–4 cm, ± convex at first, dull, margin finely striate; gills with tinge of cap colour, very narrow; stipe soon darker than cap; whole plant leathery and pliant. Densely clustered, often in circles. Mainly frondose woods, esp. beech. VII—XI. C.

Collybia dryophila

Collybia fusipes

Collybia peronata
"Wood woolly-foot"

Collybia butyracea

Collybia maculata

Collybia confluens

Collybia fuscopurpurea. Marasmius. *Cap convex-flat, dark brownish with purplish flush, drying paler; stipe darker, almost reddish-brown, lower half densely woolly-hairy to curved litter-binding base; taste mild.* Cap 2–4 cm, sometimes depressed, margin sl. striate; gills ± distant, cap colour; stipe hairs greyish-yellow. Frondose woods, esp. beech. IX–XI. O.

Collybia tuberosa. *Small; cap flat, dirty white, dry; grows from purple-brown sclerotium.* Cap 0.5–1 cm, tinged yellowish at centre; gills crowded white; stipe sl. pruinose, thin and slender or short and thick; pilose below; sclerotium oval, varying reddish-brown or black; among decaying gill fungi, esp. *Russalaceae.* VIII–XI. C.

Cantharellula umbonata. *Shallow funnel-shaped; blunt edged dichotomous gills ± decurrent; spores amyloid.* Cap 3–4 cm, with small central papilla, grey to black, edge paler, surface ± tomentose-flocculose; gills repeatedly branched finally reddish spotted. On gravelly acid soils, often with *Calluna* and mosses near conifers. IX–XI. O.

Collybia cookei, cirrhata. *Similar to previous species but sclerotium yellowish (or absent).* Similar habitats. VIII–XI. C.

Melanoleuca

Medium to large species, cap ± greyish to greyish or yellowish brown, hygrophanous. Like Tricholoma, to which they were formerly referred, but spores with amyloid warts, and other microscopical characters very different.

Melanoleuca cognata. *Dirty yellowish-tan—almost wholly; stipe striate, sub-bulbous.* Cap 6–10 cm, convex-flat, smooth; gills somewhat more yellow, emarginate: stipe slender, longer than cap diam. Grassy places by roads; paths in woods, mainly coniferous. IX–XI. R–O. The illustration shows an unusually yellowish colour.

Melanoleuca melaleuca. *Cap convex- flat,± umbonate, sooty-brown, umbo darker; gills white.* Cap 4–8 cm, smooth, somewhat moist; drying out paler; gills emarginate; stipe tall, whitish with brownish longitudinal fibrils; flesh flushed brownish from base upwards. Woods and pastures. VIII–XI. F–C.

There are several closely related species.

Lentinellus

Lentinellus cochleatus. Lentinus, *Tufted; aniseed smell; cap irregular, ± funnel-shaped, buff to pale date-brown; gill edge toothed; spores amyloid.* Cap 2–5 cm. wavy, smooth; gills decurrent, pale watery-brown tinged pinkish with age; flesh rather tough. On stumps, esp. beech. VIII–XI. O–F.

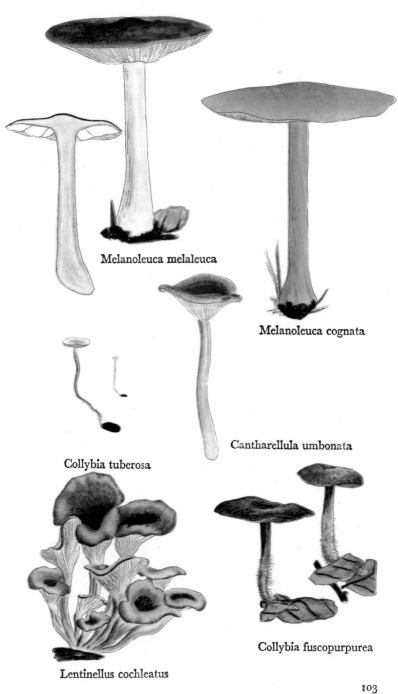

Melanoleuca melaleuca

Melanoleuca cognata

Cantharellula umbonata

Collybia tuberosa

Collybia fuscopurpurea

Lentinellus cochleatus

Schizophyllum commune. *Cap fan-shaped, ± lobed, greyish-tomentose; gill edge longitudinally split; on wood.* Cap 1–4 cm, drying whitish; gills greyish-violet, edge pubescent, each split half revolute in dry weather, ± straight in wet; stipe rudimentary or absent; flesh leathery-tough. On hardwoods; trunks, newly-felled wood, stacked timber, dead branches; almost restricted to South-East England. I–XII. C.

Panellus

Caps small to medium; gill edge even; stipe short, thick, lateral; spores amyloid, except P. nidulans.

Panellus stypticus. Panus. *Clay brown or pale tan; leathery; stipe flattened and dilated above; on frondose wood.* Cap 1–3(4) cm, convex-flat, ± reniform, minutely mealy; gills narrow, crowded, sometimes pale cinnamon; stipe almost whitish, short; flesh bitter. Stumps, often imbricate. I–XII. C.

Panellus mitis. Pleurotus. *Entirely white, becoming pale reddish-clay colour; on coniferous wood.* Cap 1–2 cm, shell-shaped to broadly ligulate, pellicle separable; gills crowded; stipe flattened and dilated above, somewhat mealy; flesh ± spongy, taste mild. Esp. on spruce. X–XII. F–C.

Panellus serotinus. Pleurotus. *Cap ± olive-green; gills yellow, stipe with brownish scales; on frondose trees.* Cap 3–8 cm, at first ± cushion-shaped and tomentose; finally fan-shaped with incurved margin and viscid; gills narrow, crowded; stipe lateral, somewhat dilated upwards; flesh gelatinous to tough. Trunks of frondose trees. X–XII. O.

Panellus (Phyllotopsis) nidulans. Crepidotus. *Cap yellowish to ± orange-yellow; gills ± orange-ochre.* Cap 2–5 cm, ± shell-shaped or reniform, velvety, sometimes resupinate, edge involute; gills crowded, narrow; stipe absent; flesh firm, gelatinous-spongy, yellow. Spores pale pinkish clay. On stumps esp. beech. X–XII. R.

Pleurotus *sensu restricto*

Medium to very large species; stipe excentric, lateral or absent; on wood. The genus formerly included all bracket-like agarics with smooth edge to gill and white spores.

Pleurotus dryinus, corticatus. *Cap whitish with soft greyish scale; young gills covered by very fugacious veil.* Cap 5–12 cm, fleshy, often yellowish with age, margin with velar remnants; gills decurrent, anastamosing, white, discolouring yellowish; stipe stout, ± eccentric, sometimes with ring-like velar remains; flesh white, finally ± corky. On trunks of often living, frondose trees. IX–II. O–F.

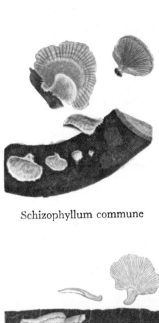

Schizophyllum commune

Panellus stypticus

Panellus mitis

Panellus nidulans

Panellus serotinus

Pleurotus dryinus

Pleurotus ostreatus. *Young cap deep greyish-blue to almost black, with waxy lustre; often imbricate.* Cap 3–15 cm, ± shell-shaped, smooth or sl. cracked, sometimes paler bluish, brownish with age, margin involute; gills whitish, decurrent; stipe excentric short, or lateral and longer, whitish, strigose below; flesh soft, firm, whitish. Spore mass lilac. Causes considerable damage on frondose trees, esp. beech; occasionally attacks conifers; less common on newly felled wood. I–XII. C. *Edible and good, esp. when young.*

Lentinus lepideus. *Cap pale yellowish with brownish scales; gill edge serrate.* Cap 4–10 cm, irregularly convex, scales coarse; gills whitish, sinuate, rather distant; stipe stout, white, fibrillose to brownish squamulose, base hard ± rooting; flesh white, hard, tough. On coniferous wood: railway sleepers, poles, paving blocks; also in houses where reduced light results in cap being replaced by branched antler-like growths. V–X. O–F.

Panus torulosus, conchatus. *Tough; caps irregularly infundibuliform; stipe, at least at first, with ± violet down.* Cap 4–8 cm, varying yellowish flesh colour, ± smooth, often lobed; gills narrow, pale brown at first, tinged, flesh-colour to violaceous; stipe excentric to lateral, stout, the down soon disappearing; flesh white. Stumps of various trees, often in small clusters. V–X. O–F.

Oudemansiella mucida. Armillaria. *Cap shining white, very slimy; stipe with ring; on beech.* Cap 3–8 cm, greyish in button stage; gills broad, distant, white; stipe short, slender often sl. greyish and squamulose below membranous greyish ring. On beech: dead trunks, weakened trees, often several metres up. VIII–XI. C.

Oudemansiella radicata. Collybia. *Cap yellowish-brown, often with olive tinge, slimy, ± radially wrinkled gills pure white, broad, distant; stipe hard, with "taproot".* Cap 3–9 cm, finally flattened, usually rather umbonate; gills adnexed, sometimes edged brown; stipe whitish, tapering upwards, fibrillose, the long taproot sooner or later in contact with wood. Frondose woods, esp. beech. VI–XI. C.

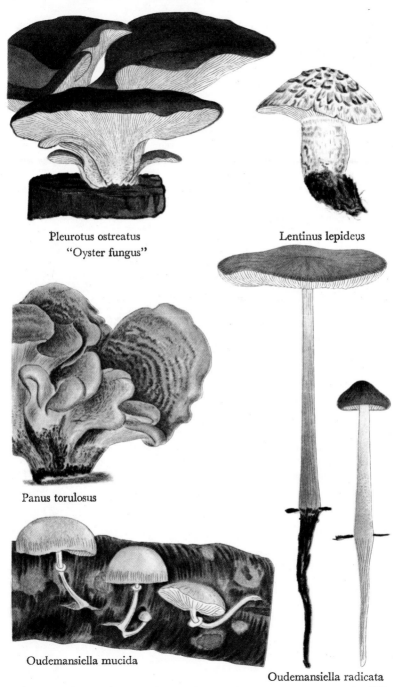

Pleurotus ostreatus
"Oyster fungus"

Lentinus lepideus

Panus torulosus

Oudemansiella mucida

Oudemansiella radicata

107

Flammulina velutipes. Collybia. *Cap ± yellow-ochre, somewhat orange towards centre, slimy; stipe densely dark brown velvety; tufted on wood.* Cap 2–6 cm, convex, then expanded; gills pale yellow, finally ± brownish, adnexed; stipe apex pale yellow, pruinose, tough. On stumps, trunks, branches of frondose trees. IX–III. C. *Edible, but stipes tough.*

Macrocystidia cucumis. Naucoria. *Cap conico-campanulate and, like stipe, dark brown, almost black; strong fishy-cucumber smell.* Cap 1–6 cm, sl. pruinose, paler at its rather striate margin; gills finally pinkish-ochre, narrow; stipe paler at apex; flesh rather fragile. Spores reddish-ochre-brown. On damp rich soil, esp. along woodland paths. IX–XI. O–F. The spore colour is unusual for this section.

Xeromphalina campanella. *Rusty yellowish-brown; decurrent gills connected by veins; spores amyloid; fasciculate on Pinus stumps.* Cap 1–2 cm, ± campanulate, toughish, striate when moist; gills yellow; stipe date-brown, horny, polished, base tawny strigose. VIII–X. O. More frequent in Scotland.

Mycena

Small, sometimes minute, thin fleshed species with ± parabolic cap and margin when young never incurved; gills white to greyish, never truly decurrent; stipe thin, slender, ± polished.

Mycena galericulata. *Cap and smooth stipe greyish-brown; gills white at first, usually pinkish when old, cross-connected by veins at base; on wood.* Cap 2–5 cm, striate to umbo; gills rather distant, broad, adnate; stipe ± strigose, rooting. Usually clustered on frondose stumps, esp. alder, birch. I–XII. C.

Mycena tintinnabulum. *Densely tufted; cap dark brown, often slimy, margin not overlapping the broad, arcuate, almost decurrent gills.* Cap 1–2(3) cm, convex to expanded, fades to greyish-brown, edge sl. striate; gills pale greyish; stipe short, often curved, pale above, dark and strigose below, rooting sl. Stumps of frondose trees. X–II. R.

Mycena inclinata. *Tufted on oak; stipe whitish, flushing rufous from below upwards.* Cap edge ± dentate overlapping gills, gills ascending not arcuate, whitish to pale grey; stipe shining, smooth, strigose below, rooting. Often in knot holes. VIII–XI. F-C.

Flammulina velutipes

Macrocystidia cucumis

Mycena galericulata

Mycena inclinata

Mycena tintinnabulum

Xeromphalina campanella

Mycena alcalina. *Distinct nitric acid smell; cap dull grey to almost black; tufted on or around stumps.* Cap 1–3 cm, convex-campanulate, striate; gills whitish-grey; stipe paler than cap, hairy below, ± rooting. VIII–X. C.

Mycena leptocephala is ± solitary, smaller, more slender, growing among leaves and grass.

Mycena polygramma. *Cap steel-grey; stipe grey with whitish raised longitudinal lines.* Cap 1–4 cm, campanulate to expanded, usually with darker umbo, ± striate or sulcate towards margin, often with whitish bloom; gills whitish-grey, sometimes pink-spotted; stipe tall and stiff, strigose below, rooting. On or near stumps, twigs etc. of frondose trees, esp. alder, hazel. VII–XI. F–C.

Mycena vitilis. *Cap dull grey to brownish, convex or expanded with prominent umbo; stipe long.* Cap to 1.5 cm, margin sl. striate; gills whitish-grey, rather distant; stipe slender, almost white, polished, stiff, strigose below, ± rooting. Often on buried sticks in frondose woods, solitary or a few together. VII–I. C.

Mycena galopus. *Broken stipe yields white latex.* Cap to 1.5 cm, ± bell-shaped, greyish to pale tan with darker disc, or pure white (var. *alba*); gills white; stipe ± cap colour, smooth, hairy below. In woods generally among leaves, needles, on sticks. VIII–XII. C.

M. leucogola, on peaty or burnt ground, has cap and stipe dark brown to almost black.

Mycena crocata. *Broken stipe yields bright orange to saffron latex; in beechwoods.* Cap 1–2 cm, bell-shaped, expanding, ± umbonate, dull brown to greyish, margin paler, striate; gills whitish; stipe saffron (from sap) when young, paler with age, base rooting, hairy. Cap and gills tend to become blotched with the latex. On sticks, foliage. IX–XI. F. in some years.

Mycena haematopus. *Broken stipe yields brownish-red latex.* Cap 1–3 cm, campanulate to convex, sometimes dull greyish-brown with vinaceous tinge, often with white bloom; gills whitish; stipe ± cap colour but paler above, often deep brownish-red below. Often clustered on frondose stumps. VIII–XI. O. The usually solitary *M. sanguinolenta* also yields a reddish latex, is much more slender and the gills are edged with red (lens). Common in moss and foliage.

Mycena epipterygia. *Cap olive-brown to yellowish with slimy, separable pellicle; stipe yellow, slimy.* Cap 1–2 cm, ± bell-shaped, striate, margin serrate when young; gills whitish. Woods, esp. coniferous, heaths. VIII–XI. C.

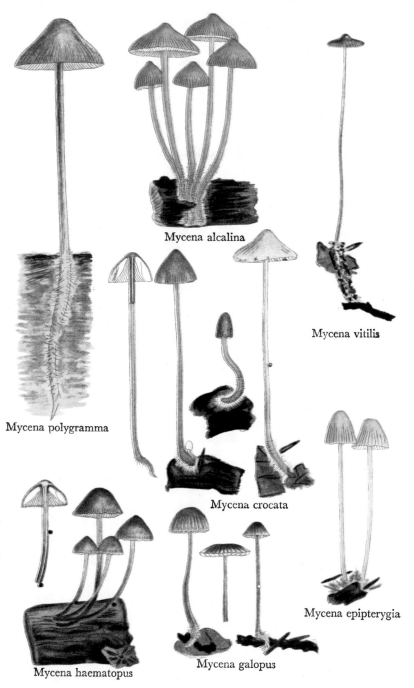

Mycena alcalina

Mycena vitilis

Mycena polygramma

Mycena crocata

Mycena epipterygia

Mycena haematopus

Mycena galopus

Mycena vulgaris. *Cap greyish-brown, slimy, pellicle separable; gills almost decurrent; stipe whitish, slimy.* Cap to 1 cm, convex to flat, somewhat depressed, margin striate; gills broad with swollen gelatinous edge; stipe with strigose base. In troops on needle cover of coniferous woods. (Illustration unusually greenish.) IX–XI. F.

Mycena pura. *Cap rose to lilac, striate; gill edge not dark purple; strong radish smell on bruising.* Cap 2–5 cm, convex, soon flattened; gills broad, whitish with tinge of cap colour; stipe ± cap colour or paler, smooth, base woolly; flesh pinkish. Among leaves etc. in woods generally. V–XII. C.

The beechwood *M. pelianthina* is rather similar, with same smell, but has gills edged with dark purple.

Mycena adonis. *Cap c.5–1 cm, ± coral-red; stipe white.* Cap convex to campanulate; smooth, tending to fade; gills tinged with cap colour; stipe sl. strigose, rooting. Grassy places of frondose woods. IX–XI. R.

The more common *M. acicula* is smaller with more orange cap; stipe lemon-yellow. Among twigs, dead foliage. V–X.

Mycena metata. *Campanulate ± flesh pink; faint smell of iodoform; amongst conifer needles.* Cap 1–2 cm, sometimes greyish or watery brown background colour, striate when moist; gills finally pinkish to pinkish-grey; stipe longish, ± cap colour but whitish above, strigose at base. Gregarious. F–C. IX–XII.

Mycena flavo-alba. *Ivory white; stipe short, curved; in grass.* Cap to 1.5 cm, convex to flat, yellowing sl. with age, edge minutely striate; gills narrow whitish; stipe whitish. Esp. lawns, pastures. VIII—XI. C.

Mycena (Fayodia) bisphaerigera. Omphalina. *Spores spherical, amyloid.* Cap 1–3 cm, convex-flat, sl. depressed, dark brown when moist, pellucid-striate margin, drying paler; gills rather distant, adnate to decurrent, pale grey; stipe tall, stiff, paler than cap; spores minutely prickly. Among sticks on rich soil in coniferous and frondose woods. VIII–X. R. So far only known from Scotland.

Baeospora myosura. Collybia conigena. *Gills very crowded, narrow; stipe springing from buried pine cone; spores amyloid.* Cap 1–3 cm, almost flat, ± tan to dull date-brown; stipe with tinge of cap colour, long rooting. X–II. F.

Pseudohiatula esculenta. Collybia. *Gills moderately crowded, rather broad; stipe mostly from buried spruce cones; spores non-amyloid.* Cap 1–3 cm, soon flattened, usually shining, dark date-brown, but varying to pale ochre; stipe ± cap colour but pale above, long rooting. Occasionally on cones of Douglas fir, but not pine cones. X–V. O–F.

Mycena vulgaris

Mycena pura

Mycena flavo-alba

Mycena adonis

Mycena metata

Baeosphora myosura

Mycena bisphaerigera

Pseudohiatula esculenta

113

Marasmius ramealis. *Cap off-whitish to pale flesh colour; stipe mealy; gregarious on dead twigs.* Cap 1 cm, ± flat and wrinkled, more flesh colour at middle; gills distant, narrow, whitish; stipe short, usually curved, cap colour. VI–X. C.

Marasmius foetidus. *Cap date-brown to grey with radiating dark furrows; smell foetid; on rotten branches.* Cap 1–3 cm, soon flat, sl. depressed at centre, viscid; gills distant, paler than cap; stipe short, dark brown, almost black below, shortly velvety tapering downwards. Esp. beech, hazel. VIII–XII. R–O.

Marasmius (Micromphale) perforans. *Cap pale brownish to flesh colour,* ± *wrinkled; stipe densely velvety, almost black, springing from dead conifer needles.* Cap to 1.5 cm, almost flat; gills rather distant; stipe slender; flesh when bruised with unpleasant smell. Gregarious. VIII–X. R–O.

Marasmius androsaceus. " Horse-hair fungus ". *Cap pale rufous, wrinkled, striate; stipe shining black like a horse hair.* Cap about 1 cm, flattened, umbilicate, centre darker; gills rather distant, ± cap colour; stipe rigid, arising black from mycelium. On heather, conifer needles, sticks. V–XI. C.

Marasmius rotula. *Cap whitish,* ± *grooved radially; gills joined to collar round stipe apex.* Cap 0.5–1.5 cm, ± convex, sl. depressed, margin grooved; gills distant; stipe thin, slender, shining, black, horny. On decaying sticks, roots, in woods esp. on damp rich soil.

Marasmius alliaceus. *Cap clay-brown; stipe black; strong garlic smell.* Cap 1–4 cm, hemispherical, then convex-expanded, margin striate; gills whitish; stipe tall, minutely velvety; flesh tough. On buried stick, dead leaves, esp. of beech. VIII–XI. F–C.

M. scorodonius is similar but has shining light reddish glabrous stipe and grows in grass.

Marasmius oreades. " Fairy-ring champignon ". *Cap pinkish-tan to buff-colour; gills broad, widely spaced; in grass, esp. lawns.* Cap 2–6 cm, convex to ± expanded, usually sl. umbonate, margin ± grooved when adult; gills paler than cap; stipe pale buff, smooth, whitish and tomentose below. Causes the well-known fairy rings on lawns. VI–XI. C. *Edible and good.*

Marasmius lupuletorum. *Cap convex, pale brown; gills wide spaced; stipe* ± *fawn colour darker towards densely woolly strigose base; mainly in beech woods.* Cap 1–2 cm often slightly striate, sometimes grooved; gills broad, yellowish; stipe slender. Solitary or in twos or threes in leaf litter of frondose woods. IX–XI. F.

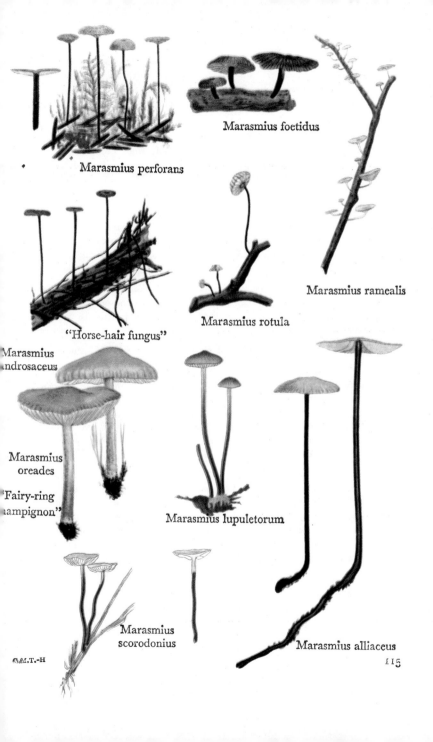

Marasmius foetidus

Marasmius perforans

Marasmius ramealis

"Horse-hair fungus"

Marasmius rotula

Marasmius
androsaceus

Marasmius
oreades

"Fairy-ring
champignon"

Marasmius lupuletorum

Marasmius
scorodonius

Marasmius alliaceus

G.M.T.-H

Amanita

Large fungi, when young entirely enclosed within a universal veil; when expanded, usually with basal bulb and volva or volval remains, membranous ring and detachable warts or scales on cap. Gills free, white. Some species deadly **poisonous.**

All illustrations half natural size.

Amanita muscaria. " Fly Agaric ". *Cap scarlet to orange-red with white warts or patches.* Cap 6–16 cm, hemispherical to convex, finally $\pm$ expanded, fading or washing out to orange or yellowish; gills crowded; stipe white, ring pendant from apex, basal bulb with several concentric, $\pm$ warty rings; flesh white, yellow beneath cap cuticle. Pine and birch on poor soils. VIII—XI. C. **Poisonous** *and dangerous, but rarely fatal.*

Amanita vaginata. Amanitopsis. " Grisette ". *Cap pale to ash-grey, margin pectinate-sulcate; stipe without ring.* Cap 4–9 cm, soon expanded, umbo darker, sometimes with white velar remains; gills crowded; stipe white to pale grey, basal volva bag-like greyish outside. In frondose woods, esp. beech, also heaths. VII–X. O–F. *Edible.*

Amanita fulva. Amanitopsis. " Tawny Grisette ". *Cap $\pm$ orange to date brown, otherwise very similar to previous species.* Cap 4–7 cm; stipe and outside of volva $\pm$ tinged with cap colour. In frondose woods, esp. birch on peaty soil. V–XI. C. *Edible and good.*

Amanita strangulata. (Illustrated on endpapers, life size.) Mostly larger than *A. fulva* and somewhat darker. Cap warty, scaly.

Amanita virosa. " Destroying Angel ". *Wholly white, stipe scaly, ring present.* Cap 5–9 cm, convex, often sl. umbonate, $\pm$ viscid shining, smooth without velar remains; gills crowded; stipe slender, ring $\pm$ frayed, volva bag-like. Cap $+$ KOH: chrome yellow. In frondose woods, usually on poor soil. VIII–X. R. **Deadly poisonous.** (White edible mushrooms—*Agaricus* spp—all have grey or pink to finally chocolate coloured gills and no volva.)

Amanita phalloides. " Death Cap ". *Cap pale yellowish with sl. greenish tinge, faintly streaked with radiating fibrils; stipe with ring and bag-like volva.* Cap 7–12 cm, sl. viscid, rarely olive-green, usually without velar remains when adult, gills crowded; stipe white, smooth, volva with upper limb free and irregularly lobed, basal bulb large; flesh white, greenish beneath cap cuticle, with faint but distinct nauseous smell when mature. Gills $+$ conc. H_2SO_4: pinkish-lilac. In frondose woods, esp. beech, oak. VII–X(XI). O–F. **Deadly poisonous.**

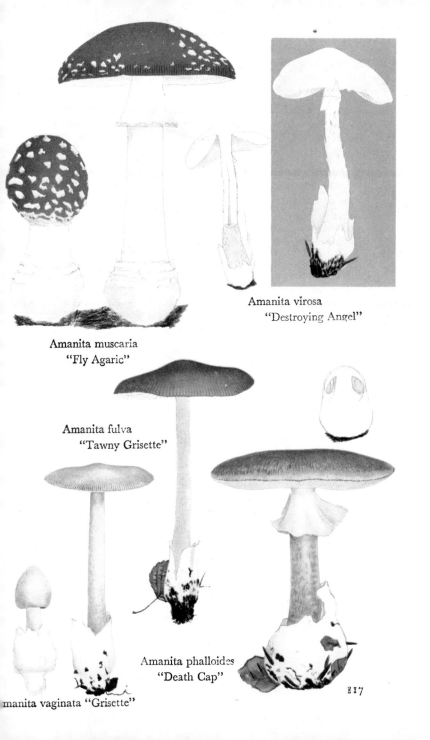

Amanita virosa
"Destroying Angel"

Amanita muscaria
"Fly Agaric"

Amanita fulva
"Tawny Grisette"

Amanita phalloides
"Death Cap"

manita vaginata "Grisette"

Amanita pantherina. *Cap ± smoky-brown often with olive tinge, warts white, margin striate, ring smooth above.* Cap 5–8 cm, convex soon flattened; stipe with 2(3) ± concentric " hoops " (volva remnants) between basal bulb and ring. Cap flesh кон : ± orange yellow. Frondose woods, esp. edges of beech woods. VIII–X. O. **Poisonous,** *often fatal.*

Amanita porphyria. *Cap greyish brown with sl. purple tinge.* Cap 5–9 cm, convex, smooth; gius and stipe white, volva usually with upper flap free on one side; bulb large; ring high up on stipe, underside tinged with cap colour. Coniferous woods. IX–X. O. *Not poisonous, but unpleasant taste.*

Amanita citrina, mappa. *Cap ± lemon-yellow with patches of velar remains; basal bulb large, smelling of raw potatoes when broken.* Cap 5–9 cm, hemispherical, then expanded, velar remains rarely absent; gills white; stipe smooth, white, ring ± flaring; upper limb of volva very short forming circular " gutter " round top of large basal bulb. In coniferous and frondose woods, esp. beech, oak. VII–XI. C.
   Var. *alba* is a frequent wholly white form.   Neither is poisonous, but taste disagreeable; easily confused with *A. virosa* and even *A. phalloides.*

Amanita excelsa, spissa. *Cap greyish-brown with grey rice-paper-like patches, margin smooth; basal bulb indistinct.* Cap 6–12 cm, convex soon expanded; gills and stipe ± white, ring striate above; volva reduced to faint greyish-brown belts. In coniferous and frondose woods. VI–X. F. *Harmless.*

Amanita rubescens. " The Blusher ". *Cap ± dull reddish-brown, with off-white patches, margin smooth; flesh reddening esp. where damaged by insect bites etc.* Cap 6–12 cm, long remaining convex, finally expanded; gills when older with reddish spots; stipe whitish, flushed sl. reddish below, membranous ring striate above; basal " bulb " hardly differentiated, but with a few warty scales from remains of volva. Frondose and coniferous woods. VII–X(XI). C. *Indigestible when raw but harmless and good when cooked.*

All illustrations half natural size.

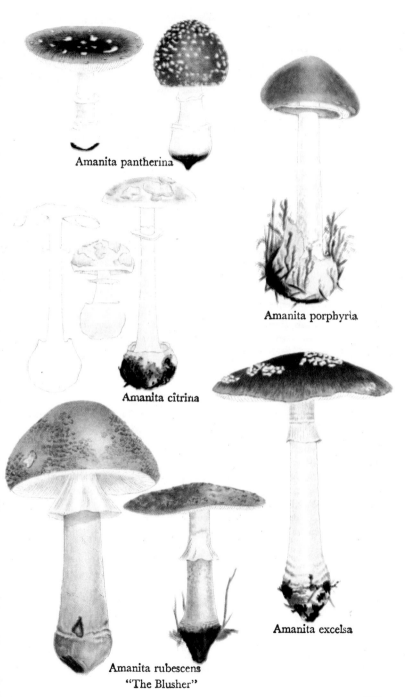

Amanita pantherina

Amanita porphyria

Amanita citrina

Amanita excelsa

Amanita rubescens
"The Blusher"

Limacella guttata, lenticularis.   Lepiota.   *Cap $\pm$ viscid, dull ochre to very pale tan, tinged sl. flesh-colour; ring membranous becoming olivaceous.*   Cap 6–10 cm, ovate at first, then $\pm$ expanded, smooth; gills white; stipe somewhat paler than cap, weakly clavate, sparsely squamulose; flesh has sl. mealy smell.   Damp rich soil in woods generally.   In wet weather ring and gills tend to " weep ".   In dry weather, cap often dirty grey with drop-like spots.   VII–X.   O.   *Edible.* $\times \frac{1}{2}$.

Volvariella.   Volvaria

Base of stipe with bag-like volva; no ring; gills free, becoming deep salmon coloured like the spores.   The genus includes a number of small and rare species.

Volvariella speciosa.   *Cap whitish to $\pm$ greyish-brown, esp. towards centre, smooth, viscid, volva externally $\pm$ greyish.*   Cap 5–10 cm, campanulate, finally convex to expanded;   gills broad, long remaining white, finally deep salmon; stipe tall, $\pm$ cap colour, smooth, dry.   Rich manured ground, rotting grass, straw, compost heaps.   VII–X.   O.   *Edible.* $\times \frac{1}{2}$.

Volvariella surrecta, loveiana.   *Cap whitish-grey; parasitic on Clitocybe nebularis.*   Appears first on half-decayed *Clitocybe* as small greyish-white " buttons ".   As host decays, differentiation occurs: cap 2–5 cm, $\pm$ silky and fibrillose; gills salmon colour; stipe short, curved, volva white.   Densely clustered.   X.   Extremely rare.   Also reported on *C. clavipes.* $\times \frac{1}{2}$.

Volvariella bombycina.   *Cap silky-fibrillose, white; volva long, discolouring dirty yellowish; on wood.*   Cap 5–10 cm, $\pm$ ovate, sometimes pale creamy; stipe swollen below;   volva membranous.   Trunks of frondose trees, esp. knot holes.   VI–X.   R–O. $\times \frac{1}{2}$.

Pluteus

Cap flattened; easily separable by slight twist from stipe; gills free, finally deep salmon coloured as are the spores; ring and volva absent.   The larger species are found on wood.

Pluteus cervinus.   *Cap $\pm$ sooty-brown; stipe streaked with darker fibrils; on wood, sawdust.*   Cap 3–8 cm, campanulate, soon expanded to flattened, innately radially fibrillose; gills at first white, broad stipe tall, brownish grey from fibrils; flesh white, soft.   Stumps, trunks and sawdust of frondose trees, solitary or a few together.   (I–)V–XI(XII).   C.   *Edible.* $\times \frac{1}{2}$.

A similar but darker and larger sp. with gills edged almost black is *P. atromarginatus,* on coniferous wood.   *Edible.*

Volvariella surrecta

Limacella guttata

Volvariella speciosa

Pluteus cervinus

Volvariella bombycina

Pluteus petasatus. *Large, fleshy; cap whitish $\pm$ squamulose; stipe $\pm$ sulcate at base.* Cap 5–15 cm, convex to expanded, squamules often brownish towards centre; gills very crowded, long remaining white; stipe stout, whitish. On sawdust, often $\pm$ fasciculate. R–O.

Pluteus lutescens. *Small; cap $\pm$ bistre; stipe yellowish from base upwards.* Cap 2–4 cm, $\pm$ expanded and umbonate, somewhat powdered mealy, otherwise smooth; young gills pale sulphur, stipe slender. On decayed frondose wood or rich soil. V–X. O–F.

Pluteus plautus Fr. sensu J. Lge. *Cap sooty brown, $\pm$ radially veined and umbonate; stipe brownish squamulose below; on coniferous wood.* Cap 2–4 cm, minutely velvety, umbo $\pm$ flattened; stipe whitish above. Not yet recorded from this country. Specimens under this name are *P. pearsonii.*

Pluteus aurantiorugosus, coccineus. *Cap $\pm$ orange-scarlet; gills at first, and stipe orange yellow.* Cap 2–5 cm, convex, margin minutely striate; stipe apex paler above. On rotten stumps of frondose trees, esp. elm, ash. X. R. (The three overlapping circles to the right of the illustration are magnified cells from cap cuticle.)

Pluteus salicinus. *Cap greyish with blue-green tinge; umbo brownish, $\pm$ squamulose.* Cap 3–6 cm, soon flattened, finely fibrillose, stipe slender, whitish, tinged glaucous below. On stumps of frondose trees, esp. willow, but also beech. IV–X. O.

Pluteus cinereo-fuscus. *Cap glaucous grey, edge sl. striate and wrinkled; stipe white.* Cap 3–5 cm, campanulate with darker umbo, minutely mealy (lens), stipe tall, slender, finely silky-fibrillose, hollow. Rich soil in frondose woods. IX–X. R.

Lepiota

Cap $\pm$ scaly, separable from stipe; gills free, stipe with distinct or rudimentary ring sometimes forming discontinuous sheath from base upwards. Spores typically white, red-brown in iodine (=dextrinoid). On soil.

Lepiota excoriata. *Large; cap dirty-whitish, minutely squamulose, adult cuticle often falls short of margin; stipe about equals cap diam.* Cap 6–10 cm, ovate, finally $\pm$ expanded and sl. umbonate; gills crowded, broad, white; stipe rooting, ring narrow, $\pm$ flaring. Pastures on light soil. VIII–XI. O. *Edible.*

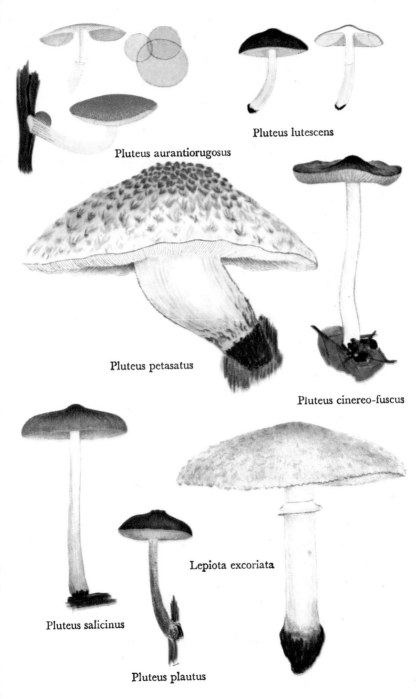

Pluteus lutescens

Pluteus aurantiorugosus

Pluteus petasatus

Pluteus cinereo-fuscus

Pluteus salicinus

Lepiota excoriata

Pluteus plautus

Lepiota procera. " Parasol Mushroom ". *Expanded cap greyish-brown with dark-brown, coarse scales; stipe concentrically scaly belted.* Cap 10–20 cm, almost smooth before expansion, finally sl. umbonate; gills white; stipe about twice cap diam., bulbous below, ring double; flesh white, not changing when cut, soft. Frondose wood margins, clearings, grassy places. VII–XI. O–F. *Edible and excellent.*

Lepiota rhacodes. " Shaggy Parasol ". *Expanded cap, coarse, dark-brown, scaly; stipe without scales; flesh orange-yellow when cut.* Cap 8–15 cm, ovate at first, broadly umbonate when expanded, umbo shining dark brown; stipe dirty white, somewhat tinged brown, bulbous; ring double, free; flesh firm. In woods, gardens, parks, esp. on rich ground. VII–XI. O–F. *Edible and good.*

Lepiota leucothites, naucina. *Wholly white, except for adult gills tinged flesh colour; ring narrow, free.* Cap 6–10 cm, soon flattened, ± silky fibrillose; gills at first white; stipe equal, smooth, ring high up. Spores white. Pastures, gardens. VIII–X. O–F. *Edible.*

Lepiota friesii, acutesquamosa. *Cap with ± bistre, conical, deciduous warts; ring lax, membranous.* Cap 5–10 cm, rather conical at first, later expanded to umbonate, pale brown between warts; gills crowded, usually forked, whitish, often spotted brown; stipe off-white, ± dark scaly belted towards swollen base; flesh of stipe brownish, smell unpleasant. Pastures and frondose woods. VIII–XI. O.

All illustrations half natural size.

Lepiota rhacodes
"Shaggy Parasol"

Lepiota friesii

Lepiota procera
"Parasol Mushroom"

Lepiota leucothites

125

Lepiota clypeolaria. *Cap pale brownish from ± concentric rings of granular scales; stipe felty-squamulose from below to ill-defined ring.* Cap 3–7 cm, finally ± expanded-umbonate (yellowish-brown to pale rufous and almost smooth before opening), margin with teeth-like veil fragments; gills white, very soft; stipe slender, equal; flesh with faint smell of gas. Woods, on needle cover or deep foliage. IX–XI. O–F.

Lepiota cortinarius J. Lge. *Cap soon cracking into pale brownish, minute, dense-set scales; stipe ± fibrillose, bulbous, veil filamentous.* Cap 5–8 cm, convex then flattened to umbonate; stipe pale brownish downwards, base slightly squamulose, veil long and persistent. Under conifers. Not yet recorded in Britain.

Lepiota cristata. *Cap pallid, umbo and scales reddish-brown, smell strong, unpleasant, stipe smooth.* Cap 2–4 cm, ± umbonate, the reddish-brown scales dispersed on a white background; gills white, crowded; stipe ± slender, pale brownish flesh colour below, paler above, ring ± membranous; flesh pallid. Lawns, pastures, less often by paths in woods. VIII–XI. F–C. *Edibility suspect, best avoided.*

Lepiota castanea. *Umbo and scales ± chestnut to rusty brown, granular; gills somewhat scaly; stipe clavate, bruising and ageing with rufous patches.* Cap 2–4 cm, background pale yellowish-brown; stipe brownish flushed, ring inconspicuous. On rich soil in woods, gardens. IX–X. O.

Lepiota grangei. *Cap and stipe with green ± velvety scales.* Cap 2–4 cm, convex-umbonate, dry, background pallid; the green somewhat browning with age; gills white; stipe with belt-like, hardly membranous ring, flesh with faint unpleasant smell. Frondose woods. X–XI. R.

Lepiota (Melanophyllum) echinata, haematosperma. *Cap mealy-granular, ± dark brown, edge denticulate from granular veil; gills almost blood-red.* Cap 1–3 cm, virtually uncracked, varying dirty brown to dark clay; gills browner red with age; stipe mealy granular; flesh ± red. Rich soil, esp. by paths in woods. Spores greyish on shedding, drying out ± reddish. VIII–XI. O–F.

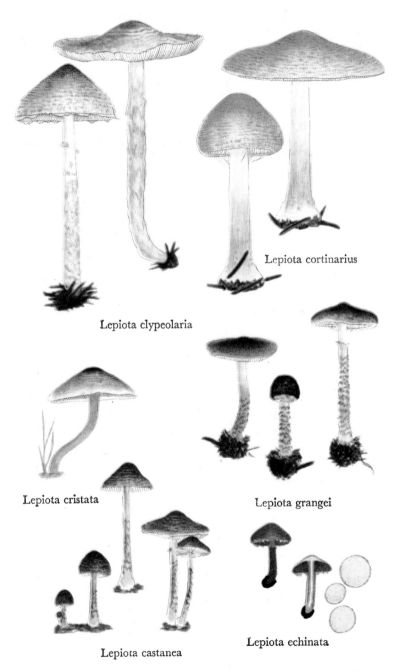

Lepiota clypeolaria

Lepiota cortinarius

Lepiota cristata

Lepiota grangei

Lepiota castanea

Lepiota echinata

Lepiota eyrei. *Cap greyish brown from granular mealy coating; gills $\pm$ glaucous.* Cap 1–3 cm, margin denticulate from mealy velar remains; stipe mealy granular like cap, darker downwards. Spores pale green. On damp rich soil. VIII–X. R–O. The only British species with green spores.

Lepiota sistrata, seminuda. *Cap almost pure white to flesh colour, mealy; stipe reddish below.* Cap to 2 cm, convex, often sl. darker at centre, margin $\pm$ fringed with velar remains; stipe flexuose, mealy below, ringless as soon as veil breaks.

Lepiota fulvella. *Cap $\pm$ brownish-tawny, indistinctly squamulose with adpressed scales; ring inconspicuous.* Cap 2–4 cm, $\pm$ umbonate, varying rusty brown to yellowish-brown; gills white with tinge of cap colour; stipe paler than cap, $\pm$ floccose with belts to ring-like zone. On damp rich soil in woods, often with nettles. IX–X. O.

Lepiota fuscovinacea. *Cap dark purplish-pink felty, darker scales; stipe densely felty-fibrillose.* Cap 3–4 cm, $\pm$ umbonate; gills whitish; stipe stoutish, brownish below, paler above the off-white fibrillose-membranous ring. Damp rich soil in woods. IX–X. R. *Edibility suspect.*

Lepiota bucknallii. *Cap whitish-grey, minutely mealy; stipe lavender blue; strong coal-gas smell.* Cap 2–3 cm, slightly umbonate, margin often $\pm$ denticulate; gills white; stipe mealy, darker bluish downwards. In frondose woods. IX–X. R–O.

Cystoderma

Small to medium species with granular cuticle; gills $\pm$ adnate; stipe $\pm$ granular squamulose from base to ring. Formerly referred to Lepiota.

Cystoderma carcharias. *Cap pinkish-grey to flesh colour; stipe almost warty below ring.* Cap 2–4 cm, soon expanded or umbonate, margin often denticulate; gills white; stipe $\pm$ cap colour, brownish with age, ring prominent, membranous. Coniferous woods. Spores amyloid; cuticle $+$ KOH: no reaction. VIII–XI. F.

Cystoderma amianthinum. *Cap $\pm$ yellow to ochre; ring inconspicuous.* Cap 2–5 cm, soon $\pm$ convex and flattened, often radially wrinkled, margin denticulate; gills white; stipe $\pm$ cap colour, ring inconspicuous. Spores amyloid; cuticle $+$ KOH: a rusty-brown colour. Among moss and needles in coniferous woods. VIII–XI. C.

Cystoderma granulosum. *Cap $\pm$ rufous-brown; stipe stout.* Cap 3–6 cm, soon expanded, obtusely umbonate; stipe rather coarsely tomentose-granular. Spores non-amyloid (weakly dextrinoid); cuticle $+$ KOH: rusty-brown colour. Coniferous woods. VIII–X. O.

Lepiota eyrei

Lepiota sistrata

Lepiota fulvella

Lepiota fuscovinacea

Cystoderma carcharias

Lepiota bucknallii

Cystoderma amianthinum

Cystoderma granulosum

Phaeolepiota aurea. Pholiota. *Cap golden-brown, scurfy or granular; stipe and lower side of membranous ring also ± scurfy and ochre brown. Spores yellowish-brown.* Cap 8–20 cm, convex, becoming expanded, slightly cracked; gills adnexed, clay colour at first, soon rusty-yellow; stipe tall, stout, sheathed from below by veil which expands near apex as conspicuous membranous ring; flesh white, smell faint, pleasant. On rich, loamy soil. IX–XI. R–O. Like a large *Cystoderma*, but spores brownish. *Edible and good.*

Agaricus. Psalliota—Mushrooms

Cap ± white and smooth or brownish from scales; gills free, white, grey or deep pink at first, finally chocolate-brown; stipe with distinct ring. Spores chocolate-brown.

Agaricus langei. *Cap with adpressed reddish-brown scales; flesh bright blood-red on cutting; stipe not bulbous; under frondose trees.* Cap 7–10 cm, bell-shaped to convex, scales densely set, ± fibrillose; gills at first deep pink; stipe stout, whitish, soon discolouring, also bruising red; smell faint, pleasant. IX–XI. O. *Edible and good.*

Agaricus silvaticus, sanguinarius. *Cap with adpressed reddish-brown fibrillose scales; cut flesh hardly reddening, stipe ± bulbous; under coniferous trees.* Cap 4–8 cm, convex, soon ± flattened; gills at first pale to deep pink; stipe off-white, somewhat yellowish when bruised, somewhat scaly downwards; flesh gives its weak reddening only when young; in old specimens, cut flesh (stipe) is already dull brownish. In thick needle cover. IX–XI. F. *Edible and good.*

Agaricus augustus. *Large. Cap yellowish-brown with darker hazel-brown minute scales; stipe bruising yellowish; smell strong of anise.* Cap 10–20 cm, semi-globate as first, then convex expanded; gills white at first, never pinkish; stipe tall, whitish, scaly below ring before cap opens, ring large, lax, membranous. Under coniferous and frondose trees. VIII–XI. O–F. *Edible and good.*

Several other ± brown to grey scale capped species of *Agaricus* are occasionally found in woods. They are all edible and good except *A. placomyces*, whose cut flesh becomes bright yellow, especially at base of stipe. See *A. xanthodermus*, p. 134
All illustrations half natural size.

Phaeolepiota aurea

Agaricus langei

Agaricus silvaticus

Agaricus augustus

131

Agaricus campestris. " Field Mushroom ". *Cap white, gills deep pink at first, even in unopened cap, flesh faintly rubescent, e.g. above gills; always in grass away from trees.* Cap 4–8 cm, unusually long in expanding, sometimes sl. squamulose towards centre; stipe short, tapering below, with narrow ring which soon falls off; no aniseed smell. Pastures, meadows. VIII–XI. O–F, but seems to be declining in frequency. *Edible and very good.*

Agaricus bisporus. *Cap ± brownish with close ± radiating brown fibrils; young gills less bright pink than previous, flesh faintly rubescent; never in grass.* Cap 5–10 cm, finally ± convex, varying fawn to pale hazel, sometimes sl. adpressed scaly with age, margin incurved, cottony; stipe equal, stoutish, ring membranous, expanded; no aniseed smell. Roadsides, manure heaps, away from grass. IX–XI. ?R–O. Probably the wild form of the many cultivated ones—all with two-spored basidia. *Edible.*

Agaricus bisporus forma **albida** J. Lge. " Cultivated Mushroom ". *Cap whitish, or sl. brownish towards centre, almost smooth.* The mushroom usually sold in shops. *Much less tasty than the " Field Mushroom ".*

Agaricus bitorquis, edulis. *Cap whitish to ochre; margin long, involute, ± even. Stipe sheathed from below upwards to second ring.* Cap 6–10 cm, flattened early, the involute margin finally expanding, often indistinctly fibrillose; gills at first dirty pink; stipe stout, the lower ring like a thin volva; flesh sl. rubescent. In gardens, along roadsides, even pushing up asphalt. V–X. O. *Edible and good.*

Agaricus subperonatus. *Cap brown with darker scales, margin jagged, not incurved; stipe sheathed from below upwards to second ring.* Cap 6–12 cm, soon convex, scales adpressed; gills pale pink at first; stipe stout, ring much as in previous species, flesh slightly rubescent, brownish where bruised. In straw-stacks, roadsides. (V) IX–X. R. *Edible and good.*

Agaricus comtulus. *Small, stipe thin; cap white, yellowish towards centre; in grass.* Cap 2–3 cm, soon convex to flattened, ± silky; gills pink at first; stipe whitish to tinged ochre, equal, ring membranous, ± expanded; flesh white, sl. yellow in base; faint smell of almonds. Always in grass. IX–XI. ?O.

All illustrations half natural size.

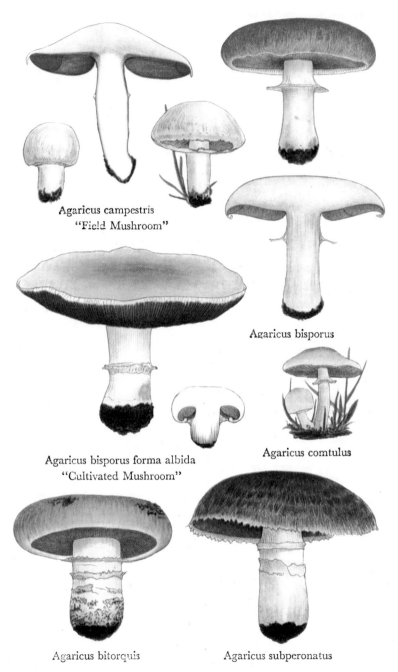

Agaricus campestris
"Field Mushroom"

Agaricus bisporus

Agaricus bisporus forma albida
"Cultivated Mushroom"

Agaricus comtulus

Agaricus bitorquis

Agaricus subperonatus

133

Agaricus silvicola. " Wood Mushroom ". *Cap white, bruising and ageing yellowish; stipe with basal bulb; smell of aniseed; in woods.* Cap 6–12 cm, soon expanding, minutely fibrillose; gills at first greyish-white tinged with flesh colour, never deep pink; stipe white smooth, ring laxly hanging, $\pm$ "double"— i.e. with second outer and lower membrane which may be split (see illustrations of this and the next species); flesh whitish to pale cream. On ground in woods generally. VIII–XI. F–C. *Edible and good.*

Agaricus arvensis. " Horse Mushroom ". *Cap white, bruising and ageing $\pm$ brassy yellow; stipe without basal bulb; smell of aniseed; found typically in pastures.* Very like previous species, esp. in young gills being $\pm$ greyish and never deep pink; differs in stipe having no basal bulb; rarely found in woods. VII–XI. F–C, becoming less so. *Edible and very good.*

Agaricus semotus, rubella. *Small; cap whitish with purplish adpressed fibrils, specially towards centre; stipe $\pm$ clavate; all parts turn yellowish on handling.* Cap 3–5 cm, convex; gills pale flesh-colour at first; stipe tapering upwards, ring $\pm$ expanded. In frondose and coniferous woods. VII–X. R. There are 2 or 3 other small purplish species, none common.

Agaricus macrosporus, villaticus. *Large; cap white to slightly ochre; stipe hardly exceeds cap diam., $\pm$ scaly as is lower side of ring.* Cap 12–26 cm, $\pm$ hemispherical, slightly scaly towards margin; gills at first greyish, never deep pink; stipe stout, ring membranous, flesh of stipe pale pinkish-orange on exposure to air, but reaction variable. Mostly in pastures, specially on chalky soils. IX–X. O–F, but season and distribution incompletely known.

A similar species, *A. bernardii*, occurs on salt marches and pastures near the sea; the cap is $\pm$ coarsely cracked into thickish scales, has a greyish colour and faintly disagreeable smell. R.

Agaricus xanthodermus. "Yellow stainer " " Yellow-staining Mushroom ". (Not illustrated here.) Not uncommon, often mistaken for both *A. campestris* and *A. arvensis*, and when eaten can cause alarming symptoms (coma, vomiting or diarrhoea, but with complete recovery within a few days. It is closely related to *A. placomyces* (p. 130) and these are the only two in which the flesh at the extreme base of the stipe goes immediately bright yellow on cutting. It is thus important to have the whole stipe intact. Some people can eat both these species without any ill effects at all. Many detect in them, when raw, a smell like writing ink. On cooking they always produce an unpleasant smell.

For a differential chemical test, see section on Chemical tests, p. 232, under Tl4 (Henry's reagent).

All illustrations half natural size.

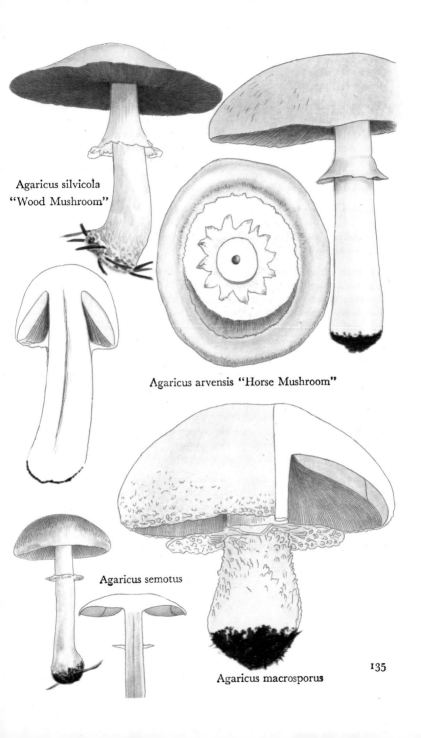

Agaricus silvicola
"Wood Mushroom"

Agaricus arvensis "Horse Mushroom"

Agaricus semotus

Agaricus macrosporus

135

Characterised in almost all species by the gradual " auto-digestion " of the gills, and sometimes the cap, into a black ink-like fluid. Gills thin and very crowded, $\pm$ free; spores black in mass, in a few species, very dark brown.

Coprinus comatus. " Shaggy cap ". " Lawyer's Wig ". *Cap at first white, almost imbricate with shaggy-woolly scales; ring conspicuous, soon disappearing.* Cap 5–12 cm high, at first cylindrical, then expanding below; gills progressively white, pink, black and autodigesting; stipe erect, slender, hollow, elongating as spores mature. Fields, roadsides, rubbish tips, often clustered. V–XI. C. Best cooked at stage shown by right-hand illustration, before auto-digestion starts. *Edible and very good; delicate taste.*

Coprinus picaceus. *Expanding cap breaks outer covering (veil) giving discrete white felty patches, on brown-black background; no ring.* Cap 5–8 cm high, narrowly oval, then conical; gills white, pale brown, finally black; stipe finally long, white. Rich soil in frondose woods. IX–XI. O.

Coprinus atramentarius. *Cap dirty, pale brownish-grey, scaly towards centre, $\pm$ grooved at margin.* Cap 3–7 cm high, ovate, then $\pm$ campanulate; gills at first off-white; stipe tapering upwards, elongating, leaving ring-like zone at sl. swollen base, whitish, smooth. Often clustered near base of frondose trees; also in fields and gardens. VIII–XII. F–C. *Edible, but can cause nausea if consumed with alcohol.* See p. 17 in connection with " Antabuse ".

Coprinus cinereus, fimetarius, macrorrhizus. *Cap centre squamosely scaly; stipe base at substrate level swollen (5–10 mm diam.) and connected with tapering " tap root ".* Cap 1–3 cm high, at first ovate cylindric with dirty whitish-brown coating which cracks and falls away as cap expands exposing greyish-brown, viscid undersurface with striate margin; finally cap splits radially, the auto-digesting segments becoming recurved over the persisting brownish middle; stipe white, smooth, enlarging downwards to swollen base. Mostly in dung and manure heaps, less often on enriched soil or rotting straw. I–XII. C.

Coprinus sterquilinus. *Cap at first white, shaggy with $\pm$ pointed, recurved, fibrillose scales; ring conspicuous.* Cap 2–3 cm, high, $\pm$ ovate at first, soon expanding, the margin splitting as auto-digestion proceeds; gills at first passing through pinkish to black; stipe white, soon elongating and becoming flushed brownish-black from apex; ring movable at or below middle of stipe. Like a small *C. comatus.* On dung. VI–X. O.

All illustrations half natural size.

Coprinus comatus
"Shaggy cap"; "Lawyer's Wig"

Coprinus picaceus

Coprinus cinereus

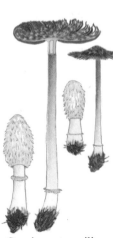

Coprinus sterquilinus

Coprinus atramentarius

Coprinus radiatus. *Small; cap at first rooted with pointed, recurved, fibrillose, scales, ± grey.* Cap 2–8 mm high, at first ovate, soon expanding, the margin splitting and revolute as coating falls away exposing greyish wholly striate undersurface: gills rather distant at maturity, auto-digesting with cap; stipe white, slender, ± pilose below and rooting. Like a miniature *C. cinereus.* On fresh horse-dung. V.–XI. C.

Coprinus lagopus. *White, pilose, fibrillose; cap finally revolute; stipe greatly elongating; hardly auto-digesting.* Cap 0.5–2 cm high, ovate at first, the hairs soon partly greyish-black and falling off; gills finally withering, looking like low thin ridges as they turn up and back; stipe finally 10–15 cm, esp. pilose downwards. On soil, sticks, amongst litter in frondose woods, usually solitary. VII–XI. C.

Coprinus bisporus. *Small; cap clay-yellow, ovate, wholly sulcate; ± fasciculate.* Cap 0.5–1.5 cm high, fairly smooth apart from the grooves, soon expanding and recurving and auto-digesting like the blackish-brown gills; stipe white, minutely pilose (lens). Usually in small tufts on old dung or compost. VIII–X. O–F.
   Several similar species..

Coprinus plicatilis. *Cap deeply sulcate to brownish disc; gills joined to collar round stipe apex, scarcely auto-digesting.* Cap 0.5–1.5 cm high, ovate at first, dull pale brownish, soon expanding and depressed at disc, and then pallid greyish; gills finally rather distant, withering like cap without dissolving; stipe brittle, whitish. Solitary, esp. grassy places, lawns, roadsides. V–XI. C.

Coprinus hansenii. *Cap ± date brown, deeply sulcate to darker disc; gills not joined to collar at stipe apex; hardly auto-digesting; ± tufted.* Cap 1–2 cm high, ovate at first, expanding and paler; gills pale to blackish brown, ± crowded; stipe tinged brownish. Not yet recorded in Britain.

Coprinus niveus. *Cap and stipe densely chalk-white mealy.* Cap 1–3 cm high, ovate at first, soon campanulate with ± upturned, split margin; gills soon blackening and auto-digesting with cap; stipe thickish. On cow and horse dung. V–XI. C.

Coprinus silvaticus, tardus. *Cap date-brown, sulcate almost to apex; ± tufted; spores verrucose.* Cap 1–3 cm high, ovate, finally ± convex bell-shape; gills crowded, brownish-black, auto-digesting with cap; stipe brownish, minutely pilose (lens). Clay soils in woods. Resembles *C. micaceus.* IX–XI. O.

Coprinus xanthothrix, domesticus. *Flat, adult cap sulcate, disc with ochre scales, rest ± greyish or creamy with granules; not auto-digesting but papery membranous.* Cap at first ovate 1–2 cm high, the scales extending more towards margin ± tinged rufous at margin; gills dark brown; stipe pallid, tuberculate-squamose at base. Wood floors, rotten timber, sticks, leaves. Season and frequency uncertain because of confusion with *C. domesticus.*

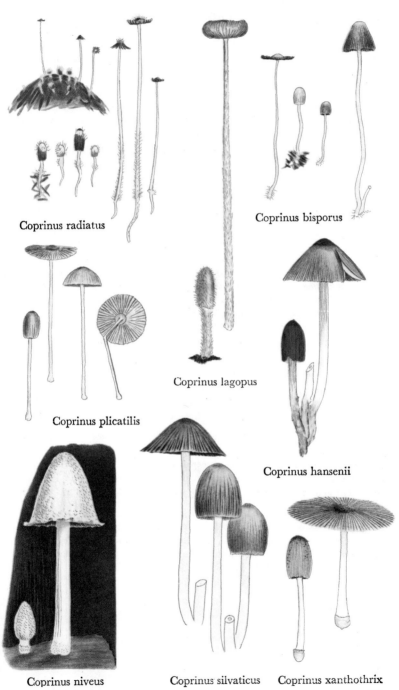

Coprinus radiatus

Coprinus bisporus

Coprinus plicatilis

Coprinus lagopus

Coprinus hansenii

Coprinus niveus

Coprinus silvaticus

Coprinus xanthothrix

139

Coprinus disseminatus. Psathyrella. *Cap membranous, yellowish-clay colour at first then grey, sulcate to disc; not auto-digesting.* Cap 0.5 cm high, at first ovate, then hemispheric; gills white then greyish, adnate; stipe short, thin, often curved, minutely pilose (lens). In large numbers, esp. round and on rotten stumps of frondose trees. V–XI. C.

Coprinus micaceus. *Cap ochre-brown to date-brown, deeply sulcate, sprinkled at first with mica-like particles which soon ± disappear, stipe shortly but densely hispid at least in young specimens (lens).* Cap 2–4 cm high, ovate then ± expanded; gills finally dark brown. Clustered on and around stumps of frondose trees. Not much auto-digestion. V–XII. C. The very similar *C. truncorum* always has a glabrous stipe.

Psathyrella

Smallish, mostly membranous species, cap often brown and pellucid-striate when water soaked (pallid, not pellucid-striate when dried out); stipe white; spores dark purplish-brown to almost black. A few large, conspicuously veiled species were formerly referred to Hypholoma.

Psathyrella (Lacrymaria) lacrymabunda. Hypholoma velutinum. *Conspicuous veil fibrillose, with remains on adult cap and cap edge; gills ± mottled, edge white, " weeping " in moist weather.* Cap 1–8 cm, ± convex and sl. umbonate, dull yellowish-brown; gills dark brown, tinged purplish; stipe sl. paler than cap, ± fibrillose to scaly, stoutish or slender. Solitary or clustered in grassy places; roadsides, paths in woods, gravelly ground. Spores warted. V–XI. F–C. *Edible.*

Psathyrella candolleana. Hypholoma. *Cap expanded-convex, pallid, with denticulate remains of veil on margin.* Cap 2–6 cm, pale yellow to almost white; gills at first greyish-lilac, finally dark brownish, narrow, crowded; stipe slender, fragile. On or near stumps of frondose trees, usually ± tufted. V–XI. C.

Psathyrella hydrophilum. Hypholoma. *Moist cap ± date-brown, drying out pale clay colour; tufted.* Cap 2–6 cm with conspicuous cobweb-like veil when young, the remains often fringing margin of expanded cap but not denticulate, gills pale brown at first, finally dark brown; stipe sometimes with faint ring-like zone. On and around stumps of frondose trees usually densely tufted. VIII–XI. C.

Psathyrella spadiceo-grisea. *Moist cap date-brown, drying pale greyish-tan; not tufted.* Cap 3–6 cm, conical at first, then expanded and sl. umbonate, without velar remains; gills finally brown with purple tinge, edge white. Solitary or in twos or threes but not tufted; frondose woods. IV–XI. O.

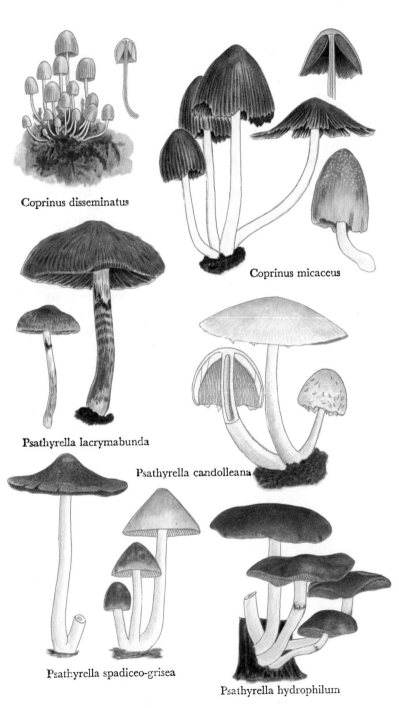

Coprinus disseminatus

Coprinus micaceus

Psathyrella lacrymabunda

Psathyrella candolleana

Psathyrella spadiceo-grisea

Psathyrella hydrophilum

Psathyrella spadicea. Psilocybe. *Moist cap date-brown, drying to pale ochre; veil absent; tufted.* Cap 2–6 cm, soon expanded convex, smooth, not striate; gills finally dull brown. Densely tufted around stumps or bases of living frondose trees. Very like *Ps. hydrophilum* but always devoid of a veil at all stages. IV–XI. R–O.

Psathyrella gracilis. *Moist cap dark brownish and striate-sulcate, drying pale tan; edge of gills ± pink (lens); stipe with short " tap-root ".* Cap 1–3 cm., ± convex, obtuse or sl. umbonate, often somewhat wrinkled, veil absent; gills broad, broadly adnate; stipe rigid, the " tap-root " fibrillose. Esp. in frondose woods, among leaves and sticks. VIII–XI. C.

There are a number of similar species which require microscopic identification.

Psathyrella conopilea, subatrata. *Adult moist cap ± conical, date brown when moist and striate to half-way, drying to very pale tan.* Cap 1–4 cm, soon conical-campanulate, veil absent; gills rather broad, finally dark brown with purplish tinge; stipe straight, tall, 10–15 cm. Frondose woods and often wet ground; gardens. IX–XI. O–F.

Psathyrella multipedata, stipatissima. *Densely tufted; moist cap, ± clay-brown, drying paler, margin finely striate.* Cap 1.5–3 cm, soon ± convex, veil none; gills crowded, adnate, dirty purplish brown; stipes slender, springing from root-like elongation. Sides of paths in woods and parks. X. R.

Psathyrella caput-medusae. Stropharia. *Cap date-brown at disc, whitish with rather broad brownish scales on lower half;* ring " double ", ± conspicuous, horizontal. Cap 3–7 cm, soon flat-convex; gills dark brown; stipe stoutish, white and smooth above ring, with brown, recurved scales below; flesh whitish with sweetish smell. Tufted on and around conifer stumps. IX–X. R.

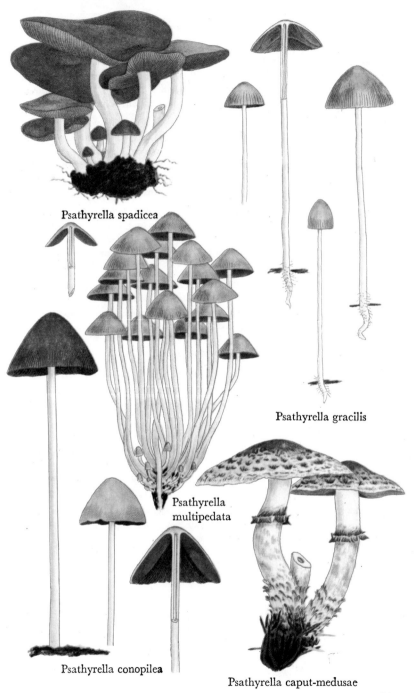

Psathyrella spadicea

Psathyrella gracilis

Psathyrella multipedata

Psathyrella conopilea

Psathyrella caput-medusae

143

Panaeolus foenisecii. Psilocybe. *Moist cap dull darkish brown with sl. rufous tinge, showing marginal belt when partly dry.* Cap 1-2 cm, bell-shaped to convex, slowly drying from apex to pale clay colour so that darker parts towards margin give a belt appearance; gills pale brown at first, then "mottled" (from unequal ripening of spores) finally ± uniformly dull dark brown; stipe paler than cap. (Spores dull brownish.) In grass, esp. lawns. VI–X. F–C.

Panaeolus rickenii, acuminatus. *Moist cap parabolic, date brown, margin striate with marginal belt when partly dry; stipe tall.* Cap 1-2 cm, drying paler and with rufous tinge from above to give "belt", smooth, veil none; gills greyish mottled, finally almost black, edge white dentate; stipe ± colour of cap but paler, apex "weeping" in moist weather. On dung and in rank grass. VII–XI. O–F.

Stropharia hornemannii, depilata. *Large, glutinous; stipe scaly to ample ± flesh ring; smell nasty; rare.* Cap 5–10(15) cm, convex to ± flat, straw colour to ± chestnut brown, often violet flushed when young; gills broad, pale, finally greyish-violet; stipe stout, whitish straw colour, the whitish scales soon disappearing, On fallen branches and chips in conifer woods. IX–XI. **Poisonous.**

Panaeolus semiovatus. Anellaria separata. *Cap ± bell-shaped, greyish to very pale tan, viscid;* stipe with ring. Cap 1-6 cm, smooth; gills greyish mottled, finally black; stipe straight, slender or stout, ring expanded, membranous. On dung and manured ground. VII–XI. F–C.

Stropharia

Stropharia coronilla. *Cap pale straw-yellow, slimy, thick-fleshed; ring radially grooved above; in grass.* Cap 1-3 cm, convex-expanded, smooth; gills ± sinuo-adnate, broad, finally dark brown; stipe stoutish, white, yellowing with age. Pastures, parks, lawns. VI–XI. O–F.

Stropharia aeruginosa. *Cap deep blue-green, slimy, white floccose when young.* Cap 2–8 cm, convex flattened, colour fading with age to dull yellowish-green; gills broad, adnate, soon chocolate coloured; stipe stout, paler than cap, smooth above the ring, ± floccose-scaly below. Esp. in grass: gardens, pastures, woods. VI–XI. C.

Stropharia semiglobata. *Cap hemispherical, straw-yellow, slimy; esp. on dung.* Cap 1-4 cm; gills adnate, soon chocolate coloured; stipe smooth, white to yellow, slimy below ring or ring-like zone. IV–XI. C.

Panaeolus foenisecii

Panaeolus semiovatus

Panaeolus rickenii

Stropharia hornemannii

Stropharia coronilla

Stropharia semiglobata

Stropharia aeruginosa

145

Hypholoma. Naematoloma

Cap usually reddish-to sulphur-yellow; gills adnate, purple black from spores, yellowish when young; stipe usually yellow; conspicuous, $\pm$ cobwebby veil. Mostly $\pm$ tufted on wood.

Hypholoma (Stropharia) squamosum. *Cap pale tan to yellow-ochre with few scales; stipe with recurved scales to $\pm$ conspicuous ring.* Cap 2–5 cm, convex to flattened, scales brownish, triangular; gills at first yellow finally violet to chocolate; stipe tall, slender (to 10 cm), yellow below ring whitish above. Generally attached to buried pieces of wood in frondose woods, esp. beech; solitary. IX–XI. F.

Hypholoma sublateritium. *Young cap brick-red, paler towards edge, gills yellow at first.* Cap 3–8 cm, convex to expanded, smooth, the edge often with velar remains; gills finally greyish-violet to chocolate; stipe stoutish, $\pm$ cap colour but yellower above, more rufous downwards and sl. scaly-fibrillose; veil yellowish-white sometimes leaving ring-like zone; flesh yellowish, almost tasteless. Densely tufted: stumps of frondose trees. VIII–XI. F–C.

Hypholoma capnoides. *Cap ochre-yellow, paler towards edge; gills whitish at first; on conifers.* Cap 2–6 cm, convex or flat to sl. umbonate, often brownish towards centre, sl. viscid; gills finally greyish-lilac to chocolate; stipe with vague remnants of veil when young, tinged brownish from base up; flesh pale yellow, taste mild. Densely tufted; never in frondose woods. IV–XI. F.

Hypholoma fasciculare. " Sulphur tuft ". *Cap sulphur-yellow, sl. fulvous towards centre; gills yellowish-green at first; taste bitter; tufted on frondose stumps.* Cap 3–7 cm, convex to $\pm$ expanded and umbonate, margin often with velar remains; gills finally olive green to chocolate; stipe slender, often with faint zone from veil remnants, cap colour but dirty brownish downwards; flesh yellow. An occasional tuft is found on conifer stumps. I–XII. C.

Hypholoma radicosum. *Cap pale yellowish-brown to tan, viscid; stipe rooting in rotting stumps.* Cap 4–8 cm, convex to expanded and $\pm$ umbonate, margin with whitish bloom and long remaining incurved; gills pallid at first, then greyish violet, finally dark brown; stipe tallish (7–8 cm), stout, with darker belt-like squamules up to vague ring-like zone; flesh pale yellow, rusty brown in rooting part. Solitary or in twos or threes, usually on conifer stumps. VIII–XI. O.

Hypholoma dispersum. *Cap dull fulvous, margin yellowish; stipe silky-striate, greyish-brown; not tufted.* Cap 2–6 cm, soon $\pm$ expanded flat, sl. umbonate; gills pale yellow becoming dark; stipe slender, rigid, 5–7 cm, sometimes with zone-like markings, darker downwards; flesh very bitter, rusty brown in stipe. Solitary or in small groups, but not tufted, on conifer stumps and chips. VIII–XI. O.

Hypholoma udum. Psilocybe. *Cap dull yellowish rufous; gills $\pm$ olive at first; veil absent; in peat.* Cap 1–2 cm, convex-flat, umbonate, varying clay colour to rufous, sl. viscid, smooth; gills finally dark chocolate brown; stipe slender, about 5 cm long (much longer—9 cm—in *Sphagnum*), $\pm$ cap colour. VIII–XI. O–F.

A similar but pale yellowish species in moss is *H. elongatum.*

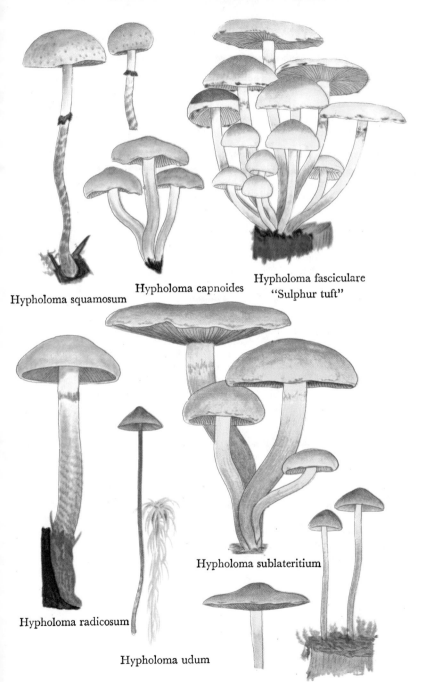

Hypholoma squamosum

Hypholoma capnoides

Hypholoma fasciculare
"Sulphur tuft"

Hypholoma radicosum

Hypholoma udum

Hypholoma sublateritium

Hypholoma dispersum

Psilocybe

Small dark spored species with moist cap on soil or dung; veil absent or rudimentary.

Psilocybe (Deconica) coprophila. *Cap hemispherical, shining, hazel to dark-brown, with detachable pellicle; gills broadly adnate; spores purplish brown; on dung.* Cap 1-2 cm, ± viscid, sl. floccose towards edge; gills almost triangular, greyish brown, finally almost black, edge whitish; stipe sl. paler than cap, often curved; flesh with mealy taste. Esp. horse-droppings, cow pats. VIII-XI. O.

Psilocybe (Deconica) montana, atrorufa. *Small; cap ± distinctly papillate, tawny-bistre when wet, striate to half-way; stipe thin, brown; among mosses, lichens.* Cap 1-2 cm, ± hemispherical to sl. expanded, drying grey-brown; gills broadly adnate, ± triangular, finally rufous brown; stipe slender, usually paler above. Chiefly sandy soils in woods, heaths. VI-XI. O-F.

Psilocybe semilanceata. "Liberty caps". *Cap pale clay colour, viscid parabolic with distinct apical cusp, pellicle separable.* Cap 0.5-1 cm across, up to 2 cm high, often with olive-green tinge; gills ± adnate finally purple-brown; stipe slender, usually wavy, whitish above. Roadsides, rich grassland. VIII-XI. F-C.

Pholiota

Medium to large sized species; stipe usually with membranous ring; cap often scaly; spores rusty or cigar-brown. Often ± tufted on wood.

Pholiota destruens. *Large; cap pale brownish ± covered with white cottony scales; esp. on poplars.* Cap 6-10 cm convex or ± expanded and broadly umbonate, margin long remaining incurved; gills finally cigar-brown; stipe short, stout, scaly like cap; flesh thick, tough, white in cap, discolouring brownish in stipe from base up, smell sweetish aromatic, taste sl. bitterish. VIII-XI. R-O. Causes a heart rot.

Pholiota flammans. *Cap and stipe bright tawny yellow with recurved ± triangular sulphur yellow scales.* Cap 2-6 cm, flat, convex, dry; gills crowded, yellow; stipe often curved; flesh yellow. On decaying trunks and stumps of conifers, generally ± solitary. VIII-X. O. (Colours often brighter than in illustration.)

Pholiota squarrosa. *Cap and stipe dry, ± straw yellow and beset with hazel brown recurved scales; ± tufted.* Cap 3-8 cm, ± convex; gills at first straw-yellow finally olive-brownish, ± arcuate-decurrent; stipe ± smooth above sl. frayed membranous ring; flesh tough, yellowish but darker in base of stipe. Base of frondose trees. IX-XI. F. *Indigestible.*

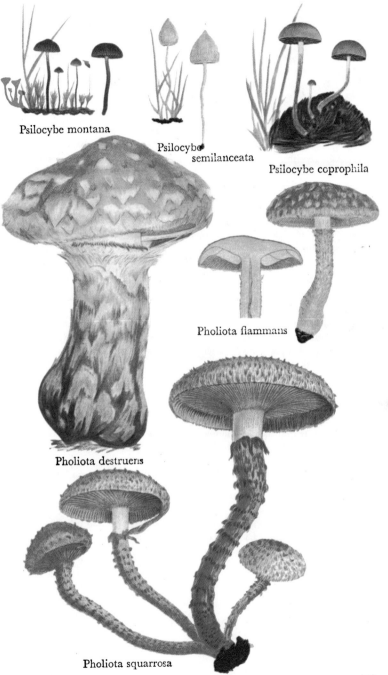

Psilocybe montana

Psilocybe semilanceata

Psilocybe coprophila

Pholiota flammans

Pholiota destruens

Pholiota squarrosa

Pholiota alnicola. Flammula. *Cap ± yellow at first, finally tinged olive towards edge and sl. fulvous towards centre; flesh bitter.* Cap 2–6 cm, convex to flattened, margin with vague remains of veil; gills pale yellow, finally clay to cinnamon; stipe ± horizontal, pale yellow above, rusty downwards, dry; flesh rusty in stipe base.   Solitary or in twos or threes almost always on alder.   IX–XI.   O.

Ph. apicrea (Flammula), is very similar, but grows on other frondose trees, esp. birch, and the flesh is not bitter.

Pholiota lenta. Flammula. *Cap slimy, pale clay colour with few disappearing white floccules; stipe with floccose squamules from base up.* Cap 3–8 cm, convex to flattened; gills pale greyish-white, finally dark clay to olive-brownish; stipe paler than cap above, flushed more brownish downwards; flesh white, brown in stipe base, faint smell and taste of radish.   Esp. in beech woods, sometimes under conifers. IX–XII.   F.

Pholiota adiposa. *Cap and stipe ± golden-brown, viscid, beset with glutinous brownish scales; ± tufted at base of beech trees or stumps.* Cap 5–10 cm, convex to expanded, scales triangular; gills straw-yellow at first, finally ± rusty ochre; stipe yellow, smooth above incomplete ring; flesh pale yellow but rusty-brown in stipe base, tough.   VIII–X.   O.

Pholiota aurivella. *Cap deep yellow, rusty towards centre, very sticky, and with rusty-brown scales; stipe dry, fibrillose.* Cap 5–12 cm, convex-expanded, scales ± adpressed; gills pale yellowish at first, finally rusty-brown, ± sinuate; stipe curved, usually short, ring ± fibrillose, soon vanishing;   flesh pale yellow, brownish in stipe base, tough.   Solitary or in twos or threes, always high up on frondose trees.   IX–XI.   O.

Pholiota lucifera. *Cap slimy, with rusty inconspicuous scales; stipe dry, fibrillose-scaly to ring; on buried frondose wood.* Cap 4–6 cm, convex-expanded; gills yellow, edge paler; stipe flesh rusty at base.   Often ± tufted.   VIII–XI.   R.

Pholiota astragalina. Flammula. *Cap viscid, saffron-red with yellow margin; stipe minutely squamulose.* Cap 2–5 cm, ± flattened, smooth; gills pale yellow at first, finally cinnamon-brown; stipe pale yellow, becoming ± rusty downwards; flesh tough, bitter.   Solitary or in twos or threes on conifer stumps.   IX–XI.   R.

Pholiota carbonaria. Flammula. *Cap viscid, ± yellowish brown; clustered in burnt coniferous areas.* Cap 1–3 cm, paler towards margin, pellicle ± separable; gills yellowish-cinnamon; stipe pale yellowish above, brownish below, ± floccose below veil zone, short.   IX–XI.   F–C.

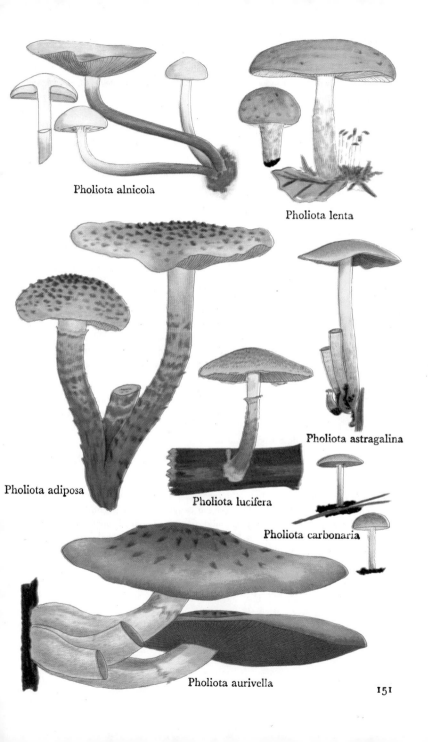

Pholiota alnicola

Pholiota lenta

Pholiota adiposa

Pholiota lucifera

Pholiota astragalina

Pholiota carbonaria

Pholiota aurivella

Pholiota (Kuehneromyces) mutabilis. *Cap date-brown when wet, drying chamois-leather colour; stipe ± scaly to membranous ring; tufted on stumps.* Cap 3–6 cm, soon flattened, drying from centre; gills finally ± cinnamon; stipe pale brown, darker downwards. Frondose woods. IV–XII. C. *Edible and good, esp. in stews.*

Conocybe

Conocybe tenera. Galera. *Cap dull ochre-brown, conical; stipe striate, powdery, with small bulb.* Cap 1–3 cm, almost without striations, drying paler; gills narrow, cinnamon; stipe to 10 cm, honey colour, finally tinged rusty. Among grass in pastures, woods. V–XII. C.

Conocybe lactea. Galera lateritia. *Cap milk-white, conical; gills cinnamon.* Cap 1–3 cm high, smooth, sometimes sl. creamy; stipe 6–10 cm, white, powdery above, base with roundish bulb; flesh thin. In grass on roadsides etc., sawdust, sand-dunes. VIII–XI. O.

Bolbitius vitellinus. *Cap bright yellow, membranous, striate at first, slimy, finally grooved; gills rusty cinnamon; in manured grass.* Cap 1–5 cm, soon expanded; gills ± free; stipe straw-yellow to whitish, ± powdery-floccose. VIII–XI. F–C.

Agrocybe

Agrocybe dura. Pholiota. *Cap ± creamy to ochre, dry; ring cottony; spores cigar brown; spring and summer.* Cap 3–7 cm, convex-flat, smooth; gills adnate, finally dull brown; stipe thickish, ± white; flesh white; taste sl. bitterish, smell not mealy. Roadsides, gardens, cultivated places on ± chalky soils. IV–VIII. O–F.

Agrocybe praecox. Pholiota. *Cap dull clay-brown (whitish when dry); stipe with pendulous membranous ring; taste and smell ± mealy, spring and early summer.* Cap 3–7 cm, ± convex, smooth; gills finally ± cigar-brown; stipe whitish; spores cigar-brown. Frondose woods, pastures. V–VII(VIII). F–C.

Agrocybe paludosa. Pholiota. *Cap ± tan; stipe slender. Very like previous sp.* In marshy meadows, reed swamps. V–VII. O.

Agrocybe erebia. Pholiota. *Wet cap bistre, sl. viscid, margin striate; whitish membranous ring grooved above.* Cap 3–6 cm convex, smooth, sl. umbonate, drying out dull clay greyish-brown; gills pallid, finally dull dark brown; stipe stoutish, at first pallid, soon bistre from base up; flesh rather thick, pale greyish-brown. On damp rich soil in frondose woods. IX–XI. O.

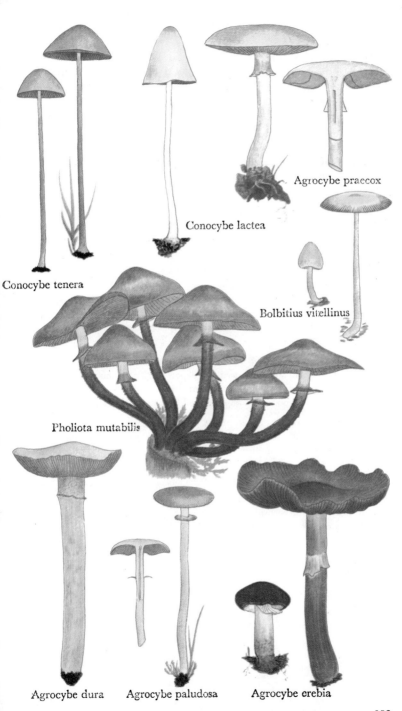

Agrocybe praecox

Conocybe lactea

Conocybe tenera

Bolbitius vitellinus

Pholiota mutabilis

Agrocybe dura   Agrocybe paludosa   Agrocybe erebia

Small to medium terrestrial species; cap ± convex or umbonate its cuticle squarrose, radially fibrillose, rarely smooth; edge of young cap with ± cobwebby veil covering the gills; spores ± dull cigar-brown, never rusty; smell often earthy or fruity. About 85 species; some dangerously **poisonous,** *even deadly, hence all best avoided. Microscopic examination of spores and cystidia important for identification. See footnote[1], p. 158.*

Inocybe corydalina. *Cap whitish clay colour, umbo often greenish; smell sickly sweet-fruity.* Cap 3–6 cm, soon ± expanded, adpressed, fibrillose, esp. towards margin, sl. viscid, whitish at first; gills pallid then pale earth brown; stipe stoutish, pale to clay grey, sl. fibrillose, without distinct bulb; flesh thick, white. Frondose woods. VIII–XI. O. Some similar species have browner caps and reddening flesh.

Inocybe flocculosa, *Cap mouse-grey to brownish, tomentose or fibrillose, ± squamulose at disc; stipe pallid, white fibrillose.* Cap 2–4 cm, soon expanded umbonate, margin with arachnoid veil; gills dirty earth-brown; stipe white below, tinged cap colour above, with vague remnants of veil; flesh with faintly spermatic smell. In frondose woods. IX-XI. O.

Inocybe lacera. *Cap convex to umbonate, cigar brown, fibrillose or squamulose.* Cap 2–4 cm, sometimes olive tinged at margin; gills broad distant, pale olive-grey at first, finally dirty olive-brown; stipe short, tapering downwards, ± cap colour, fibrillose; flesh of stipe rusty-brown. Gravelly places, heaths, coniferous woods. VI–XI. F. *Poisonous.*

Inocybe geophylla. *Cap white or lilac* (var. *lilacina) almost smooth.* Cap convex, soon expanded-umbonate, adpressed fibrillose, sl. silky shining; gills rather narrow, white, finally dirty greyish brown; stipe slender, smooth; flesh thin, smell ± spermatic. Woods, esp. on damp soil by paths. VI–XI. C. *Poisonous.*

Inocybe griseo-lilacina. *Small; cap fibrillose-squamulose; stipe pale lilac.* Cap 1–3 cm, convex or sl. umbonate, pale greyish brown without lilac tinge; gills pale lilac when young, soon dirty brown; stipe with whitish fibrils. Rich soil in frondose woods. IX–XI. O–F. *Poisonous.*

Inocybe pudica, rubescens. *Cap white, silky, flushing pink-rose to tile-red; stipe stout thickened downwards.* Cap 2–5 cm, convex-umbonate, ± fibrillose; gills pallid clay at first, then dirty brown with tile-red tinge; stipe white, soon flushed reddish. In conifer woods, on rich soil. IX–XI. O.

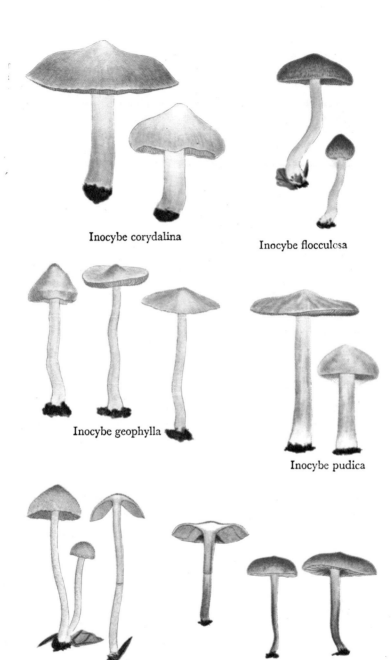

Inocybe corydalina

Inocybe flocculosa

Inocybe geophylla

Inocybe pudica

Inocybe griseo-lilacina

Inocybe lacera

Inocybe praetervisa. *Cap dark straw-yellow; stipe pale yellow with marginate white bulb.* Cap 2–4 cm, conical then expanded, umbonate, sl. rimose to about half-way, umbo sl. brownish; gills pallid, finally yellowish brown; stipe slender, pale yellowish, finely striate; flesh with spermatic smell. Along paths in woods. IX–XI. O–F. *Poisonous.*

Inocybe cookei. *Cap straw-yellow, ± rimose towards margin; stipe with marginate white bulb.* Cap 2–4 cm, convex to umbonate; gills pallid, finally clay colour; stipe tinged cap colour, smooth; flesh firm, white. Frondose woods and copses. VIII-XI. F.

Inocybe squamata. *Cap ± conical, umbonate, yellowish-brown, disc ± adpressed scaly.* Cap 3–7 cm, fibrillose, margin often irregularly split, the centre usually darker coloured; gills pale olive-yellowish, finally dirty olive brown, edge whitish, rather broad; stipe stout, fibrillose to striate, pale, finally yellowish-brown. On rich clay soil by hedges. IX–XI. R. *?Poisonous.*

Inocybe fastigiata. *Cap conical, rimose, ± acutely umbonate, yellow ochre to brownish ochre; gills yellow.* Cap 2–5 cm, ± innately-fibrillose, margin often cracked; stipe sl. fibrillose, pallid, without bulb; flesh thin, smell spermatic. Frondose woods. VI–XI. F. **Dangerously poisonous.**

Inocybe langei. *Cap ± ochre brownish, fibrillose-squamulose; stipe shorter than cap diam.* Cap 2–4 cm, flattened, ± umbonate, at first adpressed fibrillose; gills pallid, finally olive yellowish-brown, broad, rather distant; stipe whitish, stout, firm, sl. striate above; smell faintly spermatic. Damp, rich soil of frondose woods. IX–XI. O. *?Poisonous.*

Inocybe dulcamara. *Cap finally minutely felty squamulose, ± ochry with sl. tawny flush at disc; stipe brownish.* Cap 2–5 cm, ± flattened, pale brownish-yellow at first, fibrillose at margin and arachnoid veil when young; gills olive-yellow finally ± cinnamon, narrow; stipe fibrillose, pale at first, then dirty yellowish-brown; flesh pale yellowish, brownish in stipe. Light and peaty soils in conifer woods. VIII-XI. F.

Inocybe bongardii. *Cap pale brownish with sl. pink tinge, fibrillosely scaly; flesh reddening, smell of ripe pears.* Cap 3–6 cm, campanulate to convex, sl. umbonate; gills broad, whitish, finally dull cinnamon; stipe rather tall, often flexuose, finally fibrillose, white, finally brownish vinaceous. Rich soil in woods. VII–XI. O.

Inocybe praetervisa   Inocybe squamata

Inocybe cookei

Inocybe dulcamara

Inocybe langei

Inocybe fastigiata   Inocybe bongardii

Inocybe patouillardii. *Whitish when young, later yellowish-brown; bright pinkish where cracked or bruised.* Cap 4–7 cm, campanulate then expanded and ± umbonate, minutely silky-fibrillose, margin often split; gills whitish, finally olive-yellowish; stipe thickish, almost smooth, whitish with tinge of cap colour, also bruising pinkish; flesh with rank smell. Frondose woods, esp. beech, on calcareous soil. V–XI. O. **Deadly poisonous.**

Inocybe jurana. *Cap densely fibrillose, vinaceous brown.* Cap 3–7 cm, conico-campanulate, later expanded and umbonate, umbo adpressed squamulose; gills whitish grey, finally greyish brown; stipe with vague bulb, white with dirty vinaceous flush from base up; flesh tinged vinaceous esp. in umbo and stipe base. In frondose woods and copses, the stipe deep in ground. VIII–XI. O. *?Poisonous.*

Inocybe maculata. *Cap ± conical, rimose, dark brown with pale adpressed scales at disc.* Cap 3–7 cm with dark brown fibrils, disc scales pale clay and almost membranous; gills pale greyish, finally cigar-brown; stipe fibrillose striate, pallid, soon tinged with cap colour; flesh whitish with sl. aromatic smell. Mainly frondose woods, esp. along paths on rich soil. IX–XI. C. *Poisonous.*

Inocybe napipes. *Cap ± campanulate, finally acutely umbonate, dark brown to chestnut; stipe with depressed, not marginate bulb.* Cap 3–5 cm, almost smooth to minutely fibrillose; gills pallid, finally yellowish brown; stipe slender, ± cap colour, but paler above. In wet or boggy places esp. under birch. IX–XI. O–F. *Poisonous.*

Inocybe asterospora. *Cap bay-brown to chestnut, rimose; stipe with marginate bulb.* Cap 3–6 cm, expanded, obtusely umbonate, dark brown fibrils, showing pallid flesh between; gills whitish, later brown; stipe slender, brownish; flesh in cap pallid, in stipe brownish. Usually solitary in parks; along woodland paths in rich soil. IX–XI. O–F. *Poisonous.*

Inocybe casimiri, lanuginosa p.p. *Cap ± bistre with velvety squamules, erect at disc, recurved elsewhere.* Cap 2–3 cm, ± convex; gills pallid, finally clay to yellowish-brown; stipe about twice cap diam., thin, flushed cap colour from base up and beset with dark brown cottony squamules. In woods, on heaths, esp. on sandy soil; also on peat and stumps. VIII–XI. O.

---

[1] The main divisions of *Inocybe* are as follows:
  I. Spores smooth, not nodulose or spiny: sub-genus *Inocybe.*
    (a) ± fusiform, thick-walled, crested cystidia present, on sides of gill if not on edge—cystidiate Inocybes.
    (b) No such thick-walled cystidia present, but thin walled para-cystidia usually present on gill edge—acystidiate Inocybes.
  II. Spores nodulose or spiny; cystidia of type (a) above usually present: sub-genus *Clypeus.*

Inocybe patouillardii

Inocybe maculata

Inocybe napipes

Inocybe casimiri

Inocybe asterospora

Inocybe jurana

Hebeloma

Cap white to pale brown, sl. viscid; veil present or absent; gills ± sinuate finally cigar-brown from the spores; stipe pallid. No edible species, some being ± poisonous, but not deadly.

Hebeloma crustuliniforme. *Cap ± pale watery tan; veil absent; stipe short; distinct smell of radish.* Cap 3–7 cm, convex expanded, smooth, sl. viscid with paler margin and inrolled downy edge; gills at first watery greyish (" weeping " in wet weather); stipe about equal to cap diam., rather thick, whitish, coarsely powdery above; flesh whitish, firm. On damp soil in woods, gardens. VIII–XI. C. *Poisonous to some people.*

Hebeloma longicaudum. *Cap whitish pale brown, without veil; stipe tall, bulbous; almost without smell.* Cap 3–7 cm, convex, viscid, smooth, darker brown towards disc; gills at first pale greyish to flesh colour, often weeping; stipe 7–8 cm, almost smooth, white; flesh ± white. Damp woods. VIII–XI. O.

Hebeloma sinuosum. *Large; cap ± tan colour; veil absent; almost without smell.* Cap 5–12 cm, convex to expanded, usually ± undulate, smooth, sl. viscid, often with tinge of flesh colour, paler in middle; gills irregular, rather narrow; stipe tall, stout, with adpressed, brownish, scaly zones on pale background, sl. bulbous-rooting below; flesh pallid. Damp woods, often by ditches. IX–XI. O.

Hebeloma pusillum. *Small; cap reddish clay-brown, margin paler, veil absent.* Cap 1–2 cm, convex, soon expanded with small umbo, smooth, viscid; gills rather broad, at first pale greyish, often " weeping "; stipe slender, pruinose, white; flesh firm, sl. bitter. Mostly in willow bogs. VIII–X. R–O.

Hebeloma pumilum. *Small; cap brownish, edge whitish, stipe with remnants of veil, rooting; smell almost none.* Cap 1–2 cm, convex without umbo, smooth, viscid; gills rather broad, often " weeping," finally pale cinnamon; stipe sl. fibrillose, floccose above, whitish; flesh sl. bitterish. In dry frondose woods. X–XI. R–O.

Hebeloma mesophaeum. *Cap ± date-brown at disc, margin much paler; stip brownish with remains of veil.* Cap 2–4 cm., convex flattened, smooth sl. viscid; gills at first pallid; stipe whitish at first and with distinct veil, soon brownish and fibrillose; flesh pale brown, dark brownish in stipe base, taste sl. bitter. In woods and esp. pine birch heathland. VIII–XII. C.

Hebeloma sacchariolens. *Cap ± ochre-buff; strong sweetish burnt-sugar smell; no veil.* Cap 2–4 cm, convex, smooth; gills broad, pale flesh colour to cinnamon; stipe tall, stout, fibrillose, pallid, finally brownish. Damp frondose woods and copses. IX–X. O.

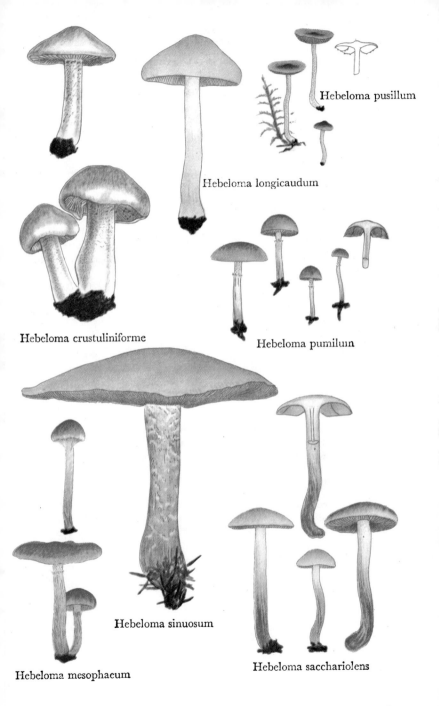

Hebeloma pusillum

Hebeloma longicaudum

Hebeloma crustuliniforme

Hebeloma pumilum

Hebeloma sinuosum

Hebeloma mesophaeum

Hebeloma sacchariolens

Naucoria. Alnicola

Small brownish species growing in alder or willow swamps. Spores ± rusty-brown, large, rough.

Naucoria escharoides. *Cap dull yellowish at first, then ± cinnamon, scurfy; stipe flushing brown from base up; under alders.* Cap 1–3 cm, convex-expanded; gills ± cap colour, adnate, narrow, stipe somewhat flexuose, fibrillose, hollow, fragile. IX–XI. C.

Naucoria scolecina. *Cap ± chesnut, striate at margin when moist; stipe ± concolorous; under alders.* Cap 1–2 cm, convex, smooth, drying out pale greyish brown; gills rusty brown; stipe shortish, flexuose, pale at apex, sl. fibrillose. IX–XI. O–F.

Naucoria langei Kühn. *Cap reddish clay-brown, paler at margin, umbonate, stipe paler, apex powdery; mostly under willows.* Cap 1–2 cm, finally expanded, smooth, almost without striations; gills rather broad, distant, dull brown, edge white. On decaying leaf humus. Best recognised by large lemon-shaped spores. No British record as yet.

Cortinarius

A very large genus with a wide variety of species., with cobweb like veil (when young) and rusty brown spores. See footnote[1], pages 164, 166.

Cortinarius elatior. *(M).* *Cap clay-brown to olive, slimy, margin wrinkled sulcate; gills transversely venose; stipe slimy, ± fusiform, whitish or bluish with incomplete belt-like scales.* Cap 4–9 cm, conical then ± expanded, margin sometimes sl. violet; gills broad, finally rusty violaceous or umber; stipe rooting, sl. grooved at apex; flesh pale yellowish. Woods, esp. beech. VIII–X. C.

Cortinarius trivialis. *(M).* *Cap clay-brown, slimy; stipe slimy with belt-like pallid scales.* Cap 5–10 cm, convex flattened, margin even; gills greyish, finally cinnamon brown; stipe tall, stout, deeply rooting, minutely striate at apex, ground colour darker than scales; flesh ± rusty brown. In frondose woods, esp. under willows, on clayey soils. VIII–X. O–F.

Cortinarius collinitus. *(M).* *Cap yellowish-brown to chestnut, slimy; stipe slimy with broad ± pale bluish belt-like scales.* Cap 5–10 cm, convex umbonate, umbo ± chestnut, rest more yellowish brown; gills pallid, finally rusty brown; stipe tall, stout, ± tapering downwards and rooting, ground colour yellowish-brown; flesh pale brown, firm. Conifer woods in deep moss. VIII–X. O–F.

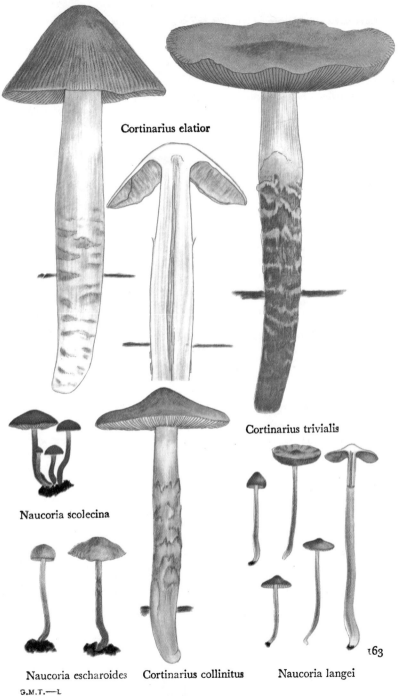

Cortinarius elatior

Cortinarius trivialis

Naucoria scolecina

Naucoria escharoides   Cortinarius collinitus   Naucoria langei

163

G.M.T.—L

Cortinarius delibutus. (*M*). *Cap pale to golden-yellow, viscid (as is stipe), young gills blue-lilac.* Cap 4–9 cm, flat-convex, smooth, more golden-yellow at disc, somewhat tinged brownish when old; gills finally cinnamon; stipe clavate, ± yellow flushed below, tinged bluish at apex with vague ring zone. Frondose trees, esp. birch, and aspen in boggy ground. VIII–XI. O.

Cortinarius albo-violaceus. (*I*). *Cap and stipe pale lilac-blue, flesh rather thick; stipe peronate to cortina by white coating.* Cap 3–7 cm, convex, finally ± flattened umbonate, sl. silky-fibrillose at margin, fading; gills rather distant, at first light bluish, finally ± cinnamon; stipe clavate, sl. bluish above; flesh whitish to pale violet, esp. at stipe apex. Frondose woods on poor soil, esp. beech; also oak. VIII–X. F. *Edible.*

Cortinarius traganus. (*I*). (Illustrated on endpapers.) *Wholly pale lilac when young, later discolouring; clavate stipe peronate with lilac veil.* Cap 5–9 cm, deep convex to ± umbonate; flesh of cap ± rhubarb colour, of stipe base ± rusty, with strong goaty smell. Conifer woods, esp. Scottish. VIII–XI. O.

Cortinarius fulgens sensu J. Lge. (*Ph*). *Cap viscid, tawny-orange to golden-brown, smooth; gills at first yellow; stipe yellowish with broad, marginate bulb.* Cap 6–10 cm, flat or convex to expanded; gills finally yellowish-rusty brown; stipe tall, stout; ochre-yellow above, more rusty downwards towards depressed bulb; flesh pale ochre in cap, ± rusty brown in stipe and bulb. Somewhat gregarious in frondose woods. IX–XI. O.

Cortinarius auroturbinatus, aurantio-turbinatus (in error). (*Ph*). *Cap viscid, shining orange-golden; gills (at first), stipe and flesh ± sulphur yellow; smell sweetish aromatic.* Cap 5–9 cm, flat or convex, often ± sulphur colour towards edge; gills usually with olive tinge; stipe stout, with large brownish-yellow, flattened or ovate bulb, apex pallid; flesh almost white in cap, lemon-yellow in bulb, and under cap cuticle. Beech woods on chalk. VIII–X. F.

Cortinarius caesiocyaneus. (*Ph*). *Cap viscid; all parts pale blue when young except large whitish marginate bulb of stipe.* Cap 6–8 cm, convex flattened, watery brownish when adult; gills at first bluish violet. Stipe squat, thick, pressed into bulb; flesh bluish-violet in cap and stipe, soon fading in cap, of bulb ± yellowish. Deep litter of beech woods, esp. on chalk. VIII–X. F.

---

[1] The genus *Cortinarius* was divided by Fries into the following sub-genera (abbreviations in parentheses). Fresh young specimens are essential.

    I. *Cap slimy, at least in wet weather; gills never at first reddish; stipe never brownish bistre, nor with reddish belt-like or other reddish markings.*
       (*a*) Stipe dry, not sticky-slimy or sl. so in spp. having marginate bulb— *Phlegmacium (Ph).*
       (*b*) Stipe ± sticky-slimy; stipe without marginate bulb—*Myxacium (M).*

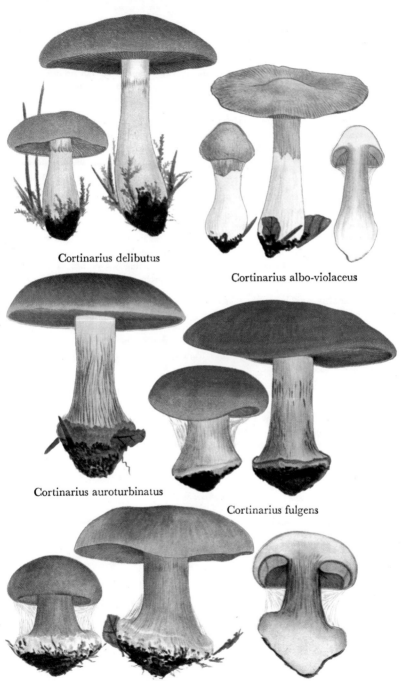

Cortinarius delibutus

Cortinarius albo-violaceus

Cortinarius auroturbinatus

Cortinarius fulgens

Cortinarius caesiocyaneus

Cortinarius melliolens. (*Ph*). *Cap viscid, pale ochre, sl. darker at disc, ± silky-hoary when young; gills at first pale watery brown; basal bulb ± round; smell ± of honey.* Cap 5–8 cm, soon expanded, sl. umbonate; gills serrulate, finally dull rusty-brown; stipe tall, slender, tinged ± cap colour, bulb not or indistinctly marginate; flesh almost white, sl. brownish when old. In deep foliage of beech. IX–X. ? O–F. One of the segregates of *C. multiformis* sensu lato.

Cortinarius (Leucocortinarius) bulbiger. *Cap pale brownish to clay; gills at first white, finally ± cap coloured, never rusty-brown; stipe with flattened bulb; spores white.* Cap 5–8 cm, convex to sl. gibbous; gills often sl. spotted along edges; stipe pale clay colour with white ± marginate bulb; flesh white, pale clay colour in stipe. A typical *Cortinarius*, apart from the white spores. Coniferous woods. IX–XI. R–O.

Cortinarius crocolitus. (*Ph*). *Cap pale ochre-yellowish, brownish at disc, ± viscid; at first with lilac flush; stipe with brownish-yellow scaly belts.* Cap 6–12 cm, ± convex to expanded, smooth or sl. squamulose at disc; gills finally rusty-tan; stipe tall (to 15 cm) somewhat clavate, pale lilac above, elsewhere pale yellow to clay colour, the belts conspicuous; flesh whitish, finally pale brown but long pale lilac in stipe apex. Frondose woods, esp. birch on peaty soil. IX–X. O–F.

Cortinarius varius. (*Ph*). *Cap yellowish tawny; gills at first violaceous; stipe clavate; flesh white; under conifers.* Cap 5–10 cm, semi-globose convex, finally ± expanded and depressed, viscid, margin paler; gills finally cinnamon ochre, edge entire violet; stipe almost smooth, whitish, tinged lilac above and pale ochre below; cortina white (finally rusty from spores). Gregarious. VIII–XI. R. *Edible and good.*

Cortinarius tabularis. (*Ph*). *Cap sl. viscid, ± clay yellowish-brown, darker at disc; gills at first pallid; stipe tall.* Cap 5–8 cm, ± convex-expanded; gills finally cinnamon, edge serrulate; stipe slender (to 10 cm) sl. swollen below, silky-fibrillose, whitish; flesh white with faint brownish tinge. But for the sl. viscid cap, it is typical of sub-genus *Dermocybe*. Frondose woods, esp. beech, amongst litter. VIII–X. F–C.

II. *Neither cap nor stipe sticky or slimy.*

  Cap not hygrophanous:

  (*d*) Cap silky or with scales or fibrils; cap flesh usually thick; stipe stout ± clavate-bulbous—*Inoloma* (*I*).

  (*d*) Cap at first silky, finally ± smooth, the flesh thin; stipe slender, cylindric or tapering upwards—*Dermocybe* (*D*).

  Cap hygrophanous:

  (*e*) Young stipe peronate or annulate with remains of universal veil in addition to a cortina—*Telamonia* (*T*).

  (*e*) Cortina only present, sometimes leaving remains on stipe—*Hydrocybe* (*H*).

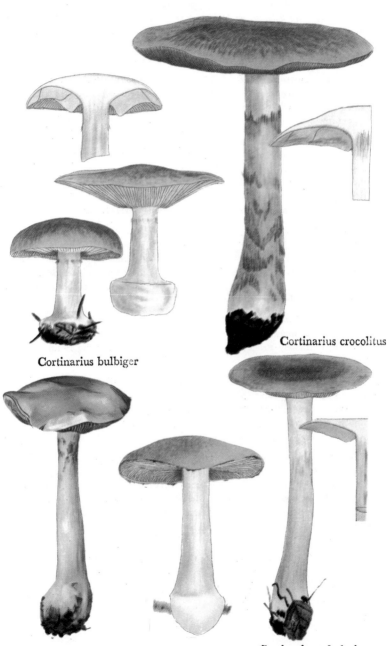

Cortinarius crocolitus

Cortinarius bulbiger

Cortinarius varius　　Cortinarius melliolens　　Cortinarius tabularis

Cortinarius bolaris. (*D*). *Cap densely cinnabar, squamose on ± cream coloured background; stipe with similar fibrillose scales.* Cap 3–5 cm, dry, convex, margin involute, squamules denser at disc; gills yellowish, finally yellowish-cinnamon; stipe usually short, coloured by the scales; flesh white, reddening. ± clustered or solitary in beech woods; also under birch. VIII–XI. O.

Cortinarius caninus. (*D*). *Cap dry, finally ± fawny-brown, gills lilac at first.* Cap 5–8 cm, convex, soon ± flat, smooth, clay-brown at first; gills rather broad and distant; finally dark cinnamon; stipe tall, stout, white, apex bluish, finally pale brown, often with median ring-like zone; flesh pale brown. Coniferous woods. VIII–X. O.

Cortinarius pholideus. (*I*). *Cap and stipe ± hazel-brownish, beset with darker, acute ± recurved flocculose scales.* Cap 3–7 cm, convex, then expanded-umbonate, the scales blackish; gills dirty lilac at first, later dark cinnamon; stipe tall, slender, apex faintly lilac; flesh pale brown, violet in stipe apex, darker brown towards base. Esp. under birch in wet peaty soil. VIII–X. C.

Cortinarius anomalus. (*D*). *Cap ± clay colour, sl. violet tinged, edge paler; gills deep violet at first; stipe ± clavate, yellowish, squamose.* Cap 3–5 cm, convex flattened, minutely fibrillose to smooth; gills finally cinnamon; stipe apex violet, pallid below a ring-like zone, the squamules minute and ± dispersed as stipe elongates; flesh ± pale violet, fading. Frondose woods, esp. beech, also oak and birch. VIII–X. F–C.

Cortinarius cinnabarinus. (*D*). *Wholly ± red-lead colour, dry.* Cap 2–4 cm, ± convex, shining; gills rather distant and broad, sl. darker than cap; stipe shortish, fibrillosely striate; flesh red, smell and taste recalling radish. Beech-woods. IX–XI. O.

Cortinarius semisanguineus. (*D*). *Cap olive-yellowish pale brown dry; gills glancing blood-red.* Cap 2–5 cm, convex to umbonate, ± fibrillose; gills finally with rusty tinge; stipe slender, ± flexuose, yellowish-brown with olive-brown fibrils; flesh yellowish-brown. Clustered or solitary in coniferous and birch woods, heaths. VIII–XI. C.

Cortinarius cinnamomeus sensu lato. (*D*). *Cap dry, yellowish olive-brown; gills ± bright yellow when young, sometimes ± tinged saffron.* Cap 2–5 cm, convex to umbonate, ± fibrillose; gills rather broad and distant, finally ± tinged brownish; flesh dirty olive-yellow. Woods generally, peaty places. VIII–XII. C. A polymorphic species, some of the varieties often regarded as species: the left-hand illustrations have been called *C. croceofolius*, those on the right *C. cinnamomeoluteus*.

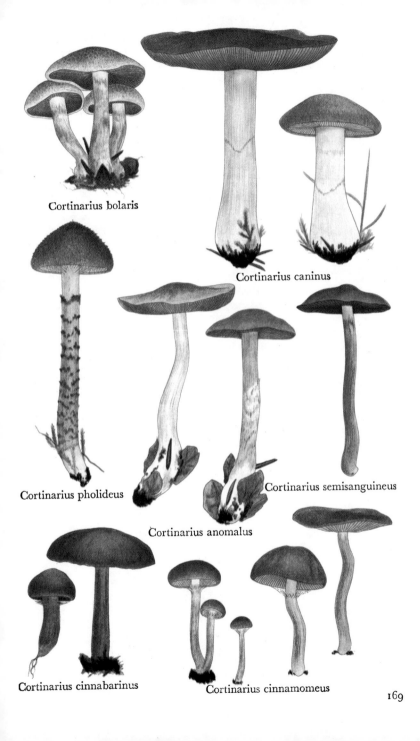

Cortinarius bolaris

Cortinarius caninus

Cortinarius pholideus

Cortinarius anomalus

Cortinarius semisanguineus

Cortinarius cinnabarinus

Cortinarius cinnamomeus

Cortinarius armillatus. (*T*). *Large; with cinnabar-red belts on stipe.* Cap 5–10 cm, ± convex, somewhat brick-red when young later ± tan brown; gills pale, finally cinnamon, broad, distant; stipe pale brown tall, slender, sl. clavate, belts oblique, usually 3–4. Woods, esp. under birch amongst heath vegetation. VIII–X. F–C.

Cortinarius glandicolor. (*T*). *Cap dry, dark brown, acutely umbonate; stipe concolorous, with white oblique ring-like belt.* Cap 2–4 cm, campanulate then convex, varying dark chestnut to blackish-brown, paler when dry, smooth, margin with white fibrils when young; gills distant, ± cap colour; stipe thinnish, ± flexuose, base pallid, sl. swollen; flesh dark brown. Boggy ground, esp. under birch and alder; also under conifers. IX–XI. O.

There are a number of other similar small dark brown spp.

Cortinarius flexipes. (*T*). *Cap acutely umbonate, with white fibrils when young gills at first dark brown and tinged violaceus; characteristic Pelargonium smell.* Cap 1–3 cm, ± dark brown, campanulate conical; gills distant; stipe whitish flocculose to ring-like belt, apex and base often ± violet. On boggy ground in woods, esp. birch. IX–XI. O–F.

Cortinarius lucorum. J. Lge. (*T*). *Cap dull brown tinged flesh colour; stipe with pallid belt-like zone towards base.* Cap 5–10 cm, ± convex, somewhat dark spotted; gills rather distant, paler than cap; stipe stout, at first whitish with pale brownish tinge, finally greyish-brown base ± swollen. Usually in beech-woods. Not authentically known in this country.

Cortinarius hinnuleus. (*T*). *Cap ochre or tawny-brown; gills distant; characteristic gas-tar smell.* Cap 3–7 cm, convex to umbonate, dry state paler, esp. towards edge; gills ochre to cinnamon; stipe sl. paler than cap with white belt-like zone above middle; flesh ochre-brownish. Frondose woods, esp. oak and in grassy clearings on poor soil. VIII–XI. F–C.

Cortinarius glandicolor

Cortinarius armillatus

Cortinarius flexipes

Cortinarius lucorum

Cortinarius hinnuleus

Cortinarius saturatus J. Lge. (*H*). *Young cap ochre yellowish-brown, flesh thick; stipe without ring, base white.* Cap 5–9 cm, convex to umbonate, smooth, sl. shining, finally chestnut colour, but drying pale brown; gills broad, distant, sl. darker than cap; stipe short, stout, ± clavate, striate with colour of cap above; flesh ± cap colour, firm. Beech woods, gregarious or ± tufted. IX–X. R. (British record doubtful).

Cortinarius saturninus. (*H*). *Cap ± chestnut to sl. tawny; gills at first and stipe apex ± violet; ± tufted.* Cap 4–8 cm, dry, bluntly umbonate, margin with white silky fibrils; gills broad, rather distant, soon dark cinnamon; stipe ± clavate, whitish soon discolouring to pale brownish; flesh violet in stipe apex. Margins of woods and copses. IX–XI. F.

Cortinarius pulchellus. J. Lge. (*H*). *Small; cap ± conical, dark violet-brown; in bogs.* Cap 0.5–1 cm, dry, minutely fibrillose; gills rather distant, dark bluish violet; stipe slender, cap colour, but paler below; when young, whole fungus less brownish and more violet. Esp. under alder, ash and birch. Known from this country, but not yet recorded.

Cortinarius decipiens. (*H*). *Cap dark brown with purplish tinge, finally depressed round blunt umbo.* Cap 2–4 cm, at first ± conical, smooth, sl. whitish, silky fibrillose towards margin, umbo usually darker, whole cap drying paler; gills rather distant, broad, greyish lilac at first, later ochre cinnamon; stipe slender, flexuose, ± silvery shining, minutely fibrillose; flesh pale lilac-brown. Mainly under conifers, but also birch, elder. IX–XI. O.

Cortinarius saniosus. (*H*). *Cap acutely umbonate, yellowish brown; stipe with yellow fibrillose scales.* Cap 1–3 cm, campanulate or convex, later expanded, varying to pale rusty brown, margin yellowish fibrillose; gills rather distant ± cap colour; stipe slender, flexuose, pallid above, the yellow fibrils ± coating stipe up to irregular ring-like zone. In boggy copses and wood margins. IX–XI. O.

Cortinarius obtusus. (*H*). *Cap yellowish brown, finally ± umbonate, margin striate, stipe ± spindle-shaped.* Cap 1–4 cm, ± campanulate at first, then expanded, smooth, drying pale tan; gills ochre cinnamon, rather distant; stipe pale brown to almost white, silky, fibrillose, rooting, often compressed. Mainly conifer woods. IX–XI. O.

Rozites caperata. Pholiota. (Illustrated on endpapers.) Recognised by dull ochre colour, cap with filmy white scales, whitish ring and pale brown, rough spores. Woods, always on acid soils. VIII–XII. O.

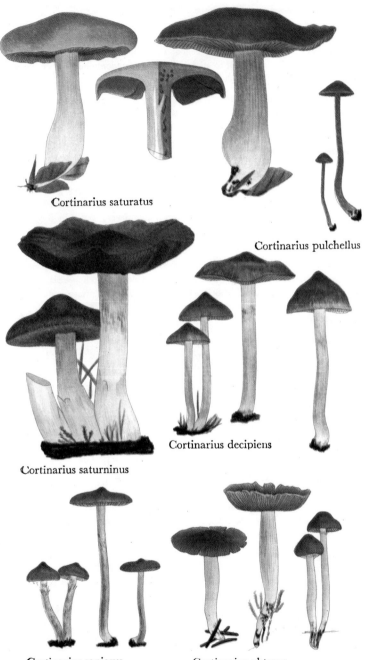

Cortinarius saturatus

Cortinarius pulchellus

Cortinarius saturninus

Cortinarius decipiens

Cortinarius saniosus

Cortinarius obtusus

173

Gymnopilus penetrans. Flammula. *Cap golden to rusty-brown; gills ± yellow, finally rusty spotted.* Cap 3–6 cm, convex, sl. umbonate, dry, smooth, minutely fibrillose, at first chrome-yellow; gills varying to tawny; stipe ± cap colour, sl. paler downwards, ring absent (but yellow veil when young); flesh yellowish, rusty in stipe, bitter. Attached to sticks, chips etc., predominantly in coniferous woods. VIII–XI. C.

Gymnopilus junonius. Pholiota spectabilis. *Cap ± golden-yellow, fibrillose; gills finally rusty-brown, ring membranous; tufted at base of frondose trunks.* Cap 6–12 cm, convex, sometimes minutely scaly, dry, varying to tawny-brown; gills crowded, narrow, at first yellow; stipe ± swollen in middle fibrillose sl. paler than cap, ring high up; flesh thick, firm, yellowish. IX—XI. O–F.

Phaeocollybia christinae (Fr.) Heim. Naucoria. *Cap shining tile-red, ± conical with mucronate umbo; stipe long rooting.* Cap 2–3 cm, somewhat viscid; gills narrow, tan, finally pale rusty; stipe slender, smooth, ± tinged cap colour, finally flushing rusty from base up. Coniferous woods. Never found here, but should occur.

Galerina. Galera

Galerina unicolor. Pholiota. *Moist cap date-brown with darker striate margin; ring membranous.* Cap 2–4 cm, convex, soon flattened, smooth, viscid, shining, margin ± chestnut, drying dull ochre-brown; gills rather narrow, pale brown; stipe pale above dark brown below ring. Often ± tufted on twigs or conifer stumps. IX–XI. O.

Galerina paludosa. *Dull honey-yellow; stipe with flocci up to distinct ring; on Sphagnum.* Cap 1–2 cm, convex to umbonate, smooth, sl. striate to about half-way, varying to brownish-yellow; gills rather distant and broad, at first tan, then cinnamon; stipe slender, flexuose, the membranous ring soon falling off. V–X. O–F.

Galerina hypnorum. *Small; wet cap pale yellow, striate almost to centre; stipe smooth.* Cap 0.5 to 1 cm, convex to campanulate, smooth; gills ± cap colour, broad, distant; stipe very delicate, often curved, pallid, pale rusty-brown downwards. Among moss in woods. heaths and bogs. VII–XI. C.

Galerina mycenopsis. *Viscid; wet cap coarsely striate to half-way; ± vivid ochre brownish; stipe tall, with silky fibrils when young.* Cap 1–2 cm, bell-shaped to ± convex, drying out pale yellow; gills rather broad, ± cap colour; stipe sl. flexuose, the white fibrils also covering young cap but soon disappearing; flesh very fragile. Among moss in damp places of coniferous woods. VIII–XI. F.

Galerina rubiginosa forma **major** J. Lge. *Moist cap ± amber-yellow with darker striations; stipe ± rusty brown, smooth but powdery apex.* Cap 1–3 cm, ± bell-shaped to convex; gills rather broad, soon dull rusty-brown. In moss on stumps. Neither type nor forma authentically recorded from this country.

Gymnopilus penetrans

Gymnopilus junonius

Phaeocollybia christinae

Galerina hypnorum

Galerina unicolor

Galerina rubiginosa
forma major

Galerina paludosa

Galerina mycenopsis

Phaeomarasmius erinaceus. Pholiota. *Cap yellowish rusty-brown with erect pointed scales; on branches.* Cap 0.5–1 cm, convex flattened, dry; gills rather distant, pale brown; stipe brown, scaly like cap, except smooth apex. Often in small groups. VIII–XI. O.

Phaeomarasmius (Flocculina) carpophilus. Naucoria. *Cap ± ochre-tan, mealy; on beech leaves and mast.* Cap 0.5–1 cm, ± convex to expanded, margin with remnants of veil; gills broad, distant, cap-colour; stipe tall, slender, densely mealy. V–X(XI). R–O.

Tubaria furfuracea. *Cap soon ± flat, clay-brown, margin with white flocci; gills sl. decurrent.* Cap 1–3 cm, convex at first, pellucid, striate, the marginal flocci soon disappearing; stipe paler than cap, smooth or with indistinct ring zone; flesh fragile. On soil, sticks, in gardens, parks, fields, wood. I–XII. C.

Ripartites tricholoma. *Cap whitish, margin ± ciliate; gills clay-brown, decurrent.* Cap 1–4 cm, convex, soon ± funnel-shaped, smooth or sl. grooved, varying to pale clay colour; gills narrow, pale at first; stipe whitish, flushing brownish upwards; flesh pallid. On ground, mostly under conifers. IX–XI. O.

Crepidotus

More or less bracket-shaped; stipe present or absent; spores ± clay-brown.

Crepidotus variabilis. *Small; ± kidney-shaped, silky white; on sticks.* Cap 0.5–2 cm, dry, margin incurved, minutely tomentose; gills rather distant, white, finally pale cinnamon; stipe lateral and very short, or absent and then attached by upper surface of cap, gills facing upwards; flesh fragile. I–XII. C.

Crepidotus mollis. *Cap finally pale yellowish-brown, spongy from thick gelatinous cuticle; on stumps.* Cap 1–5 cm ± shell-shaped, smooth, cream colour at first, drying ± whitish; gills crowded, pallid, finally dull pale cinnamon, sometimes ± spotted; stipe rudimentary, lateral, tomentose. On frondose wood, often imbricate. VII–XI. C.

Crepidotus autochthonus. *Cap greyish-white, silky-fribrillose; on soil.* Cap 2–6 cm, kidney shaped, margin incurved, and minutely tomentose; gills crowded, soon dull clay-brown; stipe rudimentary or absent, whitish tomentose; flesh without gelatinous layer. IX–X. O.

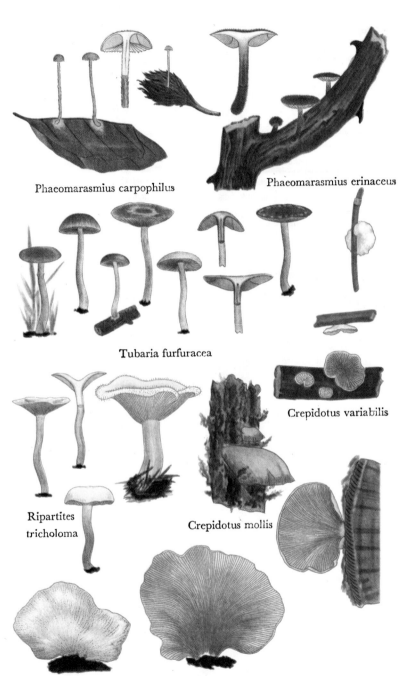

Phaeomarasmius carpophilus

Phaeomarasmius erinaceus

Tubaria furfuracea

Crepidotus variabilis

Ripartites
tricholoma

Crepidotus mollis

Crepidotus autochthonus

Clitopilus prunulus. *Cap white, with "feel" of a kid glove; gills finally dirty pinkish, decurrent; strong smell of new meal.* Cap 3–8 cm, convex, finally ± depressed, dry, smooth; gills pale cream at first; stipe usually short, sometimes eccentric, greyish white; flesh soft. Woods generally, on soil. VII–XI. C. *Edible and good.*

Rhodophyllus

A large genus with a wide species range, all having salmon-coloured spores colouring the gills at maturity; under the microscope, the spores are polygonal and angular or wavy-nodulose. The species are all terrestial. See footnote[1] on page 180.

Rhodophyllus (Entoloma) porphyrophaeus. *Cap umbonate, radially fibrillose, grey to purplish-brown with ± pale pink tinge; gills at first white.* Cap 3–8 cm, ± campanulate, then expanded; gills emarginate; stipe tall, fibrillose-striate, sl. paler than cap and more purplish-pink, base white. Among grass, esp. meadows by frondose trees. V–XI. O–F.

Rhodophyllus (Entoloma) nitidus. *Cap and stipe ± indigo-blue.* Cap 3–6 cm, ± conical-umbonate, fibrillose, sometimes minutely scaly at middle, dry; gills at first white, rather broad, emarginate; stipe straight, ± rooting, fibrillose to striate, paler below. On wet peaty soil, often under birch. VII–XI. O.

Rhodophyllus (Entoloma) prunuloides. *Cap ivory-white, umbonate, sl. viscid and shining.* Cap 5–10 cm, smooth, middle often ± cracked or scaly, margin sometimes split; gills broad, crowded, cream colour at first; stipe usually rather short, white, almost smooth; flesh white, firm, sl. mealy smell. Grassy slopes, gardens. VI–X. R–O.

Rhodophyllus (Entoloma) sinuatus, lividus. *Cap ± dull pale greyish ochre, ± expanded umbonate; gills at first yellowish.* Cap 7–12 cm, smooth, usually wavy-sinuate, sl. viscid, shining; gills broad, rather distant, almost free; stipe usually short, curved, silky-white, apex powdery; flesh thick, white, firm, faint smell of new meal or cucumber. In open frondose woods, esp. beech, oak. VIII–XI. O–F. *Poisonous, but not deadly.*

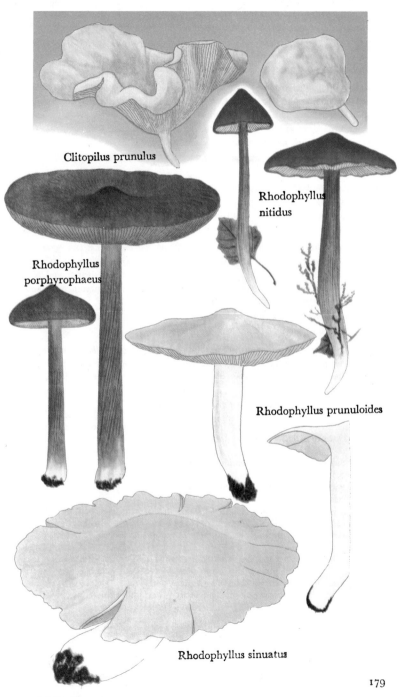

Clitopilus prunulus

Rhodophyllus
nitidus

Rhodophyllus
porphyrophaeus

Rhodophyllus prunuloides

Rhodophyllus sinuatus

179

G.M.T. M

Rhodophyllus (Entoloma) dichrous. *Cap mouse-greyish brown; stipe greyish-violet.* Cap 3–6 cm, expanded ± umbonate, minutely scaly and darker at middle, ± fibrillose towards edge; gills at first pale, rather distant, broad; stipe stoutish, greyish-violet with brownish-black fibrillose squamules; flesh greyish-violet with sweetish smell. In grass by margins of frondose woods. VII–X. O.

Rhodophyllus (Nolanea) sericeus. Entoloma. *Cap ± bistre, silky-shining; smell and taste mealy; in grass.* Cap 2–6 cm, convex, expanded, sl. umbonate, innately fibrillose, margin often split, colour paler on drying; gills at first pallid, rather broad, distant; stipe usually thin, fibrillose, paler than cap; flesh pale grey. Esp. lawns, meadows, grassy roadsides. V–X. C.

Rhodophyllus (Entoloma) clypeatus. *Cap ± greyish to yellowish-brown, often streaked with darker lines or spots; stipe rather thick.* Cap 5–10 cm, campanulate, expanded, ± umbonate, margin wavy, hygrophanous; gills at first pale grey; stipe often short and curved, sl. off-white, ± fibrillose; flesh rather thick, whitish with faint mealy smell. In small clusters on rich soil in gardens, under hedges, etc. IV–VI (IX–X). F.

Rhodophyllus (Entoloma) aprile. *Moist cap dull date-brown, umbonate, margin striate, stipe striate, tall.* Cap 3–6 cm, convex, expanded, silky-grey when dry (right-hand illustration, which is too yellowish); gills rather distant and broad, pale grey at first; stipe slender, whitish to pale grey; flesh firm, somewhat hollow in stipe, pale grey, smell faint. In frondose copses. IV–V. O. *Rhodophyllus (Entoloma) nidorosus* is a somewhat similar but autumnal species having a fairly distinct nitrous smell.

Rhodophyllus (Nolanea) staurosporus. *Moist cap ± date-brown, margin striate to half-way; spores quadrangular-stellate.* Cap 2–4 cm, parabolic, yellowish-brown when dry and then not striate; gills at first off-whitish; stipe slender, straight, striate, sl. paler than cap, base white tomentose; flesh without smell or taste. In moss and grass in pastures and clearings of woods. VI–X. F–C.

The genus *Rhodophyllus* was divided by Fries into four sub-genera, regarded by some authorities as independent genera. In the following Key, the genus *Claudopus* has been included as it, also, has deep salmon-pink ± polygonal spores.

1. Small, with excentric or lateral stipe—*Claudopus.*
1. Stipe central, 2.
2. Rather small, cap depressed or umbilicate, gills ± decurrent —*Eccilia.*
2. Not so, 3.
3. Stipe slender often ± bluish (3–8 cm × 2–3 mm), polished, not fibrillose; cap finally convex (edge incurved when young), fibrillose squamulose, sometimes ± umbilicate; gill edge sometimes coloured—*Leptonia.*
3. Otherwise 4.
4. Like *Mycena:* cap thin, conical or campanulate, often striate when moist; gills ascending under cap, stipe slender, less than 5 mm diam., coloured inside or outside (not bluish)—*Nolanea.*
4. Like *Tricholoma:* cap fleshy, convex to ± flat; gills sinuate (or emarginate); stipe usually more than 5 mm diam.—*Entoloma.*

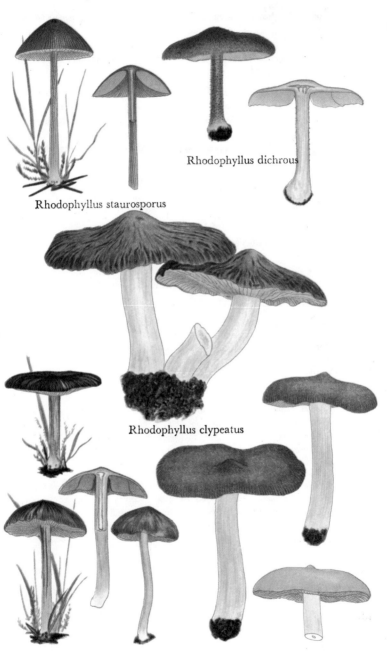

Rhodophyllus staurosporus

Rhodophyllus dichrous

Rhodophyllus clypeatus

Rhodophyllus sericeus

Rhodophyllus aprile

Rhodophyllus (Nolanea) cetratus. *Moist cap yellowish-tan, margin striate to half-way; coniferous woods.* Cap 2–4 cm, broadly conical to convex, disc often sl. depressed, shining, paler and non-striate when dry; gills rather broad, at first pale yellowish; stipe slender, striate, ± tinged with cap colour; flesh fragile, without distinct smell. Mostly among moss. IX–XI. C.

Rhodophyllus (Nolanea) icterinus. *Cap pale sulphur-yellow; smell variously described as oil of wintergreen, bananas, raspberries.* Cap 1–2 cm, ± convex, margin sl. striate; gills rather distant and broad, at first white; stipe shortish, sl. flexuose, smooth, apex powdery, pale yellowish-brown, darker towards base; flesh fragile. Solitary, on damp rich soil in copses and along paths in woods. VIII–XI. O.

Rhodophyllus (Leptonia) sericellus. Entoloma. *Mature cap sl. infundibuliform, ± very pale ochre; gills adnate.* Cap 0.5–2 cm, at first convex or flat, smooth or sl. squarrose; gills white at first, broad, distant, often with decurrent tooth; stipe short, thin, whitish; flesh fragile, smell faintly earthy. Grassy places on poor soils; wood clearings. VII–X. O–F.

Rhodophyllus (Leptonia) asprellus. *Cap bistre, disc blackish-blue, striate; gills grey at first; stipe ± blue.* Cap convex expanded, sl. depressed at disc; gills broad, rather distant, finally tinged pink; stipe slender, smooth, shining, sometimes ± flushed brownish. Wet meadows and pastures. Not authentically recorded in this country.

Rhodophyllus (Leptonia) lampropus, sensu J. Lge. *Cap and stipe typically dark blue; young gills white.* Cap 1–3 cm, ± convex expanded, minutely scaly to fibrillose, varying to brownish; gills broad, adnate, finally ± free; stipe slender, smooth, base whitish. Meadows and pastures. VIII–XI. O–F.

Among other blue *Rhodophyllus* species is *Rh.* (*Leptonia*) *euchrous* which grows on stumps esp. of alder and hazel.

Rhodophyllus (Leptonia) incanus. *Cap greenish-olive with brown streaks, finally ± umbilicate; stipe yellowish-greenish bruising ± bluish.* Cap 1–3 cm, convex, sl. striate, disc more brownish, sometimes sl. squarrose; gills at first whitish, sl. decurrent, distant, rather narrow; stipe short, thin, sometimes almost sulphur yellow. In grass; pastures and heaths. VIII–XI. O–F.

Rhodophyllus (Eccilia) undatus. Eccilia sericionitida. *Cap dull dark or paler grey-brown, ± zoned; gills decurrent.* Cap 1–3 cm, convex at first, later expanded and depressed in middle, minutely silky, fibrillose; gills rather narrow, dirty brown at first; stipe short, sl. flexuose, smooth, ± cap colour. Damp pastures and woodland bogs. IX–X. O.

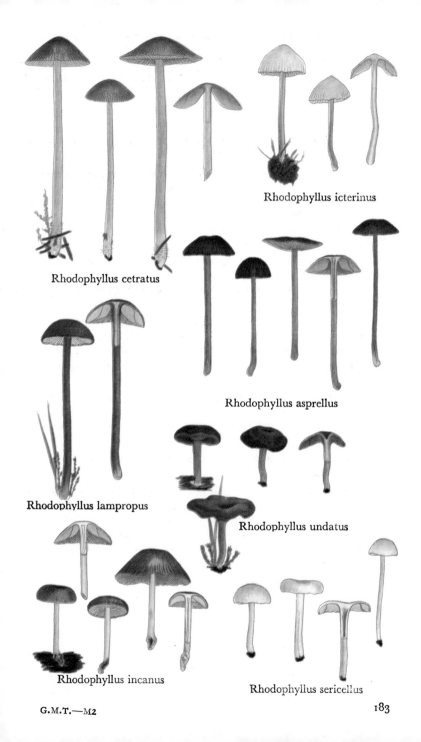

Rhodophyllus icterinus

Rhodophyllus cetratus

Rhodophyllus asprellus

Rhodophyllus lampropus

Rhodophyllus undatus

Rhodophyllus incanus

Rhodophyllus sericellus

Hygrophoropsis aurantiaca. Cantharellus. Clitocybe. *Cap orange-yellow; gills mostly forked.* Cap 3–7 cm, expanded—± funnel shaped, dry; gills decurrent, orange-red; stipe short, smooth, ± cap colour; flesh yellowish, rather tough. Spores dextrinoid. Coniferous woods; heaths. VIII–XI. C. *Edible.*

BOLETINEAE
Paxillus

Stipe ± central to lateral or absent, brownish; gills decurrent, ± anastomosing, easily pushed off from cap; spores ± ochre-brown.

Paxillus involutus. *Cap ± olive-brown, young edge incurved, woolly; gills bruising brown; stipe ± central and smooth.* Cap 5–12 cm, sl. viscid when moist, margin crenate; gills narrow, soft, yellowish, finally olive-yellow to dark clay-brown; stipe short, cap colour; flesh thick, soft, ± yellowish-brown. Mixed woods generally, esp. under birch. VIII–XI. C. *Harmless if cooked, of little value; slightly poisonous to some when raw.*

Paxillus atrotomentosus. *Cap ± sooty brown; stipe ± excentric, short, stout, densely black-velvety.* Cap 5–15 cm, convex to flattened, often ± excentric, sometimes with rufous tinge; gills crowded, decurrent, ochre-yellow; flesh whitish, firm, thick. On conifer stumps. VIII–XI. O–F.

Paxillus panuoides. *No stipe; cap bracket-like, olive-yellow.* Cap 3–8 cm, ± shell-shaped, irregular, dry, often with violet tinge; gills narrow, at first sl. paler than cap, finally ochre-yellow; flesh thin. Decayed conifer stumps, poles and sawdust; sometimes causes decay of softwoods in houses. VIII–XI. O–F.

Gomphidius rutilus, viscidus. *Cap viscid, brown with reddish tinge; flesh in base of stipe ± rhubarb-yellow; under pines.* Cap 4–10 cm, expanded minutely fibrillose-scaly, acutely umbonate, ± saffron towards edge; gills decurrent, broad, distant, brownish, finally dirty purplish; stipe paler than cap, apex with remnants of veil; flesh in cap reddish-yellow to pale tan. Usually solitary. VII–XI(XII). F.

G. roseus. (Illustrated on endpapers.) Cap deep rose-pink; esp. under young pines. VIII–XI. C.

Gomphidius glutinosus. *Cap slimy, greyish-violet; flesh in base of stipe light yellow; under conifers.* Cap 3–7 cm, convex, sl. depressed when older, smooth, often spotted; gills decurrent, narrow, distant, pale grey at first, finally blackish-grey; stipe stout, short, apex pale grey with slimy veil remains, greyish-brown and tapering downwards; flesh in cap thick, pale grey. Usually on poor soils. VII–XI. F–C.

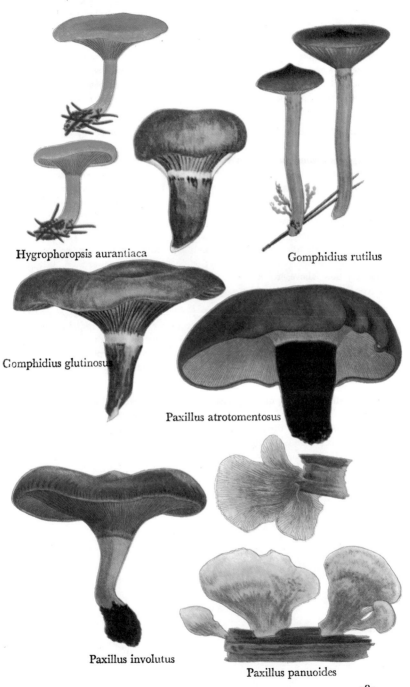

Hygrophoropsis aurantiaca

Gomphidius rutilus

Gomphidius glutinosus

Paxillus atrotomentosus

Paxillus involutus

Paxillus panuoides

Boletus

Fleshy terrestial (one parasitic on Scleroderma) toadstools with central stipe but with vertical tubes opening below by pores, in place of radiating gills. Formerly grouped with polypores, but true affinities with gill-fungi. At once distinguished from polypores by their tubes being easily and cleanly removable from the overlying cap flesh, which is not the case with polypores. The latter, too, are mostly bracket-like and attached to wood. Spores smooth, reticulate only in the genus Strobilomyces.

Boletus (Gyroporus) cyanescens. *Cap with pale brownish flocci on pale ochre ground; stipe finally cavernous.* Cap 5–10 cm, convex, dry; tubes and minute pores white, finally pale yellow, bruising blue; stipe stout, ventricose, tapering, smooth and whitish above, $\pm$ velvety and ochre downwards; flesh whitish, at once turning deep blue when cut. Woods on poor soil, esp. under spruce. VII–XI. R. *Edible and good.*

Boletus pulverulentus. *Cap reddish-brown, finally blackish; tubes pores and flesh of cap and upper stipe $\pm$ yellow, turning blackish-blue on bruising or cutting.* Cap 4–7 cm, convex flattened, dry, often lobed, minutely tomentose, yellow when very young; pores rather wide, finally olive-yellow; stipe tapering downwards, sl. velvety, orange-yellow above, reddish-brown downwards, flesh reddish towards stipe base. Damp frondose woods, esp. on calcareous soil. VIII–XI. O. *Edible.*

Boletus luteus. *Cap slimy, brownish to brownish-yellow with sl. tinge of purple; stipe with ring; under conifers.* Cap 5–10 cm, convex-expanded, $\pm$ radially streaked with darker lines; tubes at first covered by white membranous veil, pale yellow, finally yellowish-olive. Stipe yellow and $\pm$ granular above purple-brownish ring, white or brownish below; flesh pale yellow, unchangeable. Often in grass. VIII–XI. C. *Edible and good.*

Boletus elegans. *Cap slimy, $\pm$ light yellow; stipe with ring; under larch.* Cap 5–12 cm, convex later $\pm$ flat, sometimes tinged brownish esp. at disc; tubes sulphur-yellow finally dirty yellow; stipe tallish, brownish-yellow, $\pm$ punctate above the yellowish-white membranous ring; flesh rhubarb-yellowish, turning sl. lilac. III–XI. C. *Edible.*

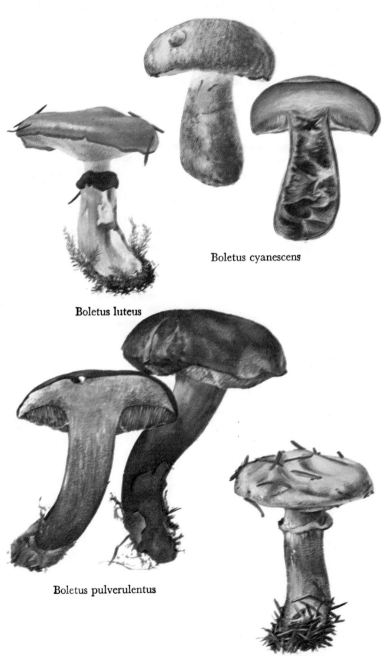

Boletus cyanescens

Boletus luteus

Boletus pulverulentus

Boletus elegans

187

Boletus bovinus. *Cap slimy, buff to reddish-buff; tubes ± decurrent, pores compound; no ring.* Cap 4–8 cm, ± convex to flat, often irregular; tubes finally olive-brown, the pores at surface divided into smaller pores below surface (compound); stipe shortish, tapering downwards, ± cap colour; flesh yellowish to pinkish, very faintly blueing. Under pines, sometimes in twos or threes. VII–XI. C.

Boletus granulatus. *Cap slimy, rufous-yellow; stipe apex granulate, ring absent.* Cap 5–10 cm, convex to expanded, smooth, shining; tubes and pores yellow, finally olive, at first oozing milky drops; stipe pale yellow; flesh yellowish, unchanging. Under conifers VIII–XI. F–C. × ½.

Boletus variegatus. *Cap dull yellowish-brown with soft darker scales.* Cap 6–12 cm, slimy in wet weather, broadly expanded; tubes pallid, finally brownish-olive, pores ± bluish when bruised; stipe stout, yellowish-brown above, brownish below, **dry**; flesh yellowish, reddish at base of stipe, turning somewhat blue in parts. Under conifers esp. pines on poor soil. VIII–XI. C.

Boletus piperatus. *Cap sl. slimy, yellowish-brown to cinnamon (usually less olive than illustration); base of stipe and mycelium bright yellow; taste peppery.* Cap 2–6 cm, convex to flattened; tubes tawny, pores coppery-reddish, wide, angular; stipe ± cinnamon upwards; flesh yellow, ± rhubarby in cap. In sandy, coniferous woods. VIII–XI. F. *Best avoided on account of the taste; not poisonous.*

Boletus subtomentosus. *Cap dry, tomentose, brownish-olive, often cracking, showing yellowish flesh; pores remaining bright, golden-yellow.* Cap 4–10 cm, flat-convex; pores rather coarse; stipe shortish, yellowish above, usually with sl. raised reddish ribs, more brownish and tapering downwards. Frondose woods. VIII–XI. C.

Boletus chrysenteron. *Cap dry, ± reddish-brown or with olive tint, often cracking to show red flush; pores finally dirty olive, slowly greening when bruised; stipe usually with reddish flesh.* Cap 4–10 cm, convex to flat, minutely tomentose; tubes finally dirty olive; stipe yellow above, paler at tapering base; flesh soft, red beneath cap cuticle, elsewhere ± yellowish and slowly turning light blue, finally ± reddish-buff. Mostly in frondose woods. The cap is sometimes almost red to reddish-purple, when it is known as *B. rubellus.* VIII–XI. C.

Boletus bovinus

Boletus granulatus

Boletus variegatus

Boletus piperatus

Boletus subtomentosus

Boletus chrysenteron

Boletus parasiticus. *Cap ± olive yellowish-brown; on Scleroderma.* Cap 2-6 cm, convex, often irregular, sl. tomentose, cracked; tubes and pores ± golden, finally dull olive-brown, often blotched red; stipe slender, curved, brownish-yellow; flesh yellow, reddish in stipe. Mostly on peaty ground; often under birch. IX–X. O.

Boletus badius. *Cap bay-brown; mature pores bruising greenish.* Cap 5–12 cm, convex, viscid, polished when dry, smooth; tubes and pores whitish at first, finally pale yellowish-green; stipe pale brown, ± striate, paler above, white and tomentose at base; flesh white to pale yellowish, turns faintly bluish esp. in yellowish flesh above tubes. Mostly under conifers. VIII–XI. C. *Edible and good.*

Boletus impolitus. *Cap clay colour to ± tawny-olive; pores yellow; stipe robust; flesh unchanging; smell unpleasant.* Cap 6–20 cm, hemispherical to convex, minutely tomentose-fibrillose; tubes sulphur-yellow gradually with orange tinge, small; stipe sl. paler than cap, here and there with reddish flush; flesh thick, white to cream, more sulphur above tubes and beneath cuticle of stipe. On clayey calcareous soil, often in grass under frondose trees. VI–X. O. $\times \frac{1}{2}$.

Boletus edulis. *Cap brownish, smooth; pores white to pale yellowish-green; stipe swollen, apex with white network of sl. raised veins.* Cap 6–20 cm, ± hemispherical, viscid at first; pores not bruising bluish; stipe pale brown; flesh white, firm, unchanging. Predominantly in frondose woods, esp. beech. A small, young specimen illustrated. (VIII) IX–XI. F–C. *Edible and excellent.* $\times \frac{1}{2}$

Boletus calopus. *Cap greyish; pores bruising greenish-blue; stipe ± scarlet, with white to pink network.* Cap 6–18 cm, convex, sometimes sl. tinged olive-brown, minutely tomentose; tubes and pores yellow; stipe ± robust, apex often yellow; flesh yellowish in cap, fading, turning blue in patches esp. in stipe, taste bitter. Frondose and coniferous woods. VIII–XI. O–F. *Not eaten on account of bitter taste but not poisonous.* $\times \frac{1}{2}$.

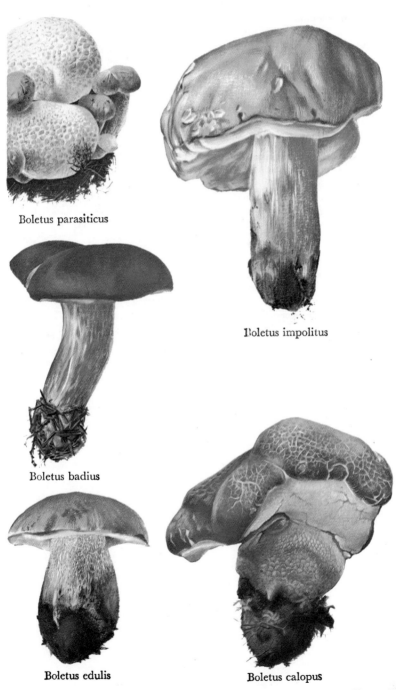

Boletus parasiticus

Boletus impolitus

Boletus badius

Boletus edulis

Boletus calopus

Boletus satanas (not illustrated) is a poisonous, but not deadly, species not unlike *B. calopus*. It has a greyish or grey-greenish cap, blood-red pores when mature, $\pm$ reddish swollen stipe, yellow at apex and base, red network of veins at apex; pores turn blue on touching, the white flesh becoming pale blue on cutting. It grows under frondose trees on calcareous soils. VII–X. R–O.

Boletus queletii. *Cap yellowish-brown to $\pm$ rufous; pores finally $\pm$ olive-brownish, blue-black on bruising; cut flesh turns greenish-blue, purplish-red in base of stipe.* Cap 5–15 cm, dry, minutely tomentose; young tubes and pores $\pm$ orange; stipe $\pm$ yellowish-brown above, $\pm$ flushed reddish-brown below; flesh $\pm$ yellow. Frondose woods on rich calcareous soil. VIII–X. R.

Boletus luridus. *Cap mostly brown with olive tinge; mature tubes green, pores $\pm$ orange-red; stipe covered by wide-mesh red network; flesh turning blue.* Cap 5–20 cm, convex, varying brown to almost rufous, dry, minutely tomentose; stipe yellowish, often red flushed; flesh yellowish, purplish-red above tubes, sometimes reddish-brown at base of stipe. Frondose woods and parks. VIII–XI. O. Cf. *B. satanas* and *B. calopus*.

Boletus erythropus. *Cap mostly dark brown; mature pores red, blue to touch; stipe densely red-punctate above; flesh turning blue.* Cap 5–20 cm, sometimes with reddish or olive tinge, minutely tomentose, dry; tubes yellow-green; stipe $\pm$ robust, ground colour yellowish obscured above by the red stippling; no net; flesh yellow. Woods generally, on poor soils. VIII–XI. F–C. *Edible.*

Boletus (Tylopilus) felleus. *Cap $\pm$ ochre to honey-colour; mature pores pink; stipe with network; flesh bitter, unchanging.* Cap 5–12 cm, convex, later $\pm$ expanded, sl. tomentose, dry; tubes and angular pores at first white, dirty brownish where touched; stipe sl. clavate, pale clay above, more olive-brownish below, the net wide-meshed and darker. Woods generally, more esp. coniferous. The pink pores, wide mesh net and very bitter taste separate it from *B. edulis*. VIII–XI. C.

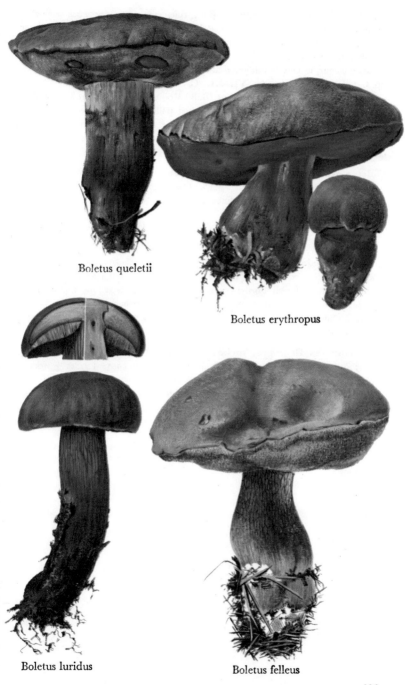

Boletus queletii

Boletus erythropus

Boletus luridus

Boletus felleus

Boletus testaceoscaber, versipellis p.p.; rufescens. *Cap ± yellowish or reddish-orange; striate stipe with black, scurfy scales.* Cap 8–25 cm, hemispherical, later convex, tomentose, dry; pores minute, round, finally pale dirty greyish-brown; cut flesh white, slowly (10 mins.) and unevenly turning dull dirty pinkish-lilac or ± slate colour, usually bluish-green at base of stipe; taste mild. Mainly a birch sp. but also in conifer woods. VII–XI. C. *Edible and good.* ×1

The closely related *B. aurantiacus* (Bull.) Roques, has a more brownish-red or brownish-orange cap, the stipe scales at first pallid and finally reddish-brown; cut flesh becomes slowly (10 mins.) slate-colour to black without bluish-green patches. Under aspen and birch, but much less common than previous species known, but not yet in British lists.

Boletus scaber. *Cap greyish to ± dark brown; striate stipe with brown to black scurfy scales; flesh unchanging or sl. pinkish.* Cap 6–20 cm, convex, tomentose then smooth; pores off-white to pale dingy buff, darker where touched; stipe tallish. Under birches. VII–XI. C.

B. holopus is a rather rare species of birch bogs and is ± wholly white with sl. greenish tinge.

Boletus (Gyrodon) lividus. *Cap viscid, yellowish; tubes shallow (1–3 mm), decurrent* Cap 4–8 cm, convex, finally irregularly flattened to depressed, smooth, ± radially streaked with brownish fibrils; pores and tubes bright yellow, finally olive-yellow; stipe usually short, often ± flexuose, sl. darker than cap; flesh yellowish, becoming faintly bluish above tubes, brownish-yellow in stipe. In alder swamps. IX.–XI. R.

Strobilomyces floccopus, strobilaceus. *Cap with coarse, blackish, overlapping scales; flesh becoming reddish, finally blackish.* Cap 8–15 cm, convex, scales ± woolly-fibrillose, pointed; pores at first covered by membranous veil, whitish then greyish, reddish on bruising; stipe with greyish-black floccose sheath to ring-like zone, pallid above and smooth. Frondose woods on rich soil; often under beech. IX.–XI. R–O, but may be locally frequent. Differs from all Boletus-like toadstools by its purple-brown reticulate spores. ×½.

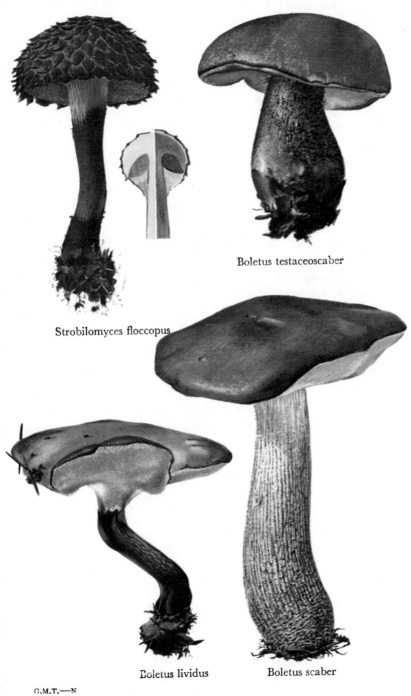

Strobilomyces floccopus

Boletus testaceoscaber

Boletus lividus

Boletus scaber

RUSSULINEAE

Russula

Medium to large species; cap ± flattened, often brightly coloured; gills white to egg-yellow, intermediate gills absent except in six species (these have white, brown or black ± depressed caps); stipe brittle, easily breaking transversely, becoming bright or dirty salmon-pink (" iron, Fe, reaction ") when rubbed with ferrous sulphate (" green vitriol ") crystal (a few important exceptions are noted below); spores (see footnote[1], page 198) white to egg-yellow; flesh yields no latex. Taste important in identifying species. See page 231.

Russula delica. *Cap dirty white, ± depressed, gills decurrent, with intermediates; flesh hard; Fe: slowly pinkish.* Cap 6–12 cm, ± funnel shaped with incurved margin, sl. tomentose, finally smooth, often rusty-brown spotted; gills narrow, often with glaucous glint, esp. at stipe apex; stipe stout, white or brownish, hard; flesh sl. acrid in gills; smell distinctive; spores almost white. Mixed woods. IX–XI. C.

Russula nigricans. *Cap white to brown, finally black; gills thick, with intermediates, distant; cut flesh becomes reddish in c. 5–10 mins.* Cap. 10–20 cm, convex to sl. funnel-shaped; gills ± straw colour, soon sooty-brown from edge inwards; stipe white, then brownish; flesh finally becomes black; Fe: dark olive; spores white. Mixed woods; but esp. frondose. VIII–XI, the black fruit bodies long persisting. C.

R. densifolia is rather similar but has crowded gills.

Russula claroflava. *Cap bright chrome or lemon-yellow; gills finally ± primrose colour; stipe white at first; soggy ground under birch.* Cap 6–12 cm, convex flattened, margin sl. striate; stipe sl. veined longitudinally, finally turns greyish and also where bruised; flesh white, mild, slowly turns grey. IX–XI. F–C. *Edible.*

Russula foetens. *Cap dirty yellowish, slimy, margin finally deeply furrowed and papillate; taste acrid, smell nauseous.* Cap 6–12 cm, at first almost globular, margin smooth, finally ± flat; gills dirty white, often brown spotted and beaded with drops; stipe whitish, stout, soon hollow; spores pale cream. Mixed woods. VIII–XI. F–C.

Russula fellea. *Cap dull ochre-yellow; gills and stipe pale honey colour; flesh bitter-acrid; characteristic smell of Pelargonium.* Cap. 3–7 cm, convex flattened, slippery, margin ± grooved and papillate when old; stipe firm, sl. flocculose above; flesh white; spores pale cream. Frondose woods, esp. beech. VIII–XI. C.

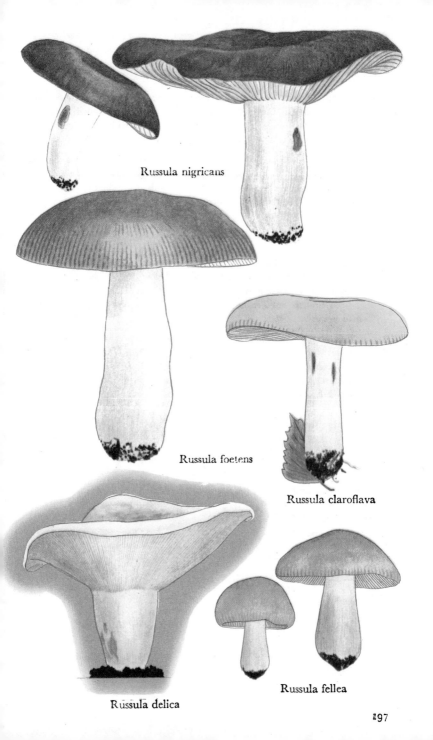

Russula nigricans

Russula foetens

Russula claroflava

Russula delica

Russula fellea

Russula ochroleuca. *Cap ± bright yellowish-ochre; gills and stipe white; flesh almost mild, no smell.* Cap 4–9 cm, convex flattened, smooth, slippery, margin sl. striate with age; stipe faintly but clearly reticulately veined and becoming pale greyish; spores pale cream. Woods generally. VIII–XI. C.

Russula solaris. *Cap lemon-yellow to bright yellow; gills finally ± straw colour; flesh acrid; beech woods.* Cap 3–6 cm, convex finally flattened and sl. depressed, smooth, slimy, often brighter at centre, margin striate with age; flesh white, fragile; spores deep cream. IX–XI. O.

Russula vesca. *Cap brownish-red to ± pinkish-buff, the cuticle in mature caps falls short of margin showing white flesh; flesh very firm; Fe: bright rusty; spores white.* Cap 4–8 cm, convex to flattened, smooth, sl. viscid; gills white finally often brown-spotted; stipe white ± rusty at pointed base; flesh reddish below cap cuticle, otherwise white. Frondose woods, esp. oak. VIII–XI. F–C. *Edible and good.*

Russula cyanoxantha. *Cap bluish-green to ± violet; Fe: no colour or very faintly olive.* Cap 5–12 cm, finally ± flattened and depressed, faintly radially veined, colours variable; gills white, elastic and greasy to touch; stipe white, sometimes flushed purplish; flesh firm, white, but reddish below cap cuticle, mild; spores white. Frondose woods esp. beech. VII–XI. F–C. *Edible and excellent.*

R. grisea is similar, but has creamy gills and spores and the iron reaction: pinkish to ± rusty.

Russula violeipes, amoena. *Cap lemon or peach colour and, like stem, often flushed violet; flesh firm, mild; smell characteristic, ± fruity; spores creamy.* Cap 4–8 cm, convex, finally flattened and ± depressed, minutely mealy or granular, like a " bloom "; gills sl. creamy, edge sometimes purplish. Mixed woods, often beech. IX–XI. O. *Edible.*

---

[1] To judge the colour of spores, a *thick fresh* spore print on white paper is required. It should be scooped up and pressed down with a cover slip. Matching is done against Crawshay's code (Pearson 1950): 8 grades A–H, from white through cream and ochre to egg-yellow. The code letters (which are given in the index to this book) and examples from easily recognised *Russula* spp. are:

White or whitish. A to A++
A. *R. emetica, cyanoxantha*
A. + +. *R. ochroleuca*

Creamy. B–D
B. *R. lepida, rosea*
C. *R. violeipes, sanguinea*
D. *R. foetens*

Ochre E–F
E. *R. xerampelina*
F. *R. claroflava, versicolor*

Egg-yellow G–H
G. *R. olivacea,*
H. *R. aurata*

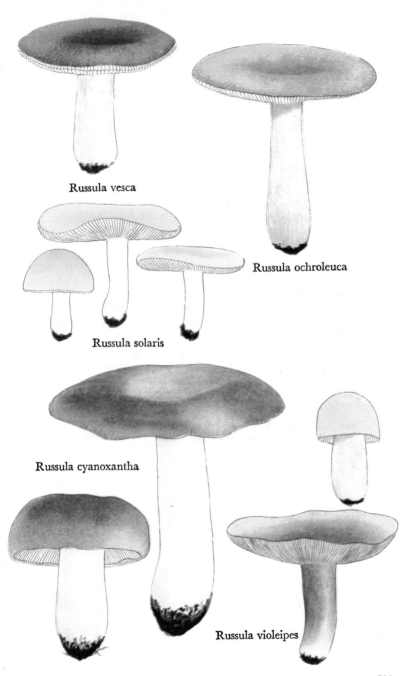

Russula vesca

Russula ochroleuca

Russula solaris

Russula cyanoxantha

Russula violeipes

Russula virescens. *Cap ± verdigris green, cuticle ± coarsely mealy, soon cracking; spores whitish.* Cap 7–12 cm, rounded, soon ± flattened, flesh white between cracks; gills white, crowded, narrow; stipe white, short, sl. tapering downwards; flesh hard, white, spongy in stipe, mild. Frondose woods esp. beech. VIII–XI. F–C. *Edible and good.*

Russula sanguinea. *Cap ± scarlet; stipe pink flushed; flesh bitter, acrid; under conifers.* Cap 3–10 cm, convex, sl. depressed at middle, margin smooth; gills crowded, narrow, ± ivory-white, later yellow-spotted, sl. decurrent; stipe tapering below; flesh white; spores cream colour. VIII–XI. O.

Russula lepida. *Cap and stipe deep rose-red; flesh hard, taste almost mild; cap cuticle with white " bloom "; not peeling.* Cap 4–8 cm, finally convex flattened, dry, somewhat fading; gills narrow, white, free; flesh white, smell characterstic, ± cedar wood, white spores; s.v. (see page 231): nil. Frondose woods, esp. beech. VIII–XI. C.

R. rosea is very similar, grows in beech woods, but has white stipe and cap cuticle peeling to about half-way, and the flesh is spongy; s.v.: red ink colour.

Russula xerampelina. *Cap purple-red to brown; characteristic crab-lobster smell when adult; Fe: deep olive-green.* Cap 5–12 cm, ± convex to expanded, depressed at middle, viscid soon dry, margin finally ± grooved; gills cream to pale ochre; stipe somewhat reticulately veined, white or ± red, stains yellowish-brown. Very variable, esp. cap colour: at once identified by iron reaction. Woods generally. VIII–XI. C. *Edible.*

Russula puellaris. *Small, fragile; cap purple-pink, margin grooved, stipe yellowish; flesh mild.* Cap 3–5 cm, soon ± flat and depressed at middle; gills white finally pale yellow, rather distant; stipe slender, ± veined; flesh (and whole fungus) tends to become suffused with wax-yellow colour; spores pale cream. Mostly under conifers. VIII–XI. F–C. *Too small to be worth eating.*

R. versicolor is very similar, but usually has ± greenish flush at cap middle; flesh ± acrid, at least in gills; ochre spores and grows in damp ground under birches, occasionally alders.

Russula xerampelina

Russula sanguinea

Russula lepida

Russula virescens

Russula puellaris

Russula atropurpurea. *Cap purplish-red, $\pm$ black at middle; gills white, stipe white, rusty at base; flesh almost mild; spores sl. off white.* Cap 5–10 cm, sl. convex to $\pm$ flat or depressed at middle, often becoming mottled with yellow; gills often rusty spotted, sl. decurrent; stipe usually grey with age; flesh white, sometimes $\pm$ acrid in young specimens. Mainly under frondose trees. VII–XI. C. *Edible, but rather dry and somewhat bitter.*

Russula emetica. *Fragile; cap $\pm$ pure scarlet (no other colour); cuticle peels completely showing $\pm$ reddish flesh; gills and spores pure white; flesh very acrid.* Cap 6–9 cm, $\pm$ convex, soon expanding and often sl. depressed, margin $\pm$ grooved; stipe usually longer than cap diam., white. Under conifers. VIII–XI. C. *May cause vomiting raw; harmless when cooked; best avoided.*

Russula mairei. *Very similar to R. emetica; confined to beech woods.* Cap 3–7 cm, cuticle usually only half-peeling, showing white flesh; stipe not exceeding cap diam; faint honey smell. VIII–XI. C. *Inedible.*

R. fragilis is similar, but has cap 2–5 cm, with purplish middle and jagged edge to gills (lens); when adult, the cap usually shows a faint olive tinge.

Russula queletii. *Cap wine-red to purplish-violet; gills finally cream to creamy-grey; stipe $\pm$ wine-red; flesh acrid; no ammonia reaction; conifers.* Cap 4–8 cm, often $\pm$ umbonate, sl. viscid at first, finally often $\pm$ spotted and with dirty olive flush; gills white at first; stipe minutely powdery; flesh white, pink under cuticle; spores pale creamy ochre. VIII–XI. C. *Inedible.*

The rather similar *R. sardonia* (*R. drimeia*), a pine wood species, is easily distinguished by stipe, flesh and esp. gills becoming $\pm$ bright red on treatment with 50% ammonium hydroxide solution. The reaction should occur within 15 mins.

Russula aeruginea. *Cap grass-green, gills and spores creamy; taste mild; under birch.* Cap 6–9 cm, soon $\pm$ depressed towards centre, margin soon $\pm$ grooved; stipe white. All parts tend to become brownish-spotted. VIII–XI. F–C. *Edible.*

Russula nitida, venosa. *Cap colours variable: usually $\pm$ wine-red and darker towards centre; margin deeply furrowed; under birch, often in Sphagnum; taste mild.* Cap 3–5 cm, flesh thin, cuticle peeling $\pm$ completely; gills cream colour, transversely veined; stipe white, clavate, $\pm$ flushed pink, soon hollow. VIII–XI. F–C.

Russula emetica

Russula aeruginea

Russula mairei

Russula atropurpurea

Russula queletii

Russula nitida

Russula paludosa. *Cap mostly ± shining brick-red; stipe usually longer than cap diam. and with rusty flesh; taste mild; wet places under conifers.* Cap 8–12 cm, convex to flattened, sometimes ± brownish or mixed colours, finally sl. grooved at margin; gills broad and distant finally cream colour, edge often reddish; stipe stout; flesh white, not greying, sl. honey smell when old. Spores creamy-yellow. Mostly in *Sphagnum.* VIII–XI. O, esp. Scotland.

In similar localities is *R. obscura* with more purplish cap and flesh which turns greyish to black. *Both species are edible.*

Russula decolorans. *Brick to orange red; flesh mild, greying with age; under conifers.* Cap 5–15 cm, semi-globate and sl. viscid when young, finally ± flattened-depressed, and colours may fade to yellowish; gills crowded, bi-furcate at stipe, finally creamy; stipe often tall and stout, striate and ± rough, white later greying; flesh of old specimens almost black. Mainly boggy areas; commoner in Scotland. VIII–XI. R–O.

Russula olivacea. *Cap mixed reddish, brownish-red, sometimes ± olive-brownish; gills finally (and spores) deep egg-yellow; stipe apex (at least) flushed deep pink; flesh mild; stipe purplish-red in 10–15 minutes with phenol water; beech woods.* Cap 8–15 cm, soon ± depressed often ± concentrically colour zoned, edge paler; gills broad, distant; stipe stout, soon spongy; flesh commonly worm infested. VIII–XI. C. *Edible.*

Russula aurata. *Cap orange to reddish-yellow; gill edge bright chrome-yellow; flesh mild.* Cap 6–9 cm, finally ± convex to depressed, sometimes with golden patches; gills finally (apart from edges) pale yellow; stipe stout, white, stained yellowish esp. towards base; flesh white, orange-yellow below cuticle. Spores egg-yellow. Beech woods. VIII–XI. O. *Edible and good.*

Russula nauseosa. *Cap thin, ± pale pinkish-purple-brownish; gills finally and spores deep egg-yellow; taste mild.* Cap 3–6 cm, soon flattened or sl. depressed, darker towards centre, cuticle peels easily, often fading to pale yellowish-brown; gills distant, may taste sl. acrid; stipe white, slender, sl. veined; flesh spongy. Damp ground under conifers. VIII–XI. F–C.

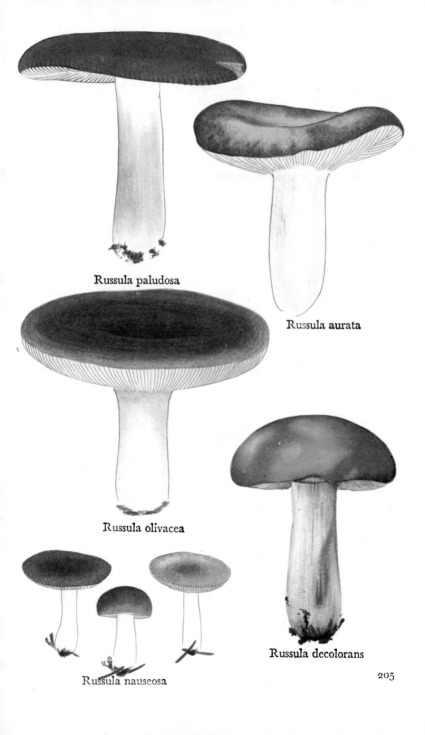

Russula paludosa

Russula **aurata**

Russula olivacea

Russula nauseosa

Russula decolorans

205

Lactarius

Fleshy species, yielding a serous, white or coloured milk where broken; spores white to deep cream. Taste important in identifying species.

Lactarius volemus. *Cap bright tawny-orange; gills bruising ± brownish, taste mild.* Cap 7–11 cm, convex to sl. depressed, paler towards margin, dry, usually ± cracked; gills cream colour, weakly decurrent; stipe smooth, ± cap colour below, whitish pruinose above; flesh firm, yellowish-white, smells of herring when old; milk white, abundant. Mixed woods. VIII–XI. O–F. *Edible.*

Lactarius fuliginosus. (Larger, right-hand illustration.) *Cap dark sooty-brown, dry, shortly velvety; flesh, but not milk, turns slowly (c. 5 mins.) pinkish-rose.* Cap 4–10 cm, soon ± depressed, sometimes with central papilla, margin often crenate; gills decurrent, cream then ochre-yellow; stipe tapering downwards ± tinged brownish; flesh sl. acrid. Frondose woods. VIII–XI. F.

A similar, more slender fungus with *white* stipe is *L. azonites* (left-hand illustration); also in frondose woods.

Lactarius vellereus. *Cap white, velvety; gills distant, pale ochre; stipe short; milk white, very acrid.* Cap 10–20 cm, convex with incurved margin, finally depressed at middle, and ± brownish stained; gills weakly decurrent; stipe velvety, stout; flesh white, firm. Frondose woods, often in groups. IX–XI. C.

Lactarius piperatus. *Cap white, tinged creamy, smooth; gills very crowded; milk-white, very acrid.* Cap 6–15 cm, margin long remaining incurved, finally ± funnel-shaped, often spotted brownish; gills ± decurrent, dichotomous, creamy-yellow with age; stipe almost as high as cap diam., stout; flesh firm. Frondose woods. VIII–XI. O.

Lactarius glyciosmus. *Cap greyish-lilac; gills ± yellowish; strong smell of coconut; under birch.* Cap 2–6 cm, soon ± depressed with central papilla, often ± minutely scaly; gills ± decurrent, sometimes tinged greyish-lilac; stipe cap colour but paler; milk white, soon ± acrid. Wettish ground. VIII–XI. C.

L. mammosus, with virtually the same coconut smell, has a brownish-bistre cap, but is otherwise rather similar. It grows under conifers and is very much less frequent.

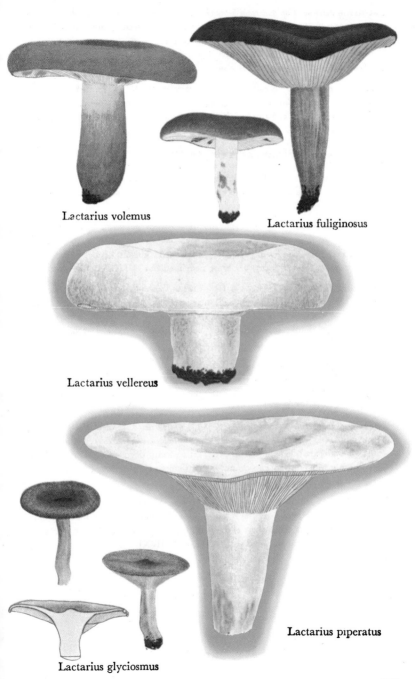

Lactarius volemus

Lactarius fuliginosus

Lactarius vellereus

Lactarius glyciosmus

Lactarius piperatus

Lactarius rufus. *Cap dull reddish-brown, papillate; milk white, very acrid in c. 45–60 seconds; under pines.* Cap 4–8 cm, convex, finally ± depressed, minutely tomentose when young, soon glabrous; gills decurrent, crowded yellowish, finally pale yellowish-rufous, often spotted; stipe ± cap colour, whitish at base. VIII–XI. C. Sometimes the cap papilla is absent. *Inedible.*

Lactarius cyathula. *Small; cap rufous chestnut, finally ± saucer-shaped, margin striate; under alder.* Cap 1–3 cm; gills pallid, finally ± cap colour; stipe pallid at first, flushing dark rufous from base up; flesh thin; milk white, scanty, mild. Wet ground. IX–XI. O–F.

Lactarius camphoratus. *Smallish; cap deep rufous; milk sl. sweetish, almost watery; characteristic ± curry-powder smell when moribund or after drying.* Cap 2–4 cm, usually papillate, finally ± depressed; gills decurrent, paler than cap; stipe ± cap colour or darker. When old, gills and stipe have purplish tint. Mainly under conifers or where conifers have been. VIII–XI. C.

Lactarius helvus. *Cap uniformly pale cinnamon to milk-coffee colour, ± felty-squamulose; smell sweet, ± of new-mown hay; milk watery-white, scanty; tasteless.* Cap 6–10 cm, dry, convex-expanded, ± depressed; gills and stipe finally ± cap colour or paler. Wet places, under or near conifers. VIII–X. O. *Inedible.*

Lactarius fulvissimus. *Cap ± orange rufous, paler at margin, dull or somewhat varnished, dry, smooth; stipe stout; white milk mild; spores deep cream.* Cap 4–7 cm, expanded to depressed; gills narrow, pale rufous, ± decurrent; stipe scarcely as long as cap diam., tapering, same colour as cap. Frondose woods, esp. on chalky soil. VIII–X. O (or overlooked).

Lactarius mitissimus. *Cap uniformly bright orange-reddish-yellow; white milk mild or sl. bitter; under conifers.* Cap 4–8 cm, expanded-depressed, umbonate, dry, margin wavy; gills ± decurrent; gills pale pinkish-ochre; stipe slender, cap colour. IX–XI. O–F.

Lactarius tabidus. *Cap ± yellowish-buff, puckered round central papilla, margin ± striate when moist; milk on handkerchief turns yellow in c. 60 seconds; taste ± mild.* Cap 2–4 cm, expanded and depressed; gills weakly decurrent, paler than cap; stipe usually longer than cap diam., ± cap colour. Frondose woods; often in *Sphagnum* under birch. VIII–XI. C.

Lactarius subdulcis. *Cap ± pinkish-tan, margin never striate; white milk, never turns yellow on handkerchief, mild to sl. bitterish.* Cap 3–6 cm, convex then expanded and depressed; gills paler than cap, ± decurrent; stipe pale at first, darkening from base up. Frondose woods, esp. beech. VIII–XI. C.

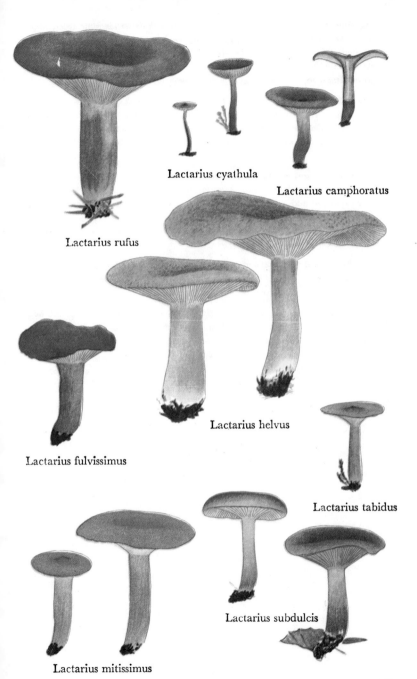

Lactarius cyathula

Lactarius camphoratus

Lactarius rufus

Lactarius fulvissimus

Lactarius helvus

Lactarius tabidus

Lactarius subdulcis

Lactarius mitissimus

Lactarius quietus. *Cap dull reddish liver-brown with darker concentric zones; faint, characteristic sweetish oily smell; strictly confined to oaks.* Cap 4–8 cm, convex, finally expanded and ± depressed; gills whitish, then ± cap colour but paler; stipe ± longitudinally furrowed, soon flushing cap colour but darker from base up; milk mild or almost so, white or tinged ± primrose. IX–XI. C.

Lactarius torminosus. *Cap ± pinkish flesh colour, with whitish concentric zones, margin incurved and very woolly-shaggy when young; milk white, acrid.* Cap 5–10 cm, convex expanded to ± depressed; gills tinged flesh colour; stipe about as long as cap diam., and ± same colour as cap. Mixed woods and heaths. VIII–XI. C. *Inedible.*

Lactarius pyrogalus. *Cap greyish-brown or yellowish-brown, usually with violaceous tinge; mature gills deep ochre; milk white, very acrid; under hazel.* Cap 4–8 cm, finally expanded and ± depressed, sl. viscid; gills decurrent; stipe dry, pale but tinged cap colour. A drop of milk on a slide turns ± deep orange-yellow with 10% potassium hydroxide. Cf. *L. circellatus* on next page. In rich soil. IX–XI. F. *Inedible.*

Lactarius pallidus. *Uniformly pale tan, sometimes with sl. flesh tinge; milk white, bitterish to sl. acrid; under beeches.* Cap 6–12 cm, soon ± flat and sl. depressed, viscid; gills crowded, narrow; stipe stout, smooth, firm. VII–XI. F. *Inedible.*

Lactarius resimus. *Large; cap and gills ± yellowish; milk bitterish, quickly turns yellowish.* Cap 10–15 cm, convex and ± deeply depressed, viscid, sl. spotted towards incurved ± tomentose (at least when young) margin; gills narrow, decurrent, yellowish; stipe short, thick, pale, cut flesh over gills at once turns yellow. Coniferous and birch woods. VIII–X. R.

L. scrobiculatus is very similar, but has the stipe pitted with deep yellow drop-like spots.

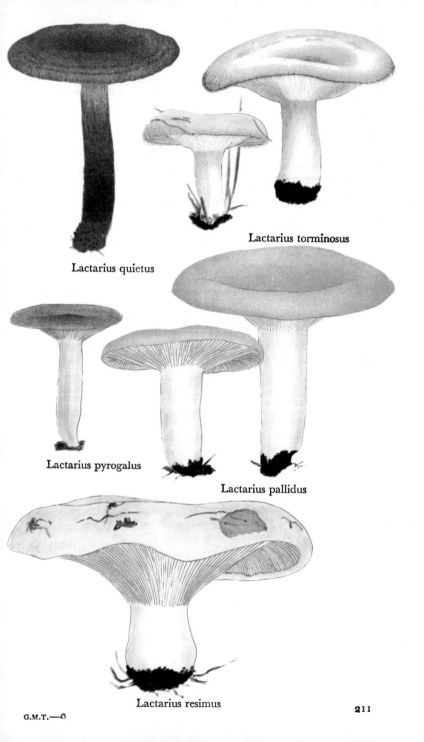

Lactarius quietus

Lactarius torminosus

Lactarius pyrogalus

Lactarius pallidus

Lactarius resimus

Lactarius repraesentaneus. *Cap yellow; margin woolly-shaggy, stipe pitted; flesh violet on bruising; milk faintly bitterish.* Cap 9–16 cm, convex, centre ± depressed, viscid and innately scaly; gills pale clay colour becoming dirty violaceous where bruised; stipe attenuated downwards, ± rooting, same colour as cap; flesh firm, smell like wild thyme, milk pale primrose. Boggy places near conifers, mainly Scotland. VIII–X. R. *Not recommended for eating.*

Lactarius vietus. *Cap dull greyish to purplish-brown; acrid white milk turns grey on gills in c. 15–30 mins.; under birches.* Cap 4–8 cm; viscid, expanded to sl. depressed; gills white, finally pale ochre, crowded; stipe pallid, ± tinged cap colour above, more ochrey below. Wet ground. (Most British specimens are more greyish than the illustration.) VIII–XI. C. *Inedible.*

Lactarius uvidus. *Cap ± dull greyish with faint lilac flush; bruised or cut flesh turns blue-lilac; flesh almost tasteless.* Cap 4–10 cm, ± viscid, convex, finally ± saucer-shaped; gills crowded, white, finally dirty pale yellow; stipe pallid, soon ± flushed ochre from base up; milk white, unchanging. Damp woods on poor soil, esp. under birch. VIII–XI. O.

L. *flavidus* also bruises blue-lilac, but the cap is ivory to straw-yellow in colour.

Lactarius blennius. *Cap olive-brown to greenish, ± zoned with concentric drop-like spots; taste very acrid.* Cap 4–10 cm, convex depressed, viscid; gills white, bruising dirty grey; stipe stoutish, ± cap colour; milk white, greying on exposure to air. Frondose woods, esp. beech. VIII–XI. C. *Inedible.*

L. *circellatus* is similar but has zoned cap and ochre yellow gills and grows under hornbeams. (Also, a drop of milk on a slide is virtually unchanged when mixed with a drop of 10% KOH, thus differing from *L. pyrogalus* as noted on previous page.)

Lactarius turpis. *Cap olive-brownish-yellow, margin shaggy and inrolled when young; white milk very acrid; under birches.* Cap 6–14 cm, expanded to ± depressed, viscid, sometimes almost blackish, margin mostly yellowish-olive; gills crowded, decurrent, dirty yellowish, soon greyish-spotted, edge brown; stipe stout, tapering, viscid, often pitted, paler than cap. Damp peaty ground. Ammonium hydroxide (50%), or any other alkali, gives a deep purple colour when applied to the cuticle. VIII–XI. C. *Inedible.*

Lactarius deliciosus. *Cap reddish-orange, ± zoned, finally staining greenish; milk mild, rapidly turns carrot colour; under conifers.* Cap 4–10 cm, convex to depressed, sl. viscid or dry, margin incurved; gills and stipe ± cap colour also flushing or spotted greenish. VIII–XI. F. *Edible; best after washing.*

Lactarius blennius

Lactarius vietus

Lactarius uvidus

Lactarius blennius

Lactarius deliciosus

Lactarius repraesentaneus

Lactarius turpis

Arcangeliella asterosperma. Octaviana. *Peridium whitish at first, becoming or bruising greenish, finally dirty brown; mature gleba purple dark brown; smell of cocoa.* Peridium 1–3 cm, irregular globose; gleba with numerous chambers, at first white. Beech woods on chalk, usually in humus. X. O–F.

Hymenogaster tener. *Peridium white, sl. discolouring, bruising reddish; gleba white, finally ± pinkish-grey, with distinct open chambers.* Peridium 0.5–2 cm, ovoid-lobed; smell ± pleasant, characteristic. In humus beneath litter of frondose woods, esp. oak, usually on calcareous soils. I–XII. F–C.
There are several similar species with clay-coloured peridium.

Rhizopogon luteolus. *Peridium dirty yellow to olive-brownish, covered by dense weft of brown threads; gleba white, finally dirty olive-yellow; garlic-like smell.* Peridium 2–8 cm, ± egg-shaped, leathery, cracked. Partly buried; pine woods on sandy soil; mainly Scotland and North England. IX–XI. O.

Melanogaster variegatus var. **broomeianus.** *Peridium finally dull reddish-brown; gleba purple-black with thick whitish-yellow chamber walls.* Peridium 1–4 cm, tuberous, ± felty with adpressed threads, blackening where bruised. Mostly on soil surface under litter of frondose trees, esp. beech. I–XII. F. Formerly sold as alternative to truffles.

Hysterangium coriaceum Hesse. *Peridium whitish, peeling off, later pale clay colour; gleba hard, olive-green, chamber walls pale; frondose woods.* Peridium 1–1.5 cm, ovoid, with prominent mycelial tuft below. Calcareous soil at base of frondose trees. No British record.

Phallus impudicus. " Stinkhorn ". *Young peridium egg-like, 3–4 cm, white, attached to white mycelial cord; soon bursts to give white, spongy, hollow receptacle 10–20 cm high with apically attached honeycombed head covered by blackish-olive sticky spore mass having offensive foetid stench.* Woods, gardens, esp. on rich soil. VII–XI. C.

Phallus hadriani (Vent.) Pers. *As previous, but grows in dunes, the " egg " has pinkish to violet flesh and olive-brown spore mass with faint sweetish smell.* R.

Mutinus caninus. *Egg ovoid, 1–2 cm, whitish-yellow; receptacle 10–12 cm high, orange-buff; head ± orange, covered with dark green, sticky spore mass with faint faecal smell.* Woods, esp. around stumps; also on rotting sawdust. VII–XI. C.

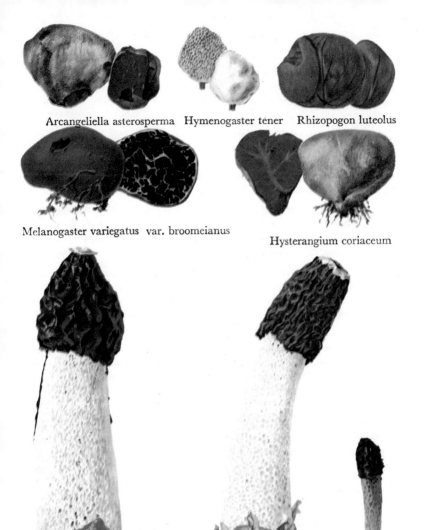

Arcangeliella asterosperma Hymenogaster tener Rhizopogon luteolus

Melanogaster variegatus var. broomeianus

Hysterangium coriaceum

Phallus impudicus
"Stinkhorn"

Phallus hadriani

Mutinus caninus

Usually pear-shaped fungi with two-layered peridium. Outer layer exoperidium bears spines, warts or granules. Gleba with or without a sterile spongy base; spores powdery at maturity intermingled with threads (capillitium). Now usually divided into 2 genera: Lycoperdon, with peridium opening by single pore; Calvatia, peridium opening by breaking away of upper part.

Lycoperdon (Calvatia) caelatum. *Open, dehisced, fruit-body cup-shaped; membrane separates sterile base from spore mass.* 6–10 cm, ± pear-shaped, whitish-grey, ± scurfy-warty, soon cracking hexagonally, finally cinnamon-brown and peeling off, showing olive-brown spore mass; base pitted, finally greyish-brown, glistening. Mostly on sandy pastures. VII–XI. O. *Edible.*

Lycoperdon (Calvatia) giganteum. " Giant puff-ball ". *Fruit-body ± globose, leathery, whitish, smooth.* Large, 15–30 or more cm across, sl. sulcate below, finally greenish-yellow; upper part flakes off; sterile base virtually absent. Woods, gardens, fields. VIII–IX. O–F but local. *Edible and good when young.*

Lycoperdon (Calvatia) excipuliforme, saccatum. *Pestle-like, sterile base tall, ± spiny-granular, furrowed above.* 8–20 cm high, head 2–10 cm across, at first whitish, with spiny warts united above, split at base, soon falling off leaving ± smooth or granular brownish fruit body, the upper part finally peeling off. Woods, heaths, pastures. VIII–XI. O. *Edible.*

Lycoperdon ericetorum, polymorphum, pusillum. *Globose to pear-shaped, ± scurfy; sterile base virtually absent.* 1–3 cm across, white to whitish-grey, finally pale yellowish-brown, sometimes spotted yellow, bronze colour below; flesh white later yellowish-green, finally cinnamon and ± powdery. Mostly sandy places, heaths. VIII–XI. O–F.

Lycoperdon perlatum, gemmatum. *Peridium pear-shaped, white to whitish-grey finally dirty yellowish-brown; warts pointed, surrounded by granules.* 4–7 cm high, 3–5 cm across, the warts soon falling off leaving ± reticulate scar pattern; sterile base with granules only, coarsely cellular within; flesh white at first, then greenish-yellow, powdery (from spores) at maturity. Woods generally, often ± tufted. VII–XII. C.

Var. *nigrescens* with shorter sterile base and blackish-brown spines surrounded by granular ring is frequent in coniferous woods.

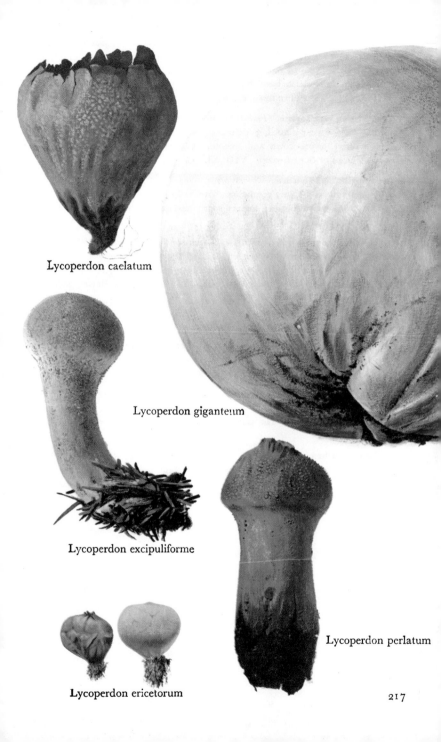

Lycoperdon caelatum

Lycoperdon giganteum

Lycoperdon excipuliforme

Lycoperdon ericetorum

Lycoperdon perlatum

217

Lycoperdon molle, umbrinum. *Spines brown, short (to 2 mm); spore mass purplish; sterile base c. 1/3 of whole.* Fruit-body pear-shaped to sub-globose, 2–5 cm, spines soon falling off exposing pale brown shiny surface; flesh whitish at first, purplish as spores mature; sterile base of coarse cells, purplish. Mostly coniferous woods. VIII–XI. F. (Size of spines and colour of spore mass variable.)

Lycoperdon pyriforme. *Fruit-body coarsely mealy, attached to wood by white thick mycelial strands.* Pear-shaped, 3–4 cm high, 2–4 cm broad, whitish at first, finally greyish or yellowish-brown and smooth. Clustered to ± tufted on frondose woody stumps or buried wood. VIII–XI. C. The only species on wood.

Lycoperdon echinatum. *Spines brown, long (3–4 mm), crowded.* Peridium 3–6 cm, ± globose, spines conniving above, falling off to expose reticulated scar pattern on brownish surface; mature spore mass dark purplish-brown. On rich soil, esp. under beech. VII–XI. R–O.

Lycoperdon depressum, hiemale. *Fruit-body white, yellowish-white, finally watery-brown; spore mass separated from sterile base by distinct membrance.* 2–4 cm, broad, at first softly and shortly spiny-granular, soon ± smooth, mature spore mass ± olive; sterile base of coarse cells. In grass; lawns, downs, pastures. VII—XI. F–C.

Bovista

Fruit-body ± spherical without sterile base; peridium of two layers: outer ± fleshy and breaking away, inner tough and papery; when mature with apical opening. Both the following species become detached and rolled about by wind.

Bovista nigrescens. *Inner layer brown-purplish at maturity, often spotted.* Fruit body 3–6 cm, outer layer whitish at first, soon cracking and peeling off; open ± jagged mature spore mass purple-brown. In grass: pastures etc. I–XII. F–C.

Bovista plumbea. *Inner layer ± lead colour at maturity, not spotted.* Fruit body 1–3 cm, outer layer at first whitish, soon cracking and peeling off; apical opening round, rather small; mature spore mass clay to olive-brown. In grass: pastures etc., also light, sandy soils. VIII–XI. O–F.

Lycoperdon molle

Lycoperdon pyriforme

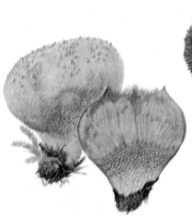

Lycoperdon depressum

Lycoperdon echinatum

Bovista plumbea

Bovista nigrescens

Geastrum—" Earth Stars "

Young fruit-bodies round, closed by outer peridium which later cracks ± stellately, exposing ± papery, globose inner peridium with apical opening.

Geastrum rufescens, fimbriatum. *Outer peridium 6–8(9) rayed; inner peridium sessile with small fringed pore.* Opened specimens 3–6 cm diam., rays ± recurved beneath fruit body, pale brownish on outermost surface, yellowish watery-brown on innermost; inner peridium smooth, ± cinnamon-buff colour. Woods. VII–XI. F (local).

Geastrum quadrifidum, coronatum. *Outer peridium purplish-brown finally 4-rayed and straddling, the tips adherent to substratum; apical pore with definite peristome; under conifers.* Opened specimens 2–3 cm across; mycelium ± flat between ray tips; inner peridium lead-grey. VIII–X. O–F (local).

Geastrum fornicatum. *Outer peridium finally of 4 acute rays, straddling, the tips adherent to substratum; apical pore with indefinite peristome; under frondose trees.* Opened specimens 5–10 cm high, rays greyish to brownish; mycelium depressed between ray tips; inner peridium with short stalk, dark brown. IV–XI. R–O (local).

Geastrum nanum. *Outer peridium 5–8 irregularly rayed, inner peridium with furrowed mouth; sand dunes; sandy places.* 2–3 cm broad and high, rays dark brown at first and sl. fleshy, later papery and grey; inner peridium stalked, greyish-brown, mouth elongated, beak-like. IX–XI. F (local).

Geastrum striatum, bryantii. *Inner peridium stalked and collar around stalk; mouth with furrowed peristome.* 3–7 cm high and broad, irregularly 6 to 12 rayed, rays dark brown, ± fleshy; inner peridium lead grey to blackish brown, mouth beak-like. Frondose woods. I–XII. O–F.

Geastrum pectinatum. *Inner peridium stalked, with no distinct collar; mouth furrowed.* 3–7 cm broad and high, irregularly 6–12 rayed, rays dark brown, ± fleshy; inner peridium usually lead grey, pruinose, stalk sometimes with loose, adherent flesh remnants. Mostly conifer woods. V–XII. O (local).

Geastrum triplex. *Rays thick, fleshy, cracked across; inner peridium sessile, usually surrounded by basal cup.* To 10 cm across, 5 to 7-rayed, rays ± flesh colour, later dark brown and ± horny; inner peridium pale brown, peristome silky to fibrous, 14 mm at base, finally grooved. Closed fruit-bodies look just like onions. Frondose woods, often beech. VIII–X. F–C.

Geastrum rufescens

Geastrum quadrifidum

Geastrum fornicatum

Geastrum striatum

Geastrum nanum

Geastrum pectinatum

Geastrum triplex

Scleroderma aurantium, vulgare. " Common earth-ball ". *Hard, sessile; peridium dirty olive-yellow,* $\pm$ *scaly-cracked, thick.* Fruit-body tuberous, 4–8 cm, peridium in section whitish to rose-pink; spore mass finally purple-black, traversed by whitish threads, powdery; spores escape by irregular cracking of peridium. Old fruit bodies are usually bored at base by beetles. Esp. on peaty ground, round birches; also woods. VIII–XII. C.

Scleroderma verrucosum. *Fruit-body greyish clay-brown with* $\pm$ *rooting stem-like base.* Peridium thin, $\pm$ warty-scaly when young, soon smoothish, finally irregularly cracking to give rather large opening; spore mass finally olive-brown, powdery. Frondose woods on rich soil. VII–XI. O–F.

Tulostoma brumale. *Globose head on long fibrillose stipe; in calcareous sand.* Head 1–2 cm diam. with minute projecting mouth, clay-brown, finally whitish-grey; stipe 2–5 cm, thin, with basal mycelial tuft. Only the head projects above the sand and thus looks like a small puff ball. Dunes; also recorded from old walls. V–II. R (local).

Crucibulum vulgare. *Peridium of one layer; fruit-body* $\pm$ *cup-shaped, at first closed, with 8–10 lens-shaped whitish " eggs ".* Fruit body 0.5–1 cm high, yellowish-white, sides shaggy, lid soon disappearing. On frondose and coniferous sticks, $\pm$ clustered. IX–III. C.

Cyathus striatus. *Peridium of three layers; fruit-body a cut-off, inverted cone, brownish and tomentose outside, fluted and shining greyish within; 10–12 grey " eggs ".* 0.5–1 cm high, closed at first by white membrane. On dead wood, stumps, twigs, fir cones, $\pm$ clustered. III–XI. C.

Cyathus olla. *Similar to previous, but trumpet shaped; not fluted internally.* 1–2 cm high, base quite narrow, closed by membrane at first, dirty yellowish-grey outside; 6–8, silky-grey " eggs ". Solitary or a few together on soil, twigs etc. III–XI. F–C.

Sphaerobolus stellatus. *Open fruit-body stellately split, orange coloured.* Globose before splitting, 0.2 cm diam.; rays $\pm$ like 5–6(8) radiating teeth, exposing central globose, olive-black spore ball which becomes shot-off, landing several feet away. On sticks, leaves, dung. I–XII. C.

Scleroderma aurantium

Scleroderma verrucosum

Tulostoma brumale

Crucibulum vulgare

Cyathus striatus

Cyathus olla

Sphaerobolus stellatus

Auricularia auricula (Hook). Under. Hirneola. "Jew's Ear". *Gelatinous when moist; ± ear-shaped, liver-brown; on elder.* 3–10 cm broad, ± translucent, varying brownish flesh colour, outer (upper) surface sl. greyish-velvety; shape more irregular with age; bone-hard when dry. Very rare on other frondose trees. I–XII, esp. X–XI. C. *Edible and good.*

Pseudohydnum gelatinosum. Tremellodon. *Fruit-body gelatinous, ± tongue-shaped, pearl-grey; underside with teeth.* 2–6 cm broad, often sl. lobed, minutely tomentose above, sometimes brownish; teeth small, whitish, flesh tough. Conifer stumps. IX–XI. O–F.

Tremella mesenterica. *Gelatinous fruit-body contorted brain-like, folded, orange-yellow; on frondose trees.* 2–10 cm broad, ± slimy; shrivelled, bone hard and dark orange when dry. Dead branches. I–XII (esp. X–XII). C.

Tremella encephala. *Gelatinous, cushion-shaped and contorted, pale flesh-colour with white hard core.* 1–4 cm broad, somewhat brownish when older. On pine wood. IX–III. O.

Exidia glandulosa. *Gelatinous, contorted brain-like, olive-black.* Fruit body 2–6 cm broad, cushion-shaped or irregular tongue-like, sometimes pendent; fertile side warty-rough; membranous, black and glistening when dry. On decaying wood of frondose trees. I–XII. esp. X–XII. C.

Exidia albida. Huds. Tremella. *Gelatinous; whitish-grey, brain-like contorted.* 2–10 cm broad, sometimes with reddish tinge, often lobed; horny and greyish when dry. Frondose branches. IX—IV. C.

Exidia recisa. *Gelatinous; top-shaped, translucent brownish-yellow; on willow branches.* 1–2 cm broad, stipe short. Often ± clustered. IX–XII. O–F. A similar black sp., *E. truncata,* occurs usually on oak.

Calocera viscosa. *Like a stags horn, orange-yellow, slimy; on conifer stumps.* 3–8 cm high, ± dichotomous, rooting deeply in stump; horny and darker orange when dry. IX–IV. C.

A similar but pale yellow unbranched species on frondose wood is *C. cornea.*

Dacrymyces deliquescens. *Gelatinous; drop-like orange yellow ± confluent bodies on decayed wood.* Fruit bodies 0.2–0.5 cm broad, sometimes ± cushion-shaped, drying dark and brownish. I–XII (after wet weather). C.

Auricularia auricula
"Jews ear"

Pseudohydnum gelatinosum

Tremella mesenterica

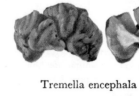

Tremella encephala

Exidia recisa

Exidia glandulosa

Exidia albida

Calocera viscosa

Dacrymyces deliquescens

INTRODUCTION TO MICROSCOPICAL CHARACTERS

FRESH MATERIAL

In addition to the ordinary free hand section—a safety-razor blade is quite adequate —there is the Percussion Technique. This involves removing a *small* piece of tissue (something between the volume of a mustard seed and a peppercorn) and making a water mount between glass slide and coverslip in the usual way. The coverslip is then tapped smartly immediately above the specimen, e.g. by dropping the unsharpened end of a new pencil from a height of about two inches, the pencil being caught on the rebound. This splays out the mounted material so that whole individual structures can be seen. The percussion may be repeated, if necessary. Too much mounting water should be avoided, as this has a cushioning effect: just enough to be covered by the coverslip is a good average guide.

ASCOMYCETES

Asci and parphyses are generally easy to see by just digging out a small piece of the hymenium, mounting in water and applying the Percussion Technique. Mounted in iodine solution, the blueing or not of the ascus tip may be observed. In the same way, the presence or absence of a lid (operculum) to the ascus can be determined.

Thin sections, more or less parallel with the hymenial layer, may also be taken in the usual way. Pith or carrot (hardened in alcohol) may be used to support small specimens.

BASIDIOMYCETES

APHYLLOPHORALES

Cystidia, which are thin- or thick-walled sterile cells of varying shapes and sizes interspersed in the hymenial layer, can be examined by taking thin sections parallel with the hymenial layer. Teasing out small portions of the same layer and mounting in water, with or without percussion, often suffices.

AGARICALES

Cap cuticle. A thin section of the surface (" scalp ") is taken with a razor from about midway between edge and centre and mounted in water. Two main types are important: (1) filamentous (Fig. 7, 1.) in which hyphae run more or less parallel with the cap surface, (2) cellular (Fig. 7, 2.) where the hyphae appear as round cells; in a few cases, for example, in the genus *Cystoderma*, the cap may have a mealy coating of round cells. The same " scalp " will also show any cap cystidia.

226

Cystidia. As mentioned before, these are thin- or thick-walled sterile cells in the hymenial layer of very varying shapes and dimensions and may occur on the margin or faces of a gill. Sometimes, they are found on cap and stipe cuticle.

For *marginal cystidia*, it is only necessary to cut out a small piece of gill edge (Fig. 8, 1.) and mount in water under a coverslip.

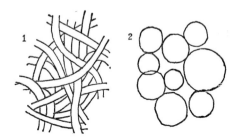

Figure 7   Cap cuticle types: 1, filamentous;
2, cellular.   ×500

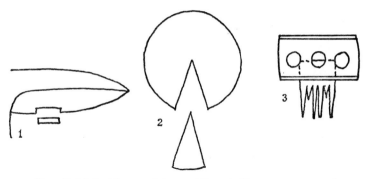

Figure 8   Method for examining cystidia and gill trama. 1, removal of gill edge for marginal cystidia. 2, removal of cap segment prior to soaking in water. 3, cutting vertical section of gill through segment of cap with a razor-blade

Facial cystidia. Cut a triangular segment from the fresh cap (see Fig. 8, 2.) and soak in water for a few minutes to get turgid. Now cut vertical sections through the gills beginning with the razor in the flesh just above the gills (Fig. 8, 3.). In this way, the cap flesh holds the sectioned gills together. Mount in water and look for cystidia on the gill sides (=faces).

A special type of facial cystidium is the *chrysocystidium*, so-called because it contains an internal body (Fig. 9, 6.) which becomes yellow when a small piece

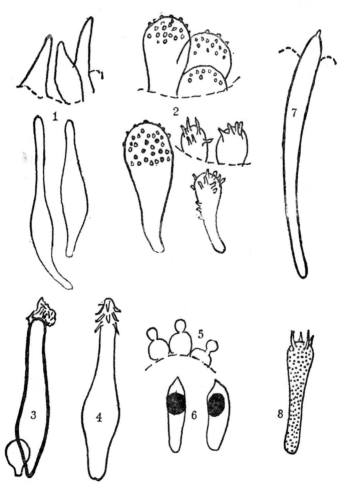

Figure 9 Types of cystidia: 1, ciliate marginal cystidia of *Mycena*. 2, granulate marginal cystidia of *Mycena*. 3, thick-walled crested cystidium of *Inocybe* (thin-walled cystidium at base on left). 4, harpoon type cystidium of Melanoleuca. 5, pin-head type cystidia of *Conocybe*. 6, chrysocystidium of *Hypholoma*, with internal stained " body ". 7, marginal cystidium of *Russula*. 8, basidium showing carminophil granules. ×500

of gill is mounted in strong ammonia solution (50%). Alternatively, the piece of gill may be mounted in Cotton Blue in lacto-phenol, when the internal body stains deep blue in about 5 to 10 minutes. This type of cystidium occurs in all

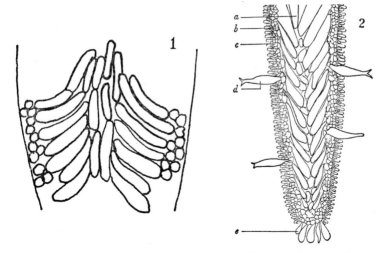

Figure 10 Types of gill trama: 1, bilateral (or divergent) gill trama of *Amanita*. × 400   2, inverse gill trama of *Pluteus* (*a*). The figure also shows: *b*, sub-hymenium; *c*, hymenium; *d*, four facial cystidia (three of them hooked); *e*, marginal cystidia (not hooked). × 200

species of *Hypholoma*, in some species of *Stropharia* and a few species of *Pholiota*, as here understood.

In all examinations for cystidia, the Percussion Technique is most valuable for revealing whole structures.

Gill trama. Proceed as for facial cystidia. These vertical sections of the gill will also show the gill trama, that is, those cells which form the greater part of the tissue between the two sides (Fig. 10). Two important types are (1) the Bilateral type, where the cylindrical hyphae curve away from the mid line towards the base of the basidia at the gill sides (Fig. 10, 1.); this type is characteristic of *Amanita* and *Limacella*. (2) the Inverse type where the more or less cylindrical cells grow away from the sides towards the mid line so that their free ends are at the mid line (Fig. 10, 2.); this type is found only in *Pluteus* and *Volvariella* amongst the Gill Fungi.

There are two other types of gill trama (3) the Regular type in which the cylindrical cells run more or less parallel with one another between the base of the basidia, that is the basidia on either side of the gill are essentially at right angles to the tramal hyphae. (4) the Irregular type: here the tramal hyphae have no direction at all but are interwoven in all directions. These last two types of trama construction are very useful in separating out the sub-genera of *Hygrophorus*.

Spores. In addition to the size and shape of spores, the type of ornamen-

229

tation is often important. This is especially so in the genera *Lactarius* and *Russula*, where the ornamentation is amyloid. Spore types of these two genera are illustrated in Fig. 11 and other kinds of spore in Fig. 12.

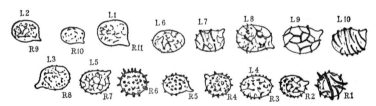

Figure 11   Spore types of *Lactarius* and *Russula*: *Lactarius*—L 1–10; *Russula*—R 1–11 × 1000.   It is important to note whether the warts or spines are isolated, or whether there are connecting lines or crests forming a partial or complete network

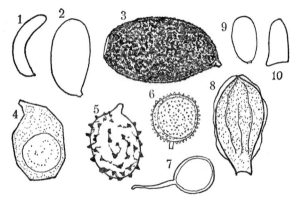

Figure 12   Various types of spores: 1, sausage-shaped (arcuate) spore of *Panellus stipticus*. 2, elliptic spore of a *Clitocybe*. 3, spore of *Panaeolus foenisecii*, showing germ pore. 4, angular polygonal spore of *Rhodophyllus* with large " oil " drop. 5, spore of *Russula* showing amyloid ornamentation. 6, prickly (echinulate) spore of *Lycoperdon*. 7, spore of *Bovista* with pedicel. 8, spore of *Hymenogaster* with wrinkled utricle. 9, spore of *Rhizopogon*. 10, projectile type of spore from *Lepiota*, section Stenosporae. Highly magnified

HERBARIUM MATERIAL

Fungi are most commonly dried by exposing them to a temperature of about 40° C. An electric fire, biscuit tin over a bunsen burner or similar device is all that is needed, the main thing being to have a good circulation of air so that the moisture can get away. Although during the drying, most of the colours go or are changed, nevertheless the microscopical characters are fully preserved and can be restored to their normal state of size and appearance either by warming a small piece of the appropriate tissue in water or by mounting it directly in 10 per cent ammonia solution or 1 to 2 per cent potassium hydroxide. The latter is perhaps a little more rapid but the reagent tends to become carbonated and this makes it rather messy to use.

CHEMICAL TESTS

Unless otherwise stated, these should be used on fresh material in good condition. The tests mentioned below are only some of the more important differential ones.

Ferrous sulphate. Esp. important in *Russula*.

Ferrous sulphate	5 grams
Distilled water	50 c.c.
Dilute sulphuric acid	1–2 drops

The stipe cuticle is lightly broken, and a few drops of the above added. The great majority of *Russula* spp. respond in about a minute to give a ± deep (dirty) salmon pink. This is the *normal* reaction and is not given in the text. The exceptional reactions only are listed, thus (*R. xerampelina*) Fe: deep olive-green, meaning this colour results and *not* the normal reaction. Fe: O (*R. cyanoxantha*) means no reaction.

The reagent should be renewed about once a month. Alternatively, a (large) crystal of ferrous sulphate (" green vitriol ") or of ferric alum may be rubbed on the stipe. Reactions are essentially similar.

Sulpho-vanillin (SV). For *Russula rosea* and for staining cystidia in cap or on gills of *Russula*. Cystidia go blue-black.

Distilled water	2 c.c.
Conc. sulphuric acid	2 c.c.
Vanillin (Vanilla)	0.25 grams

The Vanillin need not be weighed out exactly: a few crystals on a knife point to give a yellow solution. Will keep 2–3 days in stoppered, yellow bottle. For *R. rosea*, apply a drop or two (glass rod) to stipe : deep red-ink colour.

Keep away from clothes and all parts of the body, esp. the eyes. Sulphuric acid causes very painful burning. In case of accidents, wash with jet of water or *throw* water over affected part to remove acid; don't just bathe or dab with water. The acid is readily neutralised by (solid) sodium bi-carbonate or washing soda.

For cystidia. Mount a thin slip of cap cuticle or a piece of gill in a drop of SV, apply cover-slip and examine under microscope in usual way. The cystidia stain in at most 5 minutes.

Phenol 2% in distilled water.

A few drops on stipe of *Russula olivacea* gives in about 5–10 min. a beautiful black-currant juice colour. All other species give a dull chocolate brown colour.

Ammonia (NH$_3$)

50% solution of strong ammonia solution in distilled water. Gills, stipe of *Russula sardonia:* red colour (may take 30–60 min.); cuticle of *Lactarius turpis:* fine deep purple.

Potassium hydroxide (KOH). 10% in distilled water.

Keep in stoppered bottle; use glass rod; is caustic. Important for *Amanita*. *A. pantherina:* flesh of cap goes yellow-orange. *A. virosa:* cuticle goes chrome yellow. Also for *Lactarius pyrogalus*: milk + KOH goes yellow-orange.

Concentrated sulphuric acid. See under Sulpho-vanillin.

A drop of the pure acid on gills of *Amanita phalloides* gives a lilac-pinkish colour. Specific for this fungus.

Melzer's Iodine. For amyloid and dextrinoid reaction of spores.

Distilled water	20 c.c.
Potassium iodide	1 gram
Iodine	0.5 gram

Dissolve the potassium iodide in 1–2 c.c. of water, add the iodine and mix until dissolved; add remainder of water and finally,

Chloral hydrate. 20 grams (Poisonous)

The reagent is best made up fresh each season.

For amyloid reaction: add a drop to spore deposit on glass slide. A distinct blue-black coloration is positive. It requires practice to detect the coloration under the microscope.

For dextrinoid reaction: proceed as above; a reddish-brown coloration is positive: this is best seen under the microscope: individual spores are clearly seen stained reddish-brown, e.g. *Lepiota* spores.

Tl. 4. Henry's reagent : Thallium oxide	2 grams
Pure concentrated hydrochloric acid	4 c.c.
Pure concentrated nitric acid	1 c.c.
When dissolved, add slowly while gently shaking	
Sodium bi-carbonate	1 gram
When fizzing has stopped,	
Distilled water	10 c.c.

The reagent keeps indefinitely. It is poisonous. Particularly useful for separating *Agaricus xanthodermus* (" Yellow stainer ") from closely allied edible mushrooms. Apply a few drops (glass rod) to cap cuticle:

A. silvicola, arvensis: brick-red colour

A. xanthodermus: no such reaction.

Aceto-carmine. Carminophil basidia.

See genus *Lyophyllum*. Test to be made on dried material. Drying is easily done beneath a lamp or in front of a fire at a temperature of about 40° C.

Place 3–4 square millimetres of gill into 2–3 drops of aceto-carmine on a thin glass slide. Warm gently over low bunsen to just below boiling point, adding further drops of reagent so that material never dries out. Remove from flame and stir liquid on slide with mounted steel needle (mordant) till some blackening of fluid is noted. Re-heat as above 2 or 3 more times, stirring between heatings and never allowing material to dry out. Finally mount in fresh aceto-carmine and apply cover-slip. Tap cover-slip smartly (base of pencil) to splay out material and examine under oil immersion. Dozens of black staining granules are easily seen in a positive reaction, With practice, the reaction can be seen under a dry 1/16th objective.

COLLECTING FUNGI FOR IDENTIFICATION

Whether fungi are collected for purely scientific purposes or for the table, careful determination is needed if they are not recognized *in situ*. When wanted for eating, a preliminary cleaning-up, removal of stalks, etc. (where necessary), is best done at the time of gathering, but for an unrecognized fungus, the whole fruit-body must be brought home intact, and in the case of agarics, this means it must be *dug up* so as to include the base of the stem and any possible volva. Wood-inhabiting fungi may have to be cut out and removed with the underlying bark. To prevent damage and contamination with foreign spores, each species should be wrapped alone in waxed paper or a plastic bag. A few leaves or a piece of wood will help to recall the habitat, but such information is best recorded in a Field Note Book together with such data as smell, taste, latex if any, and other characters which experience soon shows are likely to fade or disappear after the fungus is brought home.

BIBLIOGRAPHY

I. GENERAL

Ainsworth, G. C. and Bisby, G. R. 1961. *Dictionary of the Fungi*. Commonwealth Mycological Institute, Kew, Surrey. Indispensable to anyone interested in fungi at whatever level.

Alexopoulos, C. J. 1963. *Introductory Mycology*. John Wiley and Sons. Excellent and clear.

Bessey, E. A. 1952. *Morphology and Taxonomy of Fungi*. The Blakiston Co., Philadelphia. Toronto. More advanced, with keys to most genera of all groups.

Cartwright, U. St. G. and W. P. K. Findlay, 1958. *Decay of Timber and its Prevention*. H. M. S. O.

Ramsbottom, J. 1953. *Mushrooms and Toadstools*. The New Naturalist. Collins, London. Full of good things about History, Natural History, Ecology.

II. SPECIAL

Christiansen, M. P. 1959, 1960. Danish Resupinate Fungi. *Dansk. Bot. Arkiv.* XIX, 1–388.

Corner, E. J. H. 1950. A monograph of Clavaria and allied genera. Oxford. Addenda: *Ann. Bot. London* 1952, 1953; *Trans. Brit. Mycol. Soc.* 1952.

Dennis, R. W. G. 1960. *British Cup Fungi and Their Allies*. Ray Society, London.

Dennis, R. W. G., Orton, P. D. and Hora, F. B. 1960. New check list of British Agarics and Boleti, Parts I, II. *Trans. Brit. Mycol. Soc.* Supplement, 1–225.

Dissing, H., and Lange, Morten. 1961. The genus Geastrum in Denmark. *Bot. Tids.* LVII, 1–27.

Eckblad, E. E. 1955. The Gasteromycetes of Norway. *Nytt. Mag. Botanikk.* IV. 19–86.

Eriksson, J. 1958. *Studies of the Swedish Heterobasidiomycetes and Aphyllophorales with special regard to the Family Corticiaceae*. Uppsala.

Hansen, E. Bille. 1954. The Danish species of Geoglossum and related genera. *Bot. Tids.* LI. 7–19.

Hawker, Lilian E. 1954. British Hypogeous Fungi. *Phil. Trans. Roy. Soc.*, B. CCXXXVII, 429–546.

Hora, F. B. 1957. The genus Panaeolus in Britain. *The Naturalist*, 77–88.

Hora, F. B. *New Check List of British Agarics and Boleti*. 1960. Part IV. Validatious, new species and critical notes.

Kühner, R. and Romagnesi, H. 1953. *Flore Analytique des Champignons Supérieurs*. Masson et Cie. Paris.

Lange, Morten. 1956. Danish Hypogeous Macromycetes. *Dansk. Bot. Arkiv.*, XVI. I.

Møller, F. H. 1950–2. Danish Psalliota species. Preliminary Studies for a Monograph on the Danish Psalliotae. I and II. Friesia IV. 1–46; 135–220.

Moser, M. 1955. Blätter und Bauchpilze; in Gams: Kleine Kryptogamenflora II b. Stuttgart.

Moser, M. 1960. Die Gattung Phlegmacium (Schleim Köpfe) Band of Die Pilze Mitteleuropas. J. Klinkhardt. Bad Heil-brunn. (With coloured plates.)

Munk, A. 1957. Danish Pyrenomycetes, a preliminary flora. *Dansk. Bot. Arkiv.* XVII.

Neuhoff, W. 1956. Die Milchlinge (*Lactarii*). Band IIb of Die Pilze Mitteleuropas. J. Kinkhardt. Bad Heilbrunn. (With coloured plates.)

Orton, P. D. Cortinarius. *The Naturalist*, 1955 (Supplement), 1–80; 1958, 81–149. University of Leeds.

Orton, P. D. 1960. New check list of British Agarics and Boleti, Part III. *Trans. Brit. Mycol. Soc.*, 1–439.

Pilát, A. 1936. *Atlas des Champignons de l'Europe: III Polyporaceae.* Prague.

Pearson, A. A. The following monographs (British species) are obtainable from the Editor, *The Naturalist*, University of Leeds.

The Genus Russula. 1950. 1–24. With Crawshay Spore Colour Chart.

The Genus Lactarius. 1950. 81–99.

British Boleti. 1950. 1–19.

The Genus Inocybe. 1954. 117–140.

The Genus Mycena. 1955. 41–63.

Schaeffer, J. 1952. Russula-Monographie, Band III of Die Pilze Mitteleuropas. J. Klinkhardt. Bad Heilbrunn. (With coloured plates.)

Singer, R. 1962. *The " Agaricales " (Mushrooms) in Modern Taxonomy.* J. Cramer Weinheim.

Supplementary Note

For species Agaricales, the most comprehensive work, as well as the most critical, is the *Flore Analytique des Champignons Supérieurs* of Kühner & Romagnesi. This also cites the most important monographs on individual genera.

For species of the Aphyllophorales, an indispensable work is: Hyménomycètes de France, by H. Bourdot & A. Galzin. Paul Lechevalier, Paris 1928. The monographs of Corner and of Pilát are most recent treatments of the Clavariaceae and Polyporaceae respectively and are complementary and supplementary to the treatment of those same group by Bourdot and Galzin.

INDEX

A–H=spore mass colour of *Lactarius* and *Russula* according to Crawshay's Colour Chart—see page 198, footnote. (In *Coprinus* A, B, C indicate cap covering types.)

L=Spore types of *Lactarius* illustrated in Fig. 11, p. 230.

R=Spore types of *Russula* illustrated in Fig. 11.

cuticle=cap cuticle.

cyst.=cystidium (ia).

iodine=Melzer's iodine—see Chemical Tests, page 231.

marg.=marginal.

p.p.=pro parte (in part).

sp.=asco- or basidiospore(s) *in this Index only*. (Elsewhere=species.)

An asterisk (*)=illustration of microscopical character(s) in Fig. 9. *All measurements are given in microns (1/1000 millimetre).*

Acetabula 38. Helvella p.p.

Agaricales 76

Agaricus. **Cuticle filamentous; sp. smooth; cyst. clavate to ±balloon-shaped.*
amethystinus=purpurellus

arvensis 134. Sp. 6½–8×4·5–5·5; cyst. obovate to sub-globose 14–20 broad

augustus 130. Sp. 7–10×4·5–5·5; cyst. clavate, *c.* 7 broad

bernardii 134. Sp. 5·5–7(10)×5–6

bisporus 132. Basidia 2-spored; sp. 6·5–8×5–6

bitorquis 132. Sp. 5–6·5×4–5; cyst. clavate, *c.* 30×6–7

campestris 132. Sp. 7–8×4·5–5·4; no cyst.

comtulus 132. Sp. 4·5–5·5×3–3·5; no cyst.

edulis=bitorquis

langei 130. Sp. 7–8(9)×4½–5; cyst. balloon-shaped, 12–20 broad

macrosporus 134. Sp. 8–12×5·5–6·5; cyst. inflated, often in a row

meleagris=placomyces

placomyces 130, 134. Sp. 4–6×3–4; cyst. balloon-shaped, 10–20 diam.

purpurellus 134. Sp. 4–5×2·5–3·5

rubellus=semotus

sanguinarius=silvaticus

semotus 134. Sp. 4·5–5·5×2·5–3·5; cyst. obovate, 6–7 broad

silvaticus 130. Sp. 5–6×3–3·5; cyst. clavate, 8–11 broad

silvicola 134. Sp. 5–6×3·5–4; cyst. sub-globose, *c.* 10–20 broad

subperonatus 132. Sp. 6–7·5×5–5·5; cyst. clavate, *c.* 35×8

villaticus=macrosporus

xanthodermus 134. Sp. 5–6·5×3–4; cyst. balloon-shaped, *c.* 10–20 (30) broad

Agrocybe. **Cuticle cellular; sp. smooth, usually with germ pore; cyst. present.*

dura 152. Sp. 11–13×6–7·5
erebia 152. Basidia 2-spored; sp.
  10–13×5–6·5
paludosa 152. Sp. 8·5–10·5×5–6
praecox 152. Sp. 8·5–10·5×5–6
Aleuria 34. Peziza p.p.
Alnicola=Naucoria
Amanita, *Gill trama bilateral (divergent); sp. smooth, amyloid or not; marg.
cyst.±inflated pyriform.*
  citrina 118. Sp. sub-globose, 8–10×
  7–8, amyloid
  excelsa 118. Sp. ovate, 8–11×5½–8,
  amyloid
  fulva 116. Sp. globose, 9–11(12),
  non-amyloid
  inaurata 116. Sp. globose, 10·5–13,
  non-amyloid
  mappa=citrina
  muscaria 116. Sp. ovate, 9–12×
  6·5–8, amyloid
  pantherina 118. Sp. ovate, 9–12×
  6·5–8, non-amyloid
  phalloides 116. Sp. sub-globose, (8)
  9–11×7–9, amyloid
  porphyria 118. Sp. sub-globose,
  7·5–9·5×6·5–7·5, amyloid
  rubescens 118. Sp. ovate, 8–10×
  5·5–6·5, amyloid
  spissa=excelsa
  strangulata=inaurata
  vaginata 116. Sp. globose, 9–11(12),
  non-amyloid
  virosa 116. Sp. globose, 8–10, amyloid
Amanitopsis=Amanita
Arcangeliella. *Sp.±shiny; gleba with
lactiferous vessels.*
  asterosperma 214. Sp. mass saffron-
  red; sp. globose, 12–14, warted
Armillaria. *Cuticle filamentous; sp.
smooth, non-amyloid.*
  mellea 92. Sp. ovate, 7·5–9×5–
  6·5
  mucida 106. Oudemansiella m.
  tabescens 92. Sp. 8–10×5–7
Ascomycetes 34
Asterophora. *Chlamydospores abundant;
basidia with *carminophil granules;
sp. c. 5·5×3·5, smooth.*
  lycoperdoides 80.   Chlamydospores

bluntly stellate, body globose, 12
  15, blunt " arms " 4–5 long
parasitica 80. Chlamydospores oval,
  smooth, c. 15×10, thick-walled
Auricularia 224. *Basidia transversely
3-septate; sp. white, smooth.*
  auricula 224. Sp. oblong, cylindric,
  curved, 16–20×5·5–8·5
Auriscalpium. *Cap leathery, laterally
stipitate.*
  vulgare 60. Sp. ovoid, 4–5·5×
  3·5–4

Baeospora. *Cuticle filamentous; sp.
amyloid, smooth.*
  conigena=myosura
  myosura 112. Sp. 3–4×1·5–2
Bolbitius. *Cuticle cellular; sp. smooth
with germ pore.*
  vitellinus 152. Sp. 12·5–14·5×7–9
Boletus. *Sp. smooth,±fusiform.*
  aurantiacus 194. Sp. 13–17×4–5
  badius 190. Sp. 12–15×4–5(6)
  bovinus 188. Sp. 7–11×3–4·5
  calopus 190. Sp. 12–16×4–5·5
  chrysenteron 188. Sp. 11–15×
  4–5·5
  cyanescens 186. Sp. broadly elliptic,
  9–12×4·5–6·5
  edulis 190. Sp. 13–17×4–5·5
  elegans 186. Sp. 7–10×3–4
  erythropus 192. Sp. 12–17×4·5–6·5
  felleus 192. Sp. 12–15×4–5
  granulatus 188. Sp. 9–10×3·5–4·5
  grevillei=elegans
  holopus 194. Sp. 16–19×5–6
  impolitus 190. Sp. (9)10–15×4·5–6
  lividus 194. Sp. broadly elliptic, 5–7
  ×3–4
  luridus 192. Sp. 11–14×5–6
  luteus 186. Sp. elliptic, 7–10×3–4
  miniatoporus=erythropus
  pachypus=calopus
  parasiticus 190. Sp. 12–18×4·5–5·5
  piperatus 188. Sp. 8–10×3·5–4
  pulverulentus 186. Sp. 11–15×
  4–5·5
  queletii 192. Sp. 11–14×5–6·5
  rubellus 188. Sp. 11–15×4·5—5·5
  rufescens=versipellis p.p.=
  testaceoscaber

satanas 192. Sp. $11-14 \times 4\cdot5-6\cdot5$
scaber 194. Sp. $15-18 \times 5-6$
subtomentosus 188. Sp. $11-14 \times 4-5$
testaceoscaber 194. Sp. $13-16 \times 4-5$
variegatus 188. Sp. $9-11 \times 3-4\cdot5$
versipellis. Includes aurantiacus and
    testaceoscaber

Bovista. *Capillitium threads free, not
attached to central column of sterile base or
to peridium inner wall.*
  nigrescens 218. Sp. smooth, globose,
    5–6, with long stalk
  plumbea 218. Sp. smooth, $\pm$ oval,
    $4-6 \times 3\cdot5-4$, with long stalk

Bulgaria. *Pore of ascus blue in iodine;
spores smooth non-septate, all or some of them
dark brown or black.*
  inquinans 44. Four upper sp.
    brownish black, $10\cdot5-14 \times 5\cdot5-$
    $6\cdot5$; four lower sp. hyaline, sl.
    smaller

Calocera. *Basidia forked, with 2 long
sterigmata.*
  cornea 224. Sp. white, arcuate,
    $7-9 \times 3-4$
  viscosa 224. Sp. yellow, ovoid,
    $8-11\cdot5 \times 3\cdot5-4\cdot5$

Calocybe 82

Caloporus. *Terrestrial, context fleshy,
white, stipe central, rarely branched;
sp. white, smooth, never fusiform nor
amyloid; cyst. absent.*
  ovinus 72. Sp. ovoid, $3.5-4 \times 3-$
    $3\cdot5$

Calycella 42. Helotium p.p.
Camarophyllus 76. A sub-genus of
Hygrophorus. *Gill trama irregular, of
narrow interwoven hyphae*

Calvatia 216. Lycoperdon p.p.
Cantharellaceae 58

Cantharellula. *Like Clitocybe but gills
repeatedly forked and edge $\pm$ rounded-
blunt; sp. amyloid.*
  umbonata 102. Sp. fusiform, $8-11 \times$
    $2\cdot5-3\cdot5$

Cantharellus. *Basidia exceptionally
slender, 6–10 times longer than wide;
hyphae with clamp connections; sp. unaffected by iodine, smooth.*
  aurantiacus 184. Hygrophoropsis a.

cibarius 58. Sp. elliptic, $7\cdot5-10\cdot5 \times$
  $4-6$
cinereus 58. Sp. ovoid, $8-10 \times 5-7$
infundibuliformis 58. Sp. elliptic,
  $9-11\cdot5 \times 6-9$
tubaeformis = infundibuliformis
Chlorociboria = Chlorosplenium

Chlorosplenium. *Pore of ascus blue in
iodine; sp. non-septate, hyaline, smooth.*
  aeruginascens 42. Sp. fusiform, 6–10
    $\times 1\cdot5-2$
  aeruginosum auct. brit. = aerugin-
    ascens

Ciboria 42. Sclerotinia p.p.

Claudopus 180; foot-note

Clavaria. *Sp. typically white.*
  abietina Cott. and Wakef. = Ramaria
    ochraceo-virens
  argillacea 54. Sp. smooth, $9-11 \times$
    $4-6$
  botrytis 56. Ramaria b.
  cinerea 54.
  corniculata 54. Sp. globose, 5–7,
    with basal apiculus, smooth
  cristata 54. Basidia usually 2-spored;
    sp.$\pm$globose, smooth, $7\cdot5-9\cdot5 \times$
    $6-7\cdot5$
  fistulosa 54. Sp. smooth, $\pm$ fusiform,
    $12-17 \times 5\cdot5-7\cdot5$
  flava 56. Ramaria f.
  formosa 56. Ramaria f.
  helvola 54. Sp. $\pm$ stellately angular,
    $5-8 \times 5-6$ including " angles "
  inaequalis Cotton and Wakf. = helvola
  invalii 56. Ramaria i.
  juncea 54. Sp. smooth, $7-11\cdot5 \times 3\cdot5-$
    $5\cdot5$
  ochraceo-virens 56. Ramaria o–v.
  pistillaris 54. Sp. pale yellowish,
    smooth, ovoid, mostly $11-16 \times 6-9$
  rugosa 54. Sp. white, smooth,
    broadly elliptic, $9-12 \times 7-10$
  stricta 56. Ramaria s.

Clavariadelphus 54

Claviceps. *Asci inoperculate, with apical
pore.*
  purpurea 48. Conidia $5\cdot5 \times 3\cdot5$;
    ascospores filiform, about 50–80
    long, finally septate

Claviciptales 48

Clavulina 54

Clavulinopsis 54

Clitocybe. *Cuticle filamentous; basidia without carminophil granules; sp. typically not reacting with iodine; typically smooth; cystidia exceptionally present.*

aggregata 80. Lyophyllum a.

asterospora 96. Sp. globose 5–7, with sparse cylindrical blunt spines 1·5–2 high

aurantiaca=Hygrophoropsis a.

clavipes 94. Sp. broadly elliptic, 4·5–5×3·5–4

connata 80. Lyophyllum c.

cyathiformis 98. Sp. elliptic, 8–11× 5–6, amyloid

dealbata 96. Sp. 4–5·5×2–3

flaccida 94. Sp. minutely prickly (best seen in Cotton Blue), sub-globose, 4–4·5×3–4

fragrans 96. Sp. 7–8×3·5–4

geotropa 94. Sp. sub-globose, comma-shaped, 6–8×5–6

gigantea 96. Sp. 6·5–8×3·5–5·5

infundibuliformis 94. Sp. 5–7×3–4

inversa=flaccida

langei 96. Sp. tear-shaped, 5–6·5× 2·5–3

nebularis 92. Sp. elliptic, 5·5–8× 3–4·5

odora 94. Sp. elliptic, 6–7·5×3–4

rivulosa 96. Sp. elliptic, 3·5–5× 2·5–3·5

suaveolens 96. Sp. 6–7×3–4

vibecina. Uncommon; most material so named is langei

Clitopilus. *Sp. with longitudinal ribs, best seen with immersion lens and sp. end-on; cyst. absent.*

prunulus 178. Sp ± fusiform, 10–14 ×4·5–6, with 5 to 7 ribs

Collybia. *Cap cuticle filamentous; sp. smooth, non-amyloid; cyst. typically absent.*

ambusta auct. 82. Lyophyllum carbonarium

butyracea 100. Sp. elliptic, 6–7× 3–4

cirrhata, sensu J. Lge.=cookei

confluens 100. Sp. elliptic, 6–7(9)× 3–4

conigena=Baeospora myosura

cookei 102. Sp. elliptic, 4–6×2–3

dryophila 100. Sp. elliptic, 4·5–6·5× 3–3·5

esculenta 112. Pseudohiatula e.

fuscopurpurea 102. Sp. ovoid-lanceolate, 6–8×3–4

fusipes 100. Sp. ± elliptic, 4·5–6× 2·5–4·5

leucomyosotis=Lyophyllum palustre

maculata 100. Sp. sub-globose, 4–5·5 ×3 5—5

mucida 106. Oudemansiella m.

murina 82. Lyophyllum m.

myosura 112. Baeospora m.

palustre 82. Lyophyllum p.

peronata 100. Sp. pip-shaped to lanceolate, 7·5–9×3–4

platyphylla 92. Tricholomopsis p.

radicata 106. Oudemansiella r.

rancida 82. Lyophyllum r.

tesquorum 82. Lyophyllum t.

tuberosa 102. Sp. ovate, 3–5×2–3

velutipes 108. Flammulina v.

Coltricia. *Cap stipitate, leathery; pores narrow, one-layered.*

perennis 62. Sp. pale yellowish, smooth, 6–9×4–6

Coniophora. *Sp. coloured, cyst. none.*

cerebella=puteana

puteana 52. Sp. brownish-olivaceous or rusty broadly elliptic, 10–14× 7–8

Conocybe. **Cap cuticle cellular; ring present or absent; spores virtually smooth (rough under immersion lens) with germ pore; *cyst. pin-headed* (Fig. 9).

lactea 152. Sp. elliptic, 11–14×6–8

tenera 152. Sp. oval, 10·5–12×5·5 6·5

Coprinus. *Three types of young cap. Type C: cap naked (no universal veil), cuticle cellular; type B: cap with universal veil of mealy or glistening particles composed of globular cells; type A: cap with felty-scaly universal veil composed of cylindrical or irregularly branched filaments. Sp. typically smooth. Marginal and facial cyst. ± balloon-shaped.*

atramentarius 136. Cap type A; sp. ovate, 7–10×5–6

bisporus 136. Cap type C; bristles on cap 60–120 long; sp. 12·5–13×

6·5–7; basidia always 2-spored

cinereus 136. Cap type A; sp. 10–11 ×6–7

comatus 136. Cap type A; sp. elliptic, 12–14×7–9

disseminatus 140. Cap type C; bristles on cap 100–130; sp. 8–11 ×4–5

domesticus sensu J. Lge.=xanthothrix *fimetarius*=cinereus

hansenii 138. Cap type C; no bristles on cap; sp. oval, 12–13×7

lagopus 138. Cap type A; sp. oval, 10–12·5×5·5–7·5

macrorrhizus=cinereus

micaceus 140. Cap type B; sp ± lemon-shaped, 7·5–12×6–7× 4·5–6

niveus 138. Cap type B; sp±lemon-shaped, 12–18×10–12×8–10

picaceus 136. Cap type A; sp. ovate, 13–17×10–12

plicatilis 138. Cap type C; sp. rounded-triangular or broadly heart-shaped, 9·5–13×9–11×5–7

radiatus 138. Cap type A; sp. oval, 11·5–12·5×6·5–7·5

silvaticus 138. Cap type C; bristles on cap *c.* 120; sp. somewhat lemon-shaped, rough, 12–15×7–9

sterquilinus 136. Cap type A; sp. ovate, 18–21×10–13

tardus=silvaticus

truncorum 140. cf. micaceus

xanthothrix 138. Cap type A, but veil becomes ± granular as cap expands; sp. oval, 7·5–9×4·5–5·5

Cordyceps. *Asci inoperculate, with apical pore; sp. filiform, fragmenting within ascus (part spores).*

capitata 48. Part sp. 10–50×3–6

cinerea 48. entomorrhiza

entomorrhiza 48. Part sp. 6–8×1·5 –2 (Tulasne)

militaris 48. Part sp. 3·5–6×1–1·5

ophioglossoides 48. Part sp. 2·5–5×2

parasitica=ophioglossoides

Corticium. *Sp. typically white, smooth.*

comedens 50. Sp. arcuate, cylindric, 15–22×5–7·5; cyst. absent

quercinum. 50. Sp. arcuate, cylin-

dric, 9–13×3–5; cyst. clavate to fusiform, 50–70×5–11

Cortinarius. *Cap cuticle filamentous; sp. always ± warty-rough; cyst. rare.*

albo-violaceus 164. Sp. ovate, 8–10× 4·5–5

anomalus 168. Sp. ovate to sub-globose, 7·5–9×6–6·5

armillatus 170. Sp. almond-shaped, 9–12×5–6

auroturbinatus 164. Sp. lemon-shaped, 12–15·5×7–8

bolaris 168. Sp. virtually smooth, obovate, 7–7·5×5

bulbiger 166. Sp. white, ovate, 7–9× 4·5

caninus 168. Sp. ovate to sub-globose, 8–10×6–7

cinnabarinus 168. Sp. ovate, pip-shaped, 7½–9×4·5–5·5

cinnamomeoluteus 168. Sp. ± elliptic, 7·5–10×4·5–5·5

cinnamomeus 168. Sp. ± elliptic, 6·5–8×4–5

caesiocyaneus 164. Sp. ± almond-shaped, 8–10·5×4·5

coerulescens sensu J. Lge.=caesiocyanus

collinitus 162. Sp. sl. lemon-shaped, 12–15×7–8·5

croceofolius 168. Sp. ± elliptic, 5–6·5 ×3·5–4·5

crocolitus 166. Sp. ellipsoid, 10–12× 6–7

decipiens 172. Sp. ovate, 8–9×5

decoloratus sensu J. Lge.=tabularis

delibutus 164. Sp. sub-globose, 7–9 ×6–7

elatior 162. Sp. 12–15(17)×7–8·5; cyst. balloon to pear-shaped, 18–26 broad

flexipes 170. Sp. elliptic to pin-shaped, 8–10×4·5–6

fulgens sensu J. Lge.=subfulgens

glandicolor 170. Sp. almond-shaped, 8–9×4·5

hinnuleus 170. Sp. ovate, 6·5–9×4·5

lucorum 170. Sp. almond-shaped 10–11×6–6·5

melliolens 166. Sp. almost smooth, elliptic, 7·5–9×4·5–5

multiformis sensu J. Lge.=melliolens

obtusus 172. Sp. almond-shaped, 7–8·5×4·5–5

pholideus 168. Sp. broadly ovate, 7–8×4·5–6

pulchellus 172. Sp. ± almond-shaped, smooth, 8–10(11)×4·5–6

sanguineus 168. Sp. ± ovate, 6·5–8×4–4·5

saniosus 172. Sp. ovate to almond-shaped, 8–9×4·5–5·5

saturatus 172. Sp. sub-globose, 5–6×4–5

saturninus 172. Sp. ellipsoid, 7–9·5×4–5

semisanguineus 168. Sp. elliptic, 6·5–8·5×4–5

subfulgens 164. Sp. ± lemon-shaped, 9–11×5–6

tabularis 166. Sp. ovate, sub-globose, 7–9(10)×5–6

traganus 164. Endpaper illustration. Sp. elliptic to almond-shaped, 7·5–10×5–6

triumphans sensu J. Lge.=crocolitus

trivialis 162. Sp. almond-shaped, 10·5–13×6–7

varius 166. Sp. almond-shaped, 10–12×5–6

Coryne. *Asci inoperculate with apical pore; asci not grouped in perithecia; hymenium not blue in iodine; spores hyaline, finally septate.*

sarcoides 44. Sp. ± oblong-fusiform, 10–18×3–5, finally 1 (3) septate

Craterellus. *Basidia exceptionally slender, 6–10 times longer than wide; hyphae with no clamp connections; sp. smooth, not reacting with iodine; basidia 2–4 spored.*

cinereus 58. Sp. ovoid, 8–10×5–7

cornucopioides 58. Sp. ovoid, 12–15×7–9

Crepidotus. *Sp. ellipsoid to globose, never polygonal; marginal cyst. ± hair-like.*

autochthonus 176. Sp. ± almond-shaped, smooth, 7–9×5–5·5

fragilis=autochthonus

mollis 176. Sp. ± almond-shaped, smooth, 6·5–8×4·5–6

nidulans 104. **Panellus n.**

variabilis 176. Sp. ellipsoid, sl. rough (immersion lens), 5·5–6×3–3·5

Crucibulum. *"Eggs" (Peridioles) attached to stalks (funicles) by small papilla.* levis 222. Sp. 7–10×3–5, smooth *vulgare*=levis

Cudonia. *Asci inoperculate, with apical pore.*

circinans 44. Pore not blue in iodine; sp. lying parallel in ascus, 30–45×2 (Dennis)

Cyathipodia 38. Helvella p.p.

Cyathus. *"Eggs" (Peridioles) attached to stalks (funicles) by small depression.*

crucibulum 222. Crucibulum levis

olla 222. Sp. smooth, broadly elliptic, 11–13=7–8

striatus 222. Sp. smooth, elliptic, 14–18×9–12

Cystoderma. *Cap surface densely mealy-granular, composed of globular cells; similar coating on stipe from base upwards. Sp. smooth, blue-black (amyloid) or red-brown (dextrinoid) in iodine.*

amianthina 128. Cap reddish with drop of 10% potassium hydroxide; sp. 5–7×3–4, amyloid

carcharias 128. Sp. ovate, 4–5·5×3–4, amyloid

granulosum 128. Sp. oval, 3·5–5×2·5–3, weakly dextrinoid

Dacrymyces. *Basidia forked bearing 2 long sterigmata; sp. become septate on germination, white to yellowish.*

deliquescens 224. Sp. ± cylindric, arcuate, 12–15×5–6

Daedalea. *Sp. white, smooth.*

quercina 66. Sp. pip-shaped, 5·5–7(9)×2·5–3

Daldinia. *Asci in perithecia, inoperculate with apical pore; sp. black or dark brown, non-septate.*

concentrica 46. Sp. lanceolate, black, flat on one side, 11–17×6–8

Deconica 148

Dialonectria 46. Nectria p.p.

Diatrype. *Asci in perithecia, inoperculate with apical pore; sp. pale brownish, non-septate.*

disciformis 46. Sp. curved, ± cylindric, 5–8×1·2

Eccilia. Sub-genus of Rhodophyllus
Elaphomyces. *Asci ± globose, powdery at maturity; sp. spherical.*
  cervinus=granulatus
  granulatus 48. Sp. finally black, 23–32 diam., densely spinous, spines 3–4 high
  muricatus 48. Sp. finally dark brown 18–25 diam., with warty spines 1·5–2·5 high
  variegatus 48. Sp. 15–25; spines 1·5–2
Entoloma 178, 180. Sub-genus of Rhodophyllus
Exidia. *Basidia vertically septate (Fig. 4, 5); sp. smooth.*
  albida 224. Sp. white, globose, 9–10 (Rea)
  glandulosa 224. Sp. white, cylindric, curved, 12–15×4–5
  recisa 224. Sp. white, cylindric, curved 15–18×4–5 (Rea)

Fayodia 112. Mycena p.p.
Fistulina. *Tubes free of each other; sp. smooth, pinkish in mass.*
  hepatica 74. Sp. ± globose, 4–6×3–4
Flammula=Pholiota or Gymnopilus
  alnicola 150. Pholiota a.
  astragalina 150. Pholiota a.
  carbonaria 150. Pholiota c.
  lenta 150. Pholiota l.
  penetrans 174. Gymnopilus p.
  sapinea auct. brit.=Gymnopilus penetrans
Flammulina. *Sp. white, smooth, nonamyloid; facial and marginal cyst. present.*
  velutipes 108. Sp. 6·5–10×3–4
Flocculina 176. Phaeomarasmius p.p.
Fomes. *Perennial, the tubes becoming stratified; cyst. or setae present; sp. white or coloured.*
  annosus 66. Sp. ± globose, white, 4–6×3·5–4·5
  fomentarius 64. Sp. white, 15–18×5·5–6
  igniarius 62. Phellinus i.

pomaceus 62. Phellinus p.
populinus 66. Oxyporus p.
marginatus=pinicola
pinicola 64. Sp. white, elliptic, 6–7×3–4

Galactinia 36. Peziza p.p.
Galera. 152. Now divided into Conocybe, Galerina
  tenera 152. Conocybe t.
Galerina. **Cap cuticle filamentous; cyst. present ± flask-shaped; sp. ± smooth.*
  hypnorum 174. Sp. 9–11×6–7
  laterita=Conocybe lactea
  marginata=unicolor
  mycenopsis 174. Sp. elliptic, 9–12×5–6·5
  paludosa 174. Sp. 9–11×6–6·5
  rubignosa f. major 174. Sp. 9–10×5·5–6; head of cyst. minutely swollen, 2·5–4 diam.
  unicolor 174. Sp. ovate, 7·5–10×4·5–6·5
Ganoderma. *Sp. tawny to brownish, thick-walled, outer wall colourless, smooth or warty and rough.*
  applanatum 64. Sp. smooth, 9–11·5×5·5–7
  lucidum 64. Sp. warty-rough, 11–14×6–8
Gasteromycetales 214
Geastrum. (Formerly spelt Geaster.)
Sp. globose ± warty or spiny, brownish.
  bryantii=striatum
  coronatum=quadrifidum
  fimbriatum=rufescens
  fornicatum 220. Sp. delicately warty, 3·5–4
  nanum 220. Sp. delicately warty, 5–6
  pectinatum 220. Sp. warts flat-topped, 5·5–7·5
  quadrifidum 220. Sp. warty, rough. 5–6
  rufescens 220. Sp. delicately warty, 4–6
  striatum 220. Sp. irregularly warty, 5–6
  triplex 220. Sp. long, echinulate, 5–6
Geoglossales 44

Geoglossum. *Asci not in perithecia, inoperculate with apical pore; sp. smooth, side by side in ascus, usually finally brown.*

cookeianum 44. Sp. sl. curved, 50–90 × 5–7, 7-septate; paraphyses ending in chain of globose cells

fallax 44. Sp. 80–100, to 12-septate; paraphyses abruptly swollen above

hirsutum 44. Sp. 110–150 × 6–8, multi-septate; septate paraphyses and setae present

virde 44. Sp. 15–20 × 5, always hyaline, finally 3-septate

Gloeophyllum. *Cap and flesh brown; cyst. present or absent.*

sepiarium 70. Sp. cylindric, white, sl. curved, 8–11 × 3–4; cyst. absent

Gloeoporus. *Flesh white, separated from tubes by thin, ± gelatinous layer; sp. hyaline, smooth; cyst. absent.*

adustus 70. Sp. pale yellow, ovate, smooth, 4–6 × 2–3·5

fumosus 72. Sp. white, elliptic, smooth, 6–7 × 3–4

Gomphidius. *Sp. elongated-fusiform, more than 15 long, smooth; cyst. large, cylindric, c. 100 long.*

glutinosus 184. Sp. 18–22 × 5–7

roseus 184, endpaper illustration. Sp. 17–21 × 5–5·5

rutilus 184. Sp. 18–24 × 6–7

viscidus=rutilus

Grifola. *Sp. white.*

frondosa 74. Sp. elliptic, 5–7 × 3·5–5 gigantea 72. Sp. broadly elliptic, 5–6 × 3·5–5·5

sulphurea 72. Sp. ovate, 5–8 × 4–5

umbellata. 74. Sp ± cylindric, 8–11 × 3–4

Gymnopilus. *Cap cuticle filamentous; sp. warty, rough (immersion lens advisable); marginal cystidia hair-like; facial cyst. usually absent.*

junonius 174. Sp. ovate, 8–10 × 5–6 penetrans 174. Filaments of cap cuticle less than 10 wide; sp. 6·5–8 × 4–5·5

spectabilis=junonius

Gyrodon 194. Boletus p.p.

Gyomitra. *Asci not in perithecia, oper-*

culate; paraphyses septate; sp. smooth, 2–3 guttate.

esculenta 38. Sp. elliptic, 18–22 × 9–12

gigas 38. Sp. apiculate, minutely prickly, c. 32 × 10–12

Gyroporus 186. Boletus p.p.

Hebeloma. *Cup cuticle filamentous; sp. minutely rough; marginal cyst. thin walled, hair-like.*

crustuliniforme 160. Sp. ± almond-shaped, 10–12·5 × 5–7(8)

elatum. Sp. lemon-shaped, 5·5–8 × 4; no marginal cyst.; facial cyst. sparse, vesiculose, c. 18 diam.

longicaudum 160. Sp. ± lemon-shaped, 10–12 × 6.5

mesophaeum 160. Sp. ovate, almost smooth, 9–11 × 4·5–5·5

pumilum 160. Sp. ± almond-shaped, 8·5–9 × 5·5

pusillum 160. Sp. ± almond-shaped, 10–14·5 × 5·5–7

saccharoliens 160. Sp. ± almond-shaped, 10·5–12 × 6·5–7

sinuosum 160. Sp. ± ovate, 10–12 × 5–7

Helotiales 42

Helotium. *Asci not in perithecia, inoperculate with apical pore; sp. smooth, either not septate or 1-septate.*

citrinum 42. Sp. in two rows, elliptic, 8–14 × 3–4

Helvella. *Asci operculate; sp. hyaline smooth usually with central oil drop.*

acetabula 38. Sp. ovate, 18–21 × 12–14

costifera 38. Sp. ovate, 18 × 14

crispa 40. Sp. elliptic, 18–20 × 9–13

elastica 38. Sp. elliptic, 18–22 × 9–12

lacunosa 38. Sp. elliptic, 17–21 × 10–13

macropus 38. Sp. elongated, 20–30 × 10–12

Hericium. *Sp. hyaline ± globose; cyst. with oily contents (gloeocystidia).*

coralloides 58. Sp. smooth, c. 4 diam.

Hirneola 244. Auricularia.

auricula. Auricularia a.

Humaria 34. Peziza p.p.

Hydnaceae 58

Hydnellum. *Flesh tough, fibrous to woody, dark-coloured; teeth dark; sp. coarsely angular or tuberculate, ± coloured.*

aurantiacum 60. Sp. yellowish, sub-globose, 4–6 × 4–5

coeruleum 60. Sp. yellowish-brown, sub-globose, 5–6 × 4–5

zonatum. Sp. dark brown, ± sub-globose, warty and rough, 4·5–6 × 4–4·5

Hydnotria. *Asci 6-8 spored; sp. ± warty and rough.*

tulasnei 42. Sp. brown, almost globose, 33–38 diam.

Hydnum (sensu restricto). *Flesh soft, sp. hyaline.*

aurantiacum 60. Hydnellum a.

auriscalpium = Auriscalpium vulgare

coeruleum 60. Hydnellum c.

coralloides 58. Hericium c.

imbricatum 58. Sarcodon i.

melaleucum 60. Phellodon m.

niger 60. Phellodon n.

repandum 60. Sp. white, smooth, sub-globose, 7–8·5 × 6–7

rufescens 60. Sp. white, smooth, sub-globose, 7–8.5 × 6–7

zonatum 60. Hydnellum z.

Hygrocybe 78. A sub-genus of Hygrophorus. *Gill trama of ± parallel, coarse hyphae.*

Hygrophoropsis. **Cap cuticle filamentous; sp. smooth, ovate, red-brown in iodine (dextrinoid).*

aurantiaca 184. Sp. 5·5–7·5 × 3·5–5·5

Hygrophorus. **Cap cuticle typically filamentous; sp. smooth, typically non-amyloid; basidia 30 or more long. See sub-genera Camarophyllus, Hygrocybe, Limacium.*

agathosmus 76. Sp. ovoid, 9–11 × 5–7

camarophyllus 78. Sp. 7–9·5 × 4·5–6

caprinus = camarophyllus

citrinus 78. Sp. 7–9 × 4–5

coccineus 78. Sp. oblong or elliptic, 7–9·5 × 4·5–5·5

conicus 78. Sp. ovate, 11–13 × 5·5–6·5

chrysaspis 76. Sp. 7·5–9 × 4–5·5

dichrous 76. Sp. ovate, 8–12 × 5–7. Exudate on some cuticular hyphae blue-green in ammonia

eburneus 76. Sp. oval or oblong, 6–8 × 4–5

glutinipes 78. citrinus var.

hypothejus 76. Sp. ovate, 7–9 × 4–5

laetus 78. Sp. oval, 5·5–7 × 4–4·5

miniatus 78. Sp. oval, 7.5–10 × 5–6

nigrescens 78. Sp. ovoid, 8–11 × 5–6

niveus 76. Sp. 7.5–12 × 4–6; basidia 2- or 4-spored

olivaceo-albus 76. Sp. 12·5–15·5 × 7–8·5

pratensis 76. Sp. elliptic, 6–8 × 4–5·5

psittacinus 78. Sp. ovate 8–9·5 × 4–5·5

puniceus 78. Sp. obovate or oblong, 8.5–12 × 5–6

pustulatus 76. Sp. ovate, 8–10 × 4·5–6

turundus 78. Sp. ovate, 8·5–12 × 5–6

Hymenochaete. *Hymenium with numerous projecting, pointed, thick-walled, brown setae.*

rubiginosa 52. Sp. hyaline, smooth, 4–6 × 2–3

Hymenogaster. *Sp. almond-shaped to ± lemon-shaped, smooth, wrinkled or warty when ripe, often with outer utricle.*

tener 214. Sp ± lemon-shaped, red-brown, warty, usually with bladder-like utricle, mostly 15–19 × 8–12

Hypholoma. **Cap cuticle filamentous, sp. smooth; marginal cyst. and (facial) chrysocystidia present.*

candolleanum 140. Psathyrella c.

capnoides 146. Sp. ovate, 7–9 × 4–5

dispersum 146. Sp. ovate, 7–9 × 4–5

elongatum 146. Sp. ovate or oblong, 9·5–11·5 × 5·5–6·5

fasciculare 146. Sp. oval, 5–7 × 3·5–4·5

hydrophilum 140. Psathyrella h.

lacrymabundum 140. Psathyrella l.

radicosum 146. Sp. oval, 6·5–8 × 3–4

squamosum 146. Sp. ovate, 11·5–14·5 × 6–8

sublateritium 146. Sp. ovate, 6–7 × 3–4·5

udum 146. Sp. ellipsoid-fusiform, (12)14–16(20) × 6–7(8)

velutinum = Psathyrella lacrymabunda

Hypochreales 46

Hypoxylon. *Asci in perithecia, inoperculate with apical pore; sp. finally brown or black, smooth 1-celled.*

coccineum = fragiforme

fragiforme 46. Sp. uniseriate, finally black, 11·5—15·5 × 5–6·5

Hysterangium. *Sp. smooth, fusiform.*

coriaceum 214. Sp. 12–13·5 × 4–4·5

Inocybe. **Cap cuticle filamentous; sp. smooth, wavy to nodulose or cylindric-spiny;* **cyst. thin-walled and ± balloon-shaped, or thick-walled, elongated-fusoid, usually capped by crystals. (Examine gill faces, if necessary.)*

asterospora 158. Sp. stellate with 5–8 bluntish protuberances, 9–12 × 7·5–9; thick-walled cyst. present

bongardii 156. Sp. smooth, bean-shaped, 10·5–14 × 6–7·5; cyst. thin walled ± clavate

casimiri 158. Sp. with numerous projecting nodules, 10 × 7; gill face without fusoid, thick-walled cyst.

cookei 156. Sp. smooth, bean-shaped, 7–10 × 4–6; cyst. thin-walled, ± pear-shaped

corydalina 154. Sp. smooth, elliptic, 8–10 × 5–6·5; cyst. thick-walled

dulcamara 156. Sp. smooth, bean-shaped, 8-10·5 × 5–5·5; cyst. thin-walled, ± club-shaped

fastigiata 156. Sp. smooth, bean-shaped, 9–12(14) × 4·5–7; cyst. thin-walled ± clavate

flocculosa 154. Sp. smooth, obliquely ovate, 8–11 × 4·5–5·5; cyst. thick-walled

geophylla 154. Sp. smooth ± obliquely ovate, 8–10·5 × 5–6; cyst. thick-walled

griseo-lilacina 154. Sp. smooth ± obliquely ovate, 8–11 × 5–6; cyst. thin-walled, ± balloon-shaped

jurana 158. Sp. smooth, bean-shaped, 10–13(14) × 5·5–7; cyst. thin-walled, clavate

lacera 154. Sp. smooth, almost cylindric, 10–15(18) × 4·5–6; cyst. thick-walled

langei 156. Sp. smooth, elliptic, 7–8 × 4–5; cyst. thick-walled

lanuginosa sensu J. Lge. = casimiri

maculata 158. Sp. smooth, bean-shaped, 9–11 × 4·5–6; cyst. thin-walled, clavate

napipes 158. Sp. nodular, with 5–6 blunt nodules, 8·5–10 × 5·5–7; cyst. thick-walled

patouillardii 158. Sp. smooth, bean-shaped, 9·5–12(14) × 5–8; cyst. thin-walled

praetervisa 156. Sp. with pointed nodules, 9–12(13) × 6–8; cyst. thick-walled

pudica 154. Sp. smooth, ± bean-shaped. 8–9·5 × 4·5–5·5; cyst. thick-walled with accompanying thin-walled ± pear-shaped ones

rubescens sensu J. Lge. = pudica

squamata 156. Sp. smooth, ± bean-shaped, 8·5–11 × 4·5–6·5; cyst. thin-walled, ± clavate

Inonotus. *Sessile; context brown finally ± corky; sp. smooth, apex not truncate.*

hispidus 62. Sp. broadly elliptic, 8–9 × 7–7·5

radiatus 62. Sp. elliptic, 5–6 × 3–3·5

Irpex. *Sessile brackets, or resupinate, annual; tubes not stratified nor forming a layer distinct from cap flesh; pores finally irregular into teeth or plates; spores hyaline, white or if faintly coloured then membrane thin and apex not truncated.*

obliquus 70. Sp. smooth, elliptic, 4–5 × 3–3·5

Kuehneromyces. Pholiota p.p.
mutabilis 152. Pholiota m.

Laccaria. *Cap cuticle filamentous; sp. globose or almost so, with pointed spines, non-amyloid.*
amethystina 98. Sp. globose 9–11; basidia 4-spored
laccata 98. Sp. globose, 7–9(10); basidia 4-spored
Lachnea 34. Peziza p.p.
Lacrymaria 140. Psathyrella p.p.
Lactarius. *At least cap flesh with scattered groups of globose cells (sphaerocysts); * sp. with amyloid ornamentation; cuticle usually filamentous.*
azonites 206. Sp. 8–9×7·5–8·5; E–F. L 9
blennius 212. Sp. 7·5–8(9)×6–7; B–C. L 7–10
camphoratus 208. Sp. 6–8×6–7; D. L 4; marginal cyst. inflated
circellatus 212. Sp. 7–8×5·5–6·5; B–C. L 10
cremor=fulvissimus
cyathula 208. Sp. 7–9×6–7
deliciosus 212. Sp. 7–9×6–7; B–C. L 3, 6, 9
flavidus 212. Sp. 8·5–10×7–9; B–C. L 7–10
fuliginosus 206. Sp. 8–9·5×8; E. L 9
fulvissimus 208. Sp. 7·5–8×6–7; D. L 4
glyciosmus 206. Sp. 7–8×5·5–6·5; D. L 7–10
helvus 208. Sp. 7–9×5·5–6·5; C. L 5
mammosus 206. Sp. 7·5–9×5·5 6·5; C(D). L 9
mitissimus 208. Sp. 7–9×6–7; B–C. L 7
necator=turpis
pallidus 210. Sp. 7·5–9×6–7; B–C. L 7–10
piperatus 206. Sp. 6–8·5×5·5–6·5; A. L 1
plumbeus=turpis
pyrogalus 210. Sp. 6·5–8×5·5–6·5; D–E. L 10

quietus 210. Sp. 7·5–9×6–7; C(D). L 6
repraesentaneus 210. Sp. 9–11×7·5–9. L 7
resimus 210. Sp. 7–8·5×6·5–7; D(E). L 6
rufus 208. Sp. 8–9·5×6–7; B. L 5
scrobiculatus. Sp. 10–12×8–9. L 6
subdulcis 208. Sp. 7–9·5×6–7·5; C–D. L 7
tabidus 208. Sp. 8–10×5–7·5; C–D. L 3; cap cuticle cellular
torminosus 210. Sp. 7·5–9·5×6–7; C–B(D). L 5
turpis 212. Sp. 7·5–8×6–7; C. L 7
uvidus 212. Sp. 9–10×7–8; E. L 8
vellereus 206. Sp. 7·5–10×6–8·5; A–B. L 2
vietus 212. Sp. 8–9·5×6–7; B–C. L 8
volemus 206. Sp. globose, 7·5–10; A. L 10
Leccinum 194. Boletus p.p.
Lentinellus. *Sp. sub-globose, less than 6·5 long, prickly, amyloid.*
cochleatus 102. Sp. 4–5×3–4
Lentinus. *Sp. non-amyloid, smooth, more than 6·5 long.*
cochleatus 102. Lentinellus c.
lepideus 106. Sp. 8–15(17)×3·5–5·5
Lenzites 70. Trametes p.p., Gloeophyllum p.p.
Leotia. *Inoperculate; sp. hyaline or sl. brownish, finally septate.*
lubrica 44. Sp. fusiform, sl. curved, 20–25×5–6, (finally 5–7), septate
Lepiota. *Sp. smooth, typically dextrinoid, gill trama never bilateral; cuticle not of mealy globular cells unless stated.*
acutesquamosa auct.=friesii
amianthina 128. Cystoderma a.
bucknallii. Cap cuticle of mealy, globular cells; sp. ± *projectile shaped, 7–9×2·5–3·5
carcharias 128. Cystoderma c.
castanea 126. Sp. *projectile-shaped, base truncate, 9–13× 3·5–5
clypeolaria 126. Sp. fusiform, 13–19×5–6

cortinarius 126. Sp. $\pm$ * projectile-shaped with oblique pedicel, 8 × 3–3·5

cristata 126. Sp. * projectile-shaped, 6–8 × 3–4

echinata 126. Cap cuticle of mealy globular cells; sp. oval, 4·5–5·5 × 2·5–3·5, with sl. brownish tint; becoming reddish on standing in mass

excoriata 122. Sp. elliptic, 12–16 × 8–10, with germ pore

eyrei 128. Cap cuticle of mealy globular cells; sp. oval, 3·5–5 × 2–2·5; greenish in mass

friesii 124. Sp. $\pm$ narrowly ellipsoid, 6–8 × 2·5–3·5; cyst. on gill edge $\pm$ balloon-shaped

fulvella 128. Sp. * projectile-shaped, mostly 8–9 × 2·5–4·5

fuscovinacea 128. Sp. ovoid, 4–5·5 × 2–3

grangei 126. Sp. * projectile-shaped, 8·5–11·5 × 3·5–4·5

granulosa 128. Cystoderma g.

haematosperma = echinata

lenticularis = Limacella guttata

leucothites 124. Sp. ovate, 7–9·5 × 5–6, white in mass, tinted pink under microscope

naucina = leucothites

procera 124. Sp. ovate, 13–17 × 8·5–11, with germ pore (? always)

rhacodes 124. Sp. oval, 8·5–11·5 × 5·5–6·5, with germ pore (? always)

seminuda = sistrata

sistrata 128. Cap cuticle of globular cells, micaceous; sp. elliptic, 3–4 × 2–2·5

Lepista 90. Tricholoma p.p.

Leptonia 178, 182. Sub-genus of Rhodophyllus

Leptopodia 38. Helvella p.p.

Leptoporus. *Sp. hyaline; pores forming a layer distinct from white or pallid, thin, homogeneous flesh of cap; cap cuticle not distinct.*

albidus = stipticus

caesius 72. Sp. sausage-shaped, 4–4·5 × 1–1·5

stipticus 72. Sp. elliptic, 4–5 × 1·5–2

Leucocortinarius. Cortinarius p.p. bulbiger 166. Cortinarius b.

Leucopaxillus 96. Clitocybe p.p.

Limacella. *Gill trama bilateral; sp. smooth almost spherical, less than 6 diam.*

guttata 120. Sp. 5–6 × 5, dextrinoid

lenticularis = guttata

Limacium 76. sub-genus of Hygrophorus. * *Gill trama divergent.*

Lycoperdon. *Sp. small round, yellowish (olive) brown, often $\pm$ warty and with pedicel.*

bovista = caelatum

caelatum 216. Sp. smooth, round, 4–5

depressum 218. Sp. virtually smooth, round, 3–5

echinatum 218. Sp. warty, round, 5–6

ericetorum 216. Sp. smooth, round, 3·5–4

excipuliforme 216. Sp. warty, round, 4–5

gemmatum = perlatum

giganteum 216. Sp. prickly, round, 4–5

hiemale = depressum

molle 218. Sp. finely warted, round, 3·5–4·5

nigrescens 216. perlatum var.

perlatum 216. Sp. round, prickly, 3·5–4·5

polymorphum = ericetorum

pusillum = ericetorum

pyriforme 218. Sp. round, virtually smooth, 4–4·5

saccatum = excipuliforme

umbrinum = molle

Lyophyllum. * *Basidia with carminophil granules; see p. 233.*

aggregatum = decastes

ambustum auct. = carbonarium

carbonarium 82. Sp. round, $\pm$ prickly, 4·5–5

connatum 80. Sp. elliptic, 6–7 × 3·5–4

decastes 80. Sp. almost round, smooth, 5·7 × 5–6

murinum 82. Sp. ovate, smooth, 6·5–8 × 4–5

palustre 82. Sp. ovate, smooth, 6–8·5×4–5

rancidum 82. Sp. elliptic, smooth, 7–8×3–4·5

tesquorum 82. Sp. broadly oval, prickly, 6–7·5×5·5–6

Macrocystidia. *Cap cuticle, gills and stipe with large, lanceolate cyst.*

cucumis 108. Sp. smooth, 7·5–10× 4–5

Marasmius. * *Cap cuticle cellular; or foetid species on wood (M. foetidus); or small leathery species, cap 1–2 cm. diam. and stipe horse-hair-like and/or not exceeding 1–2 mm. diam. and piercing substrata of vegetable remains: twigs, leaves, petioles; sp. smooth, non-amyloid.*

alliaceus 114. Sp. ovate, 9–11·5× 6–7

androsaceus 114. Sp. pip-shaped, 6·5–9×3–4; cap cuticle cells irregular and brush-like

foetidus 114. Sp. pip-shaped, 8–10× 3–4

fuscopurpureus 102. Collybia f.

lupuletorum 114. Sp. pip-shaped, 8–10×4–5

oreades 114. Sp. pip-shaped, 9·5– 10·5×5·5–6

perforans 114. Sp. pip-shaped, 5–7× 3·5; cap cuticle ± filamentous

peronatus 100. Collybia p.

ramealis 114. Sp. elliptic, 8–10× 2·5–3·5; cap cuticle of brush-like cells

rotula 114. Sp. pip-shaped, 7–10× 3·5–5

scorodonius 114. Sp. pip-shaped, 7–9×3·5–4·5; marginal cyst. brush-like

Melanogaster. *Sp. borne on basidia, falling off with remnants of sterigmata.*

variegatus var. broomeianus 214. Sp. smooth, 6–9×3–4, cylindric to ovate

Melanoleuca. *Sp. oval with amyloid warts; gills typically with conspicuous cyst. barbed at tip like a harpoon.**

cognata 102. Sp. 7–9×5–6

melaleuca 102. Sp. 7–9×4–5

Melanophyllum 126

Meruliaceae 52

Merulius. *Sp. white, smooth.*

lacrymans 52. Serpula l.

tremellosus 52. Sp. sausage-shaped, 4–5×1

Microglossum. Geoglossum p.p.

Micromphale 114. Marasmius p.p.

Mitrophora 40. Morchella p.p.

Morchella. *Operculate; alveolae separated by sterile ribs; sp. typically aguttulate, smooth.*

conica 40. Sp. yellowish in mass, elliptic, 20–24×12–14

esculenta 40. Sp. yellowish in mass, elliptic, 18–23×12–14

rimosipes=semi-libera

semi-libera 40. Sp. creamy in mass, elliptic, 22–30×12–18

vulgaris 40. Sp. yellowish in mass, elliptic, 16–18×9–11

Mutinus. *Sp. receptacle not free, but an extension of stipe.*

caninus 214. Sp. pale yellowish, oblong, 4–5×1·5–3, smooth

Mycena. * *Gill edge with granulate or ciliate cyst.; sp. amyloid or not, typically smooth.*

acicula 112. Cyst. ciliate; sp. non-amyloid, 9–11×3–3·5

adonis 112. Cyst. ciliate: awl-shaped, conical; sp. non-amyloid, 10–12×3·5–5·5; basidia 2-spored

alcalina 110. Cyst. ciliate: fusiform awl-shaped; sp. amyloid, 8–12× 4·5–6

bisphaerigera 112. Cyst. ciliate: cylindric to vesiculose or fusiform to ventricose; sp. sub-globose, prickly with amyloid perispore, 6–9; basidia 2-spored

bryophila 108. Cyst. ciliate, conical; sp. non-amyloid, spherical, coarsely warted, 6–7

capillaris 112. Cyst. granulate: with wart-like protuberances; sp. amyloid, 9–11×3–4

crocata 110. Cyst. granulate: ± warty; sp. amyloid, 7–10×4·5– 6

epipterygia 110. Gill edge with

gelatinous lining; sp. amyloid, 8–10×4·5–5

flavo-alba 112. Cyst. ciliate: ± awl-shaped to inflated conical; sp. non-amyloid, 6–8·5×3·5–4·5

galericulata 108. Cyst. granulate: ± club-shaped with finger-like protuberances; sp. amyloid, 9–12× 6–8; mostly 2-spored basidia

galopus 110. Cyst. ciliate: ± awl-shaped; sp. amyloid, 10–13×5–6·5

haematopus 110. Cyst. ciliate: ± fusiform; sp. amyloid, 7–10× 5·5–6

inclinata 108. Cyst. granulate: finely warty; sp. amyloid, 8–10×6–7

lasiosperma= bryophila

leptocephala 110. Cyst. ciliate; sp. amyloid, 10·5–12×5·5

leucogala 110. Sp. ± cylindric, 11–13×5–6·5

metata 112. Cyst. granulate; sp. amyloid, 7·5–10×4–5

mucor 112. Cyst. granulate; sp. amyloid, 9–11×3–4·5

pelianthina 112. Cyst. ciliate: cylindric-fusiform; sp. amyloid, 4–8·5 ×2·5–3·5

polygramma 110. Cyst. ciliate: ± hair-like, sometimes branched; sp. amyloid, 9–11×6–7

pura 112. Cyst. ciliate: broadly conical; sp. amyloid, 6–8×3·5–4·5

sanguinolenta 110. Cyst. ciliate: ± awl-shaped; sp. amyloid, 8–11× 4–6

tintinnabulum 108. Cyst. granulate: ± warty; sp. amyloid, 4–5×2·5–3

vitilis 110. Cyst. ciliate: ± hair-shaped; sp. amyloid, 9–12×5·5–7

vulgaris 112. Gill edge with gelatinous lining; sp. amyloid, 7–10×4–5

Naematoloma= Hypholoma

Naucoria. *Cap cuticle typically of ± round or barrel-shaped cells; sp. large, rough, ± rusty-brown; cyst. sharply pointed and hair-like, or with blunt apex and ± cylindric-clavate.*

carpophila 176. Phaeomaramius c.

christinae 174. Phaeocollybia ch.

cucumis 108. Macrocystidia c.

erinacea = Phaeomarasmiuse.

escharoides 162. Cyst. sharply pointed; sp. 10·5–11·5×5·5–6·5

langei 162. Cyst. clavate with blunt apex; sp. 13–20×7·5–9 (2-spored basidia); 12–15×6·5–7·5 (4-spored basidia)

macrospora= langei

scolecina 162. Cyst. sharply pointed; Sp. 11–14×5·5

Nectria. *Asci inoperculate, with apical pore; sp. elliptic, ± hyaline, 1-septate.*

cinnabarina, 46. Sp. 14–20×5–7, in two rows

galligena, 46. Sp. 12–27×4–9

Neotiella 34. Peziza p.p.

Noleanea 178, 180. Sub-genus of Rhodophyllus.

Nyctalis= Asterophora

Octaviana 214

Omphalia= Omphalina

asterospora, 96. Clitocybe a.

bisphaerigera 112. Mycena b.

Omphalina. *Sp. non-amyloid, mostly smooth; basidia never with carminophil granules.*

epichysium 98. Sp. 7–9×5–6

ericetorum 98. Sp. 8–9×4·5–5·5

fibula 98. Sp. 5–6×2–3

pyxidata 98. Sp. 7·5–9·5×4·5–5·5

sphagnicola 98. Sp. sub-cylindric, 8–16×3–5

swartzii 98. Sp. 5–6×2–3

umbellifera= ericetorum

Onygena. *Stalked ascocarps ± globose; asci not in a hymenium, inoperculate without apical pore; sp. smooth; saprophytic on animal debris.*

corvina 48. Sp. 5–8×2–3, colourless or pale yellow

equina 48. Sp. 6–9×4–4·5, yellowish brown

Otidea 36. Peziza p.p.

Oudemansiella. *Cuticle * cellular; sp. large, at least 9–10×6–7, non-amyloid.*

mucida 106. Sp. almost round, 13–18×12–16

249

radicata 106. Sp. ovate, 12–16×
10–12

Oxyporus. *Flesh white or pallid; cyst. crested; sp. broadly ovate, smooth, hyaline.*
populinus 66. Sp. 3·5–4·5×3–4

Pachyphloeus. *Asci with eight globose, spiny or warty sp.*
melanoxanthus 42. Sp. 13–17, excluding spines, 2·5–3

Panellus. *Sp. cylindric-elongated, smooth, amyloid (except in P. nidulans).*
mitis 104. Sp. 3·5–5×1
nidulans 104. Sp. non-amyloid, 5–6 ×2–3
serotinus 104. Sp. 4–5·5×1–2
stypticus 104. Sp. 3·5–4·5×2–2·5

Panaeolus. *Cuticle * cellular, gills mottled; sp. lemon-shaped, typically smooth, with germ pore.*
acuminatus auct.=rickenii
campanulatus. Sp. 12–14×9–10× 7–8
foenisecii 144. Sp. 12–15×7–8, rough
semi-ovatus 144. Sp. 16–20×9–12, ovate elliptic
rickenii 144. Sp. 13–16×9·5–11×9
separatus=semi-ovatus

Panus. *Sp. non-amyloid, smooth; gill edge with thick-walled cyst.*
conchatus=torulosus
torulosus 106. Sp. 5–6·5×3–3·5

Paxillus. *Sp. not more than twice as long as wide, smooth.*
atrotomentosus 184. Sp. 4·5–6·5× 3·5–4·5
involutus 184. Sp. 8–10×5–6
panuoides 184. Sp. 4–5×3–3·5

Paxina 38. Helvella p.p.

Peniophora. Corticium p.p.

Peziza. *Operculate; the ascus tip of some species are blued by iodine, others not.*
aurantia 34. Not blued; sp. 18–22 ×9–11, conspicuously reticulated; oil drops 2
badia 36. Asci blued; sp. irregularly reticulate, 17–20×9–12
catinus 34. Not blued; sp. elliptic, smooth, 20–24×10–12; oil drops 2

coccinea 34. Not blued; sp. fusiform, smooth, 26–34×11–13
costifer 38. Helvella c.
hemisphaerica 34. Not blued; sp. elliptic, rough, 20–24×10–13; oil drops 2
leporina 36. Not blued; sp. elliptic, smooth, 12–14×7–8; oil drops 2
nigrella 34. Not blued; sp. globose, smooth, 10–12(13)
onotica 36. Not blued; sp. elliptic, 10–14×5–7; oil drops 2
radiculata 34. Not blued; sp. oval, coarsely warted, 12–16×7–8; oil drops 2
repanda 36. Blued; sp. elliptic, smooth, 15–19×9–11
rutilans 34. Not blued; sp. oval, reticulated, 22–26×11–14
saniosa 34. Blued; sp. elliptic, coarsely warted (Dennis), 14–16·5 ×7–9
scutellata 34. Not blued; sp. elliptic, minutely rough, 18–22×10–13
succosa 36. Blued; sp. elliptic, with warts and ridges, 18–22×10–12
vesiculosa 36. Blued; sp. elliptic, smooth, 20–24×12–14

Phaeocollybia. *Sp. in mass rusty or rusty yellowish-brown; ± rough; ± no germ pore; stipe rooting, very cartilaginous.*
christinae 174. Sp. obliquely ovoid, 8·5–9×4·5

Phaeolepiota. *Universal veil mealy granular; sp. in mass yellowish-brown, smooth; no germ pore.*
aurea 130. Sp. 11–14×4–5

Phaeolus. *Pore layer distinct from brownish flesh of cap; cyst. absent; flesh ± violet in ammonia; sp. hyaline, smooth.*
schweinitzii 66. Sp. 7–8×3–4

Phaeomarasmius. *Cap scales comprised of filaments (round cells absent); sp. smooth.*
erinaceus 176. Sp. ± lemon-shaped, 10–11×6–8
carpophilus 176. Sp. 7–9×4–6

Phallus. *Sp. very small, smooth.*
hadrianus 214. Sp. 3–5×1·5–2
impudicus 214. Sp. 3–5×2

Phellinus. *Pores not in a layer distinct*

from coloured flesh of cap, cyst. fusiform with thick coloured walls; sp. smooth.

igniarius 62. Sp. globose, 5–7

pomaceus 62. Sp. almost globose, 6×5–6

Phellodon. *As Hydnellum, but teeth pallid.*

melaleucus 60. Sp. globose, 2·5–3, minutely prickly

niger 60. Sp. almost round, sl. angular, 3–4·5×3–4

Phlebia. *Sp. white, smooth.*

aurantiaca=radiata

merismoides 52. Sp. ± sausage-shaped, 4–5×1·5–2

radiata 52. Sp. ± sausage-shaped, 4·5–6·5×1·5–2·5

Pholiota. * *Cap cuticle filamentous; sp. mostly yellowish rusty-brown, smooth without germ pore; cyst. various.*

adiposa 150. Sp. oval, 5–6×3–3·5

alnicola 150. Sp. ovate, 7·5–9×4–5·5

apicrea 150. Sp. ovate, 8–10×4–5

astragalina 150. Sp. oval, 6–7×3–4

aurea 130. Phaeolepiota a.

aurivella 150. Sp. oblong, 8–9×4–6

caperata 172. Rozites c.

carbonaria 150. Sp. oval, 6–7×3–4

destruens 148. Sp. oval, cigar-brown, 7·5–8·5

dura 152. Agrocybe d.

erebia 152. Agrocybe e.

erinaceus 176. Phaeomarasmius e.

flammans 148. Sp. oval, 4–5×1·5–3

lenta 150. Sp. oval, clay to cocoa-brown, 6–7×3–4

lucifera 150. Sp. ± bean-shaped, 7–8×4–5·5

marginata 174. Galerina m.

mutabilis 152. Sp. ovate, 6–8×4–5

paludosa 152. Agrocybe p.

praecox 152. Agrocybe p.

spectabilis 174. Gymnopilus jun.

squarrosa 148. Sp. oval, 6–8×3–4

unicolor 174. galerina u.

Phylacteria 52. Thelephora p.p.

Phyllotopsis 104

Piptoporus. *Flesh white; spores hyaline, smooth, cylindric-arcuate; cyst. absent.*

betulinus 66. Sp. 4·5–5·5×1·5–2

Plectascales 48

Pleurotus. *Sp. smooth, ± sausage-shaped, non-amyloid; cyst. absent.*

corticatus=dryinus

dryinus 104. Sp. 11–14×3·5–4

mitis 104. Panellus m.

nidulans 104. Panellus n.

ostreatus 106. Sp. 10–11×3·5–4

serotinus 104. Panellus s.

Pluteus. * *Cuticle ± filamentous or ± mealy and comprised of globose cells; cyst. present, sometimes hooked* (Fig. 10); **gill trama inverse; sp. smooth, ± oval.*

atromarginatus 120. Cuticle filamentous; sp. 7–8×4·5–6; cyst. hooked

aurantiorugosus 122. Cuticle of globose cells; sp. 5·5×4–4·5

cervinus 120. Cuticle filamentous; sp. 7–8×5–6; cyst. hooked

cinereo-fuscus 122. Cuticle of globose cells; sp. 8–8·5×6–6·5

coccineus=aurantiorugosus

lutescens 122. Cuticle of globose cells; sp. 6·5–7×5·5–6

pearsonii. Cuticle filamentous; sp. ovoid, 5·5–6×5

petasatus. Cuticle filamentous; sp. ovoid 7–9×4–5

plautus 122. Cuticle filamentous; sp. 7–8·5×6–7

salicinus 122. Cuticle filamentous; sp. 8×5·5; cyst. hooked

Polyporus (sensu restricto). *Flesh white; sp. smooth, non-amyloid; cyst. absent.*

abietinus 70. Trametes a.

adustus 70. Gloeoporus a.

annosus 66. Fomes a.

applanatus 64. Ganoderma a.

betulinus 66. Piptoporus b.

brumalis 74. Sp. ± oblong, 5–8×1·5–2·5

caesius 72. Leptoporus c.

cinnabarinus 70. Trametes c.

fomentarius 64. Fomes f.

frondosus 74. Grifola f.

fumosus 72. Gloeoporus f.

giganteus 72. Grifola g.

hirsutus 68. Trametes h.

hispidus 62. Inonotus h.

igniarius 62. Phellinus i.

intybaceus=Grifola frondosa

lucidus 64. Ganoderma l.

marginatus=Fomes pinicola

nummularius 74. Sp. 7–9 × 2·5–3

perennis 62. Coltrichia p.

pinicola 64. Fomes p.

pomaceus 62. Phellinus p.

populinus 66. Oxyporus p.

radiatus 62. Inonotus r.

schweinitzii 66. Phaeolus s.

serialis 68. Trametes s.

stipticus 62. Leptoporus s.

squamosus 74. Sp. hyaline, oblong-elliptic, 11–14 × 4–5

sulphureus 72. Grifola s.

varius 74. Sp. oblong, 6·5–8 × 3–3·5

versicolor 68. Trametes v.

Polystictus 62, 68

Poria 68. *Resupinate; pores ± inserted directly on mycelium; sp. white or coloured.*

vaillantii 68. Sp. white, smooth, 6 × 3·5

vaporaria auct.=vaillantii

Poronia 46. *Perithecia immersed in flat surface of stipitate stroma; sp. dark coloured, non-septate, smooth.*

punctata 46. Sp. ± bean-shaped, 16–24 × 6–10

Psalliota=Agaricus

Psathyra=Psathyrella

Psathyrella 140. * *Cap cuticle cellular; sp. typically smooth, with germ pore, not violet tinted when viewed under the microscope; cystidia present.*

candolleana 140. Sp. 7–8 × 4–4·5; facial cyst. absent

caput-medusae 142. Sp. elliptic, 10–12 × 4–5

disseminata 140. Coprinus d.

conopilea 142. Cuticle with brown bristles; sp. 12·5–16 × 7·5–8; no facial cyst.

gracilis 142. Sp. elliptic, 11–13 × 5·5–6·5; facial cyst. ± capitate, not pointed

hydrophila 140. Sp. 5–7 × 3–4; facial cyst. present

lacrymabunda 140. Sp. coarsely warted, ± lemon-shaped, 8–11 × 5–6

multipedata 142. Sp. 6·5–10 × 4–5; facial cyst. present

spadicea 142. Sp. 8·5–10 × 4–5

spadiceo-grisea 140. Sp. 7–10 × 4–5; facial cyst. sack-shaped; marginal cyst. balloon-shaped

stipatissima=multipedata

subatrata=conopilea

Pseudohiatula. * *Cuticle cellular; sp. non-amyloid; cystidia present.*

esculenta 112. Sp. 5–7 × 2·5–4; cyst. blunt, crested

Pseudohydnum. *Fruit-body gelatinous.*

gelatinosum 224. Sp. smooth, broadly ovate, 5–7 × 5

Pseudoplectania. Peziza p.p.

nigrella 34. Peziza n.

Psilocybe. *Cap typically with separable pellicle; gills typically without chrysocystidia; sp. smooth, tinted violet under microscope.*

atrorufa=montana

coprophila 148. Sp. 12–14 × 6·5–8

foenisecii 144. Panaeolus f.

montana 148. Sp. 5·5–8 × 4·5

semilanceata 148. Sp. ± lemon-shaped, 12–14 × 7–8

spadicea 142. Psathyrella s.

uda 146. Hypholoma u.

Pterula. *Sp. white, typically smooth.*

multifida 56. Sp. 5–7 × 3–4

Pustularia 34. Peziza p.p.

Ramaria. *Sp. never white; smooth or not.*

boytris 56. Sp. faintly longitudinally striate, otherwise smooth, 12–18 × 4–6

flava 56. Sp. warty-rough, 10–14 × 4–6

formosa 56. Sp. ± rough, 10–16 × 3·5–5

invallii 56. Sp. shortly and sharply spiny, 6–11 × 4–6

ochraceo-virens 56. Sp. warty-rough, 5·5–9·5 × 3–4·5

stricta 56. minutely rough, Sp. 7–10 × 4–5

Rhizina. *Operculate; asci not blue in iodine; sp. fusiform, minutely rough.*

inflata=undulata

undulata 36. Sp. 24–36×8–10

Rhizopogon. *Basidia 4–8 spored; sp. smooth, hyaline or sl. coloured.*

luteolus 214. Sp. 5–8×3

Rhodophyllus. *Sp. angular polygonal* (Fig. 12, 4).

aprile 180. Sp. 8–10×7–8

asprellus 182. Sp. 10–12×7–8

cetratus 182. Sp. 10–12×6–7·5

clypeatus 180. Sp. 9–12×7–9

dichrous 180. Sp. 9–10·5×6·5–7

euchlorus=incanus

euchrous 182. Sp. 9–11×5–7·5

icterinus 182. Sp. 9–12×6–8

incanus 182. Sp. irreg. ovate, 10–13 ×6·5–9

lampropus 182. Sp. 9·5–11·5× 6·5–7

lividus=sinuatus

majalis sensu J. Lge.=aprile

nidorosus 180. Sp. 8–10×7–8

nitidus 178. Sp. sub-globose, 7–9× 6·5–7·5

porphyrophaeus 178. Sp. 10–13× 6–7

prunuloides 178. Sp. 7–9(10)× 7–8

sericellus 182. Sp. 9–11×6·5–7·5

sericeus 180. Sp. ± nodulose, 8–10 ×6–7

sinuatus 178. Sp. 9–11×8–9

staurosporus 180. Sp. ± cruciate-stellate, 9–10×7–9, with 4–6 angles

undatus 182. Sp. irregularly wavy, 8·5–9·5×5·5–6

Ripartites. *Sp. almost round, sl. angular and minutely prickly; cyst. absent.*

tricholoma 176. Sp. 4–5×3·5–4

Rozites. *Sp. elliptic, rough, without germ pore.*

caperata 172. Sp. finely warty, 11–14×7–9

Russula. * *Flesh with scattered groups of round cells (sphaerocysts); sp. with amyloid ornamentation on; cyst ± awl-shaped on gills ± stained dark blue-grey in sulphovanillin* (SV). *For spore colour grades, see p.* 198, *footnote.*

aeruginea 202. Sp. D–E, 7–8×6. R 8

alutacea auct.=olivacea

amoena=violeipes

atropurpurea 202. Sp. A–B, 8–9× 7–7·5; R 4, cyst. in cap

aurata 204. Sp. H, 8–10×7–7.5; R 3, no cap cyst.

chamaeleontina sensu J. Lge.=nauseosa 204

claroflava 196. Sp. E–F, 9–10×8; R 5, 6, no cap cyst.

cyanoxantha 198. Sp. A, 7·5–9× 6–7; R 10, no cap cyst.

decolorans 204. Sp. E, 10–14×9–12 with long spines; R 5, 6, cyst. sometimes in cap

delica 196. Sp. B, 8·5–9×6·5–7; R 4

densifolia 196. Sp. A, 7–9×6–7; R 9

drimeia=sardonia

emetica 202. Sp. A, 8–10×8–9; R 7, cyst. in cap

fellea 196. Sp. A, 7·5–8·5×6·5–7·5; R 7; cyst. in cap

foetens 196. Sp. B–C, 9–10×8; R 5, 6, no cap cyst.

fragilis 202. Sp. A–B, 8–9×7–8; cyst. in cap

grisea 198. Sp. C–D, 6·5–9×5·5–7; cyst. in cap

lepida 200. Sp. B, 7·5–9×6–7; R 4, cyst. in cap

mairei 202. Sp. A, 7–8×5·5–6; R 7, cyst. in cap

nauseosa 204. Sp. G–H, 8–11×7–9; R 4–5; cyst. in cap

nigricans 196. Sp. A, 7–10×6·5–9

nitida 202. Sp. E–G, 9–10×7–8: R 6, cyst, in cap

obscura 204. Sp. F, 10–11×8–9; R 5, 6, no cap cyst.

ochroleuca 198. Sp. B–C, 8–10× 6·5–8; R 5, no cap cyst.

olivacea 204. Sp. G–H, 8–10×7–8; R 6, no cap cyst.

paludosa 204. Sp. D–E, 8–9×7–8; R 3, cyst, in cap

puellaris 200. Sp. B–C, 9–10×7–8; R 6 cyst. in cap

queletii 202. Sp. C–D, 7·5–9×6·5–7·5; R 5, cyst. in cap

rosea 200. Sp. B, 7·5–8×6·5;
R 8

sanguinea 200. Sp. C, 7–9×6–7·5;
R 6, cyst. in cap

sardonia 202. Sp. C–F, 7–8×6–7;
R 4, cyst, in cap

solaris 198. Sp. D, 7–9×6·5–7; R 5,
cyst. in cap

vesca 198. Sp. A. 7–8×5–6; R 10,
no cap cyst.

venosa=nitida

versicolor 200. Sp. E–F, 8–9×5·5–6;
R 2; cyst. in cap

vinosa=obscura

violeipes 198. Sp. B–C, 7–9×7–8;
R 2; cyst. not blue in SV

virescens 200. Sp. B, 6·5–7·5×5·5
–6; R 9; cyst. hardly blue in
SV

xerampelina 200. Sp. E–F, 8–9·5×
7–8; R 6

Rutstroemia. *Inoperculate with apical
pore; sp. smooth.*

firma 42. Pore of ascus blued by
iodine; sp. 12–19×4–6, finally
3–5 septate

Sarcodon. *As Hydnum, but sp.* ±
coloured.

imbricatum 58. Sp. round, warty,
5–7

Sarcoscypha. Peziza p.p.

coccinea 34. Peziza c.

Schizophyllum. *Sp. non-amyloid; cyst.
absent.*

commune 104. Sp. oblong, 5·5–7×
2·5–3·5

Scleroderma. *Sp. dark, round, orna-
mented.*

aurantium 222. Sp. blackish-brown,
reticulated, 12–16

verrucosum 222. Sp. dark brown,
with prickles, 10–13

vulgare=aurantium

Sclerotinia. *Inoperculate, with apical
pore; sp. smooth, non-septate.*

batschiana 42. Apical pore blued by
iodine; sp. ovate, 7–11×4–6

tuberosa 42. Apical pore blued by
iodine; sp. 12–16×6–8

Scutellinia 34. Peziza p.p.

Serpula 52. *Sp. bright orange-yellow,
smooth.*

lacrymans 52. Sp. 9–10×5–6

Sowerbyella 34. Peziza p.p.

Sparassis. *Sp. hyaline, smooth, pale
yellowish in the mass.*

crispa 56. Sp. ± pip-shaped, 5–7×
4–5

Spathularia. *Inoperculate with apical
pore, pore not blued by iodine; sp. parallel in
ascus, cylindric, finally multi-septate.*

flavida. 44 Sp. smooth, 50–60×2–3
Sphaeirales 46

Sphaerobolus. *Basidia sessile with 5–8
sessile, smooth sp.; sp. white in mass.*

stellatus 222. Sp. oval, 6–8×4–5

Stereum. *Hymenium smooth; sp. white,
smooth, cyst. when present hyaline.*

hirsutum 50. Sp. oblong, 5–7×2·5–
3·5

purpureum 50. Sp. sl. sausage-
shaped, 5–9×3–4

rubiginosa 52. Hymenochaete r.

rugosum 50. Sp. 7–9×3–4·5

sanguinolentum 50. Sp. 8–9×2·5
3·5

Strobliomyces 186. *Sp. mass brownish-
purple; sp. broadly oval, reticulate.*

floccopus 194. Spores 10–13×8–10
strobilaceus=floccopus

Stropharia. * *Cap with separable pellicle,
epicutis flamentous; sp. smooth, tinted violet
under microscope; with germ pore; cyst.
present.*

aeruginosa 144. Sp. 7·5–9×4·5

caput-medusae 142. Hypholoma
c–m.

coprophila 148. Psilocybe c.

coronilla 144. Sp. 7–9×4–5

depilata=hornemannii

hornemannii 144. Sp. elliptic, 11–14
×6–8

semi-globata 144. Sp. 15–20×8–
10

squamosa 146. Hypholoma sq.

Thelephora. *Hymenium smooth or rough;
sp. rounded or angular, coloured.*

palmata 52. Sp. reddish-brown in
mass, angular, spiny, 8–11×7–8

terrestris 52. Sp. dark brown in

mass, angular, warted, $8-9 \times 6-7\cdot5$
Thelephoraceae 50

Trametes (sensu lato). *Sessile; corky or woody; pores not forming a distinct layer from cap flesh; pores round, angular, elongated or lamelliform; sp. white or pale yellowish, smooth.*

  abietina 70. Flesh brownish or purplish; sp. oblong, $6-9 \times 2-4$

  betulina 70. Flesh white; sp. $\pm$ cylindric, $4-6 \times 2-2\cdot5$

  cinnabarina 70. Flesh reddish; sp. $\pm$ cylindric, $5-6 \times 2-2\cdot5$

  gibbosa 68. Flesh white; sp. $\pm$ cylindric, $4-6 \times 2-2\cdot5$

  hirsuta 68. Flesh white; sp. $\pm$ cylindric, $6-8 \times 2-3$

  serialis 68. Flesh white; sp. $7-9 \times 2-3$

  versicolor 68. Flesh white; sp. $\pm$ cylindric, $5-8 \times 2-3$

Tremella. *Basidia vertically septate* (Fig. 4, 5); *hymenium gelatinous, contorted; sp. hyaline, smooth.*

  encephala 224. Sp. $10-12 \times 7\cdot5-9$

  mesenterica 224. Sp. $7-10(12) \times 5-8$ (10)

Tremellales 224

Tremellodon = Pseudohydnum

  gelatinosum 224. Pseucohydnum g.

Trichoglossum 44. Geoglossum p.p.

Tricholoma. * *Cuticle typically filamentous; sp. typically non-amyloid; basidia typically without carminophil granules; sp. smooth with central oil drop; cyst. rare.*

  aggregatum = Lyophyllum decastes 80

  albobrunnea 90. Sp. $4\cdot5-5 \times 3-4$

  album 84. Sp. $5\cdot5-6 \times 3\cdot5-4$

  argyraceum 86. Sp. $5-6 \times 3-4$

  aurantium 90. Sp. $4-5 \times 2-3$

  cerinum 82. Sp. ovoid, $3-4 \times 2-3$

  cingulatum 86. Sp. $4-5\cdot5 \times 2\cdot5-3\cdot5$

  cognatum 102. Melanoleuca c.

  columbetta 84. Sp. $5-7 \times 4-5$

  equestre = flavovirens

  flavobrunneum = fulvum

  fiavovirens 86. Sp. $5\cdot5-8 \times 4-5$

  fulvum 88. Sp. $5-7 \times 3-4\cdot5$

  gambosum 82. Sp. $5-6 \times 3-3\cdot5$; basidia with carminophil granules

  georgii = gambosum

imbricatum 88. Sp. $5-6\cdot5 \times 3\cdot5-4\cdot5$

inamoenum 84. Sp. ovoid, $7\cdot5-9\cdot5 \times 4\cdot5-6\cdot5$

irinum 90. Sp. pale pinkish, minutely prickly, $7-8 \times 3\cdot5-4$

lascivum 84. Sp. $6-7 \times 3\cdot5-4$

melaleucum 102. Melanoleuca m.

nudum 90. Sp. pale pinkish, minutely prickly, $6-8 \times 4\cdot5-5$

personatum = saevum

populinum 90. Sp. $5-6 \times 3-4$

portentosum 86. Sp. $5-6 \times 3\cdot5-4\cdot5$

psammopus 88. Sp. $5-6 \times 4-4\cdot5$

pseudoflammula 82. Sp. $3-3\cdot5 \times 2-2\cdot5$; basidia with carminophil granules

rutilans 92. Tricholomopsis r.

saponaceum 84. Sp. $5-6 \times 3\cdot5-4$

saevum 90. Sp. pale pinkish, minutely prickly, $5-7\cdot5 \times 3\cdot5-5$

scalpturatum = argyraceum

sudum 84. Sp. $5\cdot5-6\cdot5 \times 3\cdot5-4$

sulphurum 84. Sp. $8-11 \times 5-6$

terreum 88. Sp. $5-6 \times 4-5$

ustale 90. Sp. $5-6 \times 3-4$

ustaloides 90. Sp. $5-7 \times 3\cdot5-5$

vaccinum 88. Sp. $5\cdot5-6\cdot5 \times 4-4\cdot5$

virgatum 86. Sp. $6\cdot5-7\cdot5 \times 5-5\cdot5$

Tricholomopsis. *Like Tricholoma, but gill edge with large thin-walled $\pm$ pear-shaped cystidia.*

  platyphylla 92. Sp. $6\cdot5-8\cdot5 \times 6-7$

  rutilans 92. Sp. $5-7 \times 4-4\cdot5$

Tubaria. * *Cap cuticle filamentous; sp. smooth; cyst. hair-shaped clavate.*

  furfuracea 176. Sp. $7-8\cdot5 \times 4\cdot5-5$

Tuber. *Gleba venose; Asci with $1.5(6)$ sp.; sp. spiny or with a network of crests.*

  aestivum 42. Sp. reticulate, $20-40 \times 15-30$, larger spores with smaller number per ascus

  melanosporum 42. Sp. spiny, elliptic, $30-35 \times 22-25$

  nitidum 42. $20-40 \times 15-24$, larger spores with smaller number per ascus

  rufum 42. $17-46 \times 15-27$, larger spores with smaller number per ascus

Tuberales 42

Tulostoma. *Sp. coloured, globose* ± *warty.*

brumale 222. Sp. 4–5, pinkish
Tylopilus 192. Boletus p.p.

Ustulina. *Perithecia large with papillate ostiole; sp. black, non-septate, smooth.*

deusta 46. Sp. fusiform, 26–34 × 7–10

Verpa. *Operculate; sp. elliptic, smooth, with oil drops only on outer membrane; non-septate.*

conica 40. Sp. 20–24 × 12–14
Volvaria = Volvariella

Volvariella. *Gill trama inverse (see Fig. 10), sp. smooth, ± broadly oval; cyst. ± inflated clavate.*

bombycina 120. Sp. 7–9 × 5–6
loveiana = surrecta
surrecta 120. Sp. 5–6 × 3–4
speciosa 120. Sp. 13–18 × 8–10

Xeromphalina. *Like Omphalina, but stipe ± horny, never white, and base with ± tawny tomentum; sp. amyloid.*

campanella 108. Sp. ovate, 6·5–7·5 × 2·5–3·5

Xylaria. *Perithecia with conspicuous ostioles; sp. smooth, black, non-septate.*

hypoxylon 46. Sp. ± bean-shaped, 10–14 × 4–6

polymorpha 46. Sp. ± fusiform, 18–30 × 5–8

Xylosphaera 46. An earlier name for Xylaria

ENGLISH NAMES OF FUNGI

There is, as yet, no generally agreed list. The following are a few widely used names.

Blewits. *Tricholoma saevum*
Blusher. *Amanita rubescens*
Bracket Fungi. *Polyporaceae* generally
Chantarelle. *Cantharellus cibarius*
Cultivated Mushroom. *Agaricus bisporus* forma *albida*
Death Cap. *Amanita phalloides*
Destroying Angel. *Amanita virosa*
Dry Rot. *Serpula (Merulius) lacrymans*
Earthstars. *Geastrum* spp.
Earth Tongues. *Geoglossum* spp.
Fairy Clubs. *Clavaria* and *Ramaria* spp.
Fairy-ring Champignon. *Marasmius oreades*
False Morels. *Helvella* spp.
Field Mushroom. *Agaricus campestris*
Fly Agaric. *Amanita muscaria*
Grisette. *Amanita vaginata*
Honey Fungus. *Armillarea mellea*
Horse-hair Fungus. *Marasmius androsaceus*
Horse Mushroom. *Agaricus arvensis*
Ink Caps. *Coprinus* spp.
Jew's Ear. *Auricularia auricula*
Lawyer's Wig. *Coprinus comatus*
Liberty Caps. *Psilocybe semilanceata*
Morels. *Morchella* spp.
Mushrooms. *Agaricus* spp.
Orange-peel Peziza. *Peziza aurantia*
Oyster Fungus. *Pleurotus ostreatus*
Parasol Mushroom. *Lepiota procera*
Puff-balls. *Lycoperdon* spp.
St. George's Mushroom. *Tricholoma gambosum*
Shaggy Cap. *Coprinus comatus*
Shaggy Parasol. *Lepiota rhacodes*
Stinkhorn. *Phallus impudicus*
Sulphur Tuft. *Hypholoma fasciculare*
Tawny Grisette. *Amanita fulva*
Tooth Fungi. *Hydnaceae* spp.
Wood Blewits. *Tricholoma nudum*
Wood woolly-foot. *Collybia peronata*
Wood Mushroom. *Agaricus silvicola*
Yellow-staining Mushroom. *Agaricus xanthodermus*

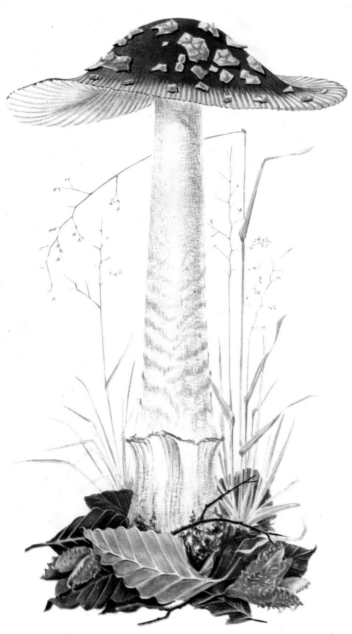

Amanita strangulata